EX LIBRIS
PACE COLLEGE

41 PARK ROW, NEW YORK

D1413955

ENTERPRISE IN SOAP AND CHEMICALS

1. Joseph Crosfield, 1792–1844

Enterprise in Soap
and Chemicals

JOSEPH CROSFIELD & SONS, LIMITED
1815–1965

by

A. E. MUSSON, M.A.

Senior Lecturer in Economic History,
University of Manchester

Augustus M. Kelley · Publishers
New York · 1967

© 1965 Joseph Crosfield & Sons, Limited

All rights reserved
MANCHESTER UNIVERSITY PRESS
MANCHESTER 13, ENGLAND

Published
in the United States
1967
by AUGUSTUS M. KELLEY · PUBLISHERS
24 East 22nd Street, New York, N.Y. 10010

PRINTED IN GREAT BRITAIN

HD
9652.9.
C7M8
1967

PREFACE

IN recent years, especially in the post-Robbins period, increasing emphasis has been laid on the importance of academic business studies. Such studies, however, must be two-way: business men may learn from the researches of economists, statisticians, sociologists, etc., but academics can equally benefit from contact with the practical problems of business life. The opportunity to write a book about Crosfield's provided me with a first-rate opportunity for such mutual stimulus.

The immediate purpose of this publication is to mark the 150th anniversary of Crosfield's foundation at Bank Quay, Warrington, and to provide an account of their development from primitive soapmaking to modern chemicals manufacture, from small family firm to big business combine. At the same time, it has enabled me to make a detailed study of the factors affecting technological change and business growth, with consideration of entrepreneurial enterprise, location, capital, trade, advertising, transport, prices, combines, rationalization, and industrial relations. The book will, it is hoped, be of interest not only to present and past employees of the firm, business associates, and customers, but also to all who are interested in the growth and organization of British business. While it emphasizes the deep-rooted influences of historical evolution upon the present-day structure and outlook of industrial firms, it also demonstrates the importance to modern British industry of applied science, economic enterprise, and adaptability.

The original opportunity for this business study was provided by Mr. A. D. Wilson, then Chairman of Crosfield's, in 1962. To him chiefly I must express my gratitude for his stimulus, interest, and friendly hospitality on many occasions. Mr. Wilson left Crosfield's in 1964, but I have received equally kind encouragement and support from his successor, Mr. J. A. Fox, who has had long associations with Crosfield's and Warrington. Other Directors of the Company have also helped me considerably, especially Mr. D. Angel and Mr. G. W. Hemy. Indeed, everyone in the Company with whom I have come into contact has

v

been most kind and helpful. To give individual acknowledgements would necessitate too long a list, with the danger of deplorable omissions, so I hope that the people concerned will accept my general thanks given here. I must, however, make particular mention of the assistance given by Mr. K. W. Michael, of the Secretary's department, whose knowledge of the nature and location of the Company's voluminous records has been invaluable; he also produced a most useful extract of statistics for the inter-war period.

Help has not been confined to present employees of the Company. The late Mr. R. C. Edwards, former Company Secretary, first put me on the rails by assisting with the firm's early records; his shrewd and kindly advice was much appreciated. Mr. S. Newall provided me with very useful information about the development of 'Persil' manufacture; Mr. R. Furness recounted Crosfield's achievements in applied scientific research; and Mr. C. Billington, above all, gave me the invaluable benefit of his astonishingly detailed memory of technical developments at Bank Quay since the beginning of this century.

Assistance has also been readily forthcoming from Unilever House. Mr. W. J. Reader has been especially helpful in guiding me through the vast collection of business records there, and his knowledge of Unilever history has elucidated a number of obscure problems. Mr. K. A. Bayley, head of Unilever Information Division, has read the whole of the typescript and very helpfully shepherded it through the final stages. I am also grateful to Mr. S. Blackhurst, the Special Projects Editor, whose expert advice has been very welcome on matters of printing and publication. Finally, I would like to thank Dr. E. G. Woodroofe, Vice-Chairman of Unilever Ltd., and Dr. J. E. Taylor, Chairman of the Unilever U.K. Chemical Group, for reading through and commenting upon the later chapters.

Outside Unilever, I have had help from a large number of people. I wish to express particularly warm thanks to Mrs. Gertrude Gaspari, Mr. Eric O. Crosfield, and Mr. G. B. Crosfield, for supplying me with material relating to the Crosfield family. The Society of Friends has also been very liberal in giving me access to its records. I am especially grateful to Mr. E. H. Milligan, Librarian at Friends House, London, and to Dr. W. Giles Howson, of Lancaster, who dug out much interesting Quaker material for me. I also wish to thank the Hardshaw East Monthly Meeting (Manchester) and the Warrington Preparative Meeting for permitting me to examine their records.

All historical researchers owe a great debt to libraries and record offices, but I wish to express particularly warm appreciation of the assistance given by Mr. G. A. Carter and his staff at Warrington Municipal Library, whereby I was able to obtain a great deal of varied historical evidence from the surviving local records. I would also like to thank Mr. R. Sharpe France and his staff at the Lancashire Record Office, Preston.

Solicitors' offices are another valuable source of historical evidence, and here, too, I was fortunate. Mr. T. H. W. Bower, of Mrs. T. Ridgway & Co., Warrington, was most kind in supplying me with Crosfield material, and I also obtained a considerable quantity of documents from Messrs. Simpson, North, Harley & Co., of Liverpool.

Some interesting material was kindly provided by the I.C.I. Alkali Division, Winnington. Mr. A. S. Irvine, Manager of their Information Service, gave me all possible assistance and some pleasant hospitality. Professor T. C. Barker and Dr. J. R. Harris were also very helpful in directing me to records relating to Joseph Crosfield's chemical and other activities in the St. Helens area, and I wish to thank the St. Helens Town Clerk, Mr. T. Taylor, for permitting me to examine records in the town hall. Mr. J. C. Jarvis, of the Customs & Excise Library, London, also provided me with some very interesting material relating to Joseph Crosfield's soapmaking activities, to which my attention was drawn by Professor Barker. The British Transport Commission's records were very helpful in regard to Joseph Crosfield's railway interests; and I wish to thank Miss Alexa Smith for some painstaking delving therein. Mr. Frank Neal, of Liverpool University, also sent me some useful evidence concerning Crosfield's ownership of ships and flats.

Professor T. S. Willan, of Manchester University, and Dr. D. W. F. Hardie, of I.C.I., very kindly read through the typescript chapters dealing with the nineteenth century and made some very helpful comments. I was particularly pleased to have the benefit of Dr. Hardie's profound knowledge of the north-west chemicals industry.

I have been greatly aided, in writing the chapters dealing with the period from the late nineteenth century, by Professor Charles Wilson's monumental *History of Unilever*, which provides such a wide-ranging and fascinating account of international developments in the soap and oils and fats trades during those years. On a few points I have differed from Professor Wilson and have made some modifications to his account, but in general I have been very much indebted to his scholarship.

To all those who have provided me with evidence or who have read the typescript, I express my very warm thanks, while recognizing, of course, that responsibility for any errors or shortcomings is entirely my own. To Mr. T. L. Jones, Secretary of the Manchester University Press, I wish to express my appreciation of the way in which this book has been produced. Finally, I wish to thank my wife for her constant encouragement and for her fortitude through prolonged periods of research and writing.

A. E. MUSSON.

Manchester, April 1965

CONTENTS

PART I
JOSEPH CROSFIELD, 1792–1844, AND 'THE SOAPERY AT BANKEY'

PART II
VICTORIAN GROWTH AND PROSPERITY, 1844–96

PART III
THE THIRD GENERATION: COMPETITION AND TECHNOLOGICAL ADVANCE, 1896–1915

CONTENTS

PART IV
CROSFIELD'S IN THE AGE OF BIG BUSINESS, 1915–65

LIST OF ILLUSTRATIONS

PART I

JOSEPH CROSFIELD, 1792–1844, AND 'THE SOAPERY AT BANKEY'

CHAPTER I

FAMILY ORIGINS

THE enormous soap and chemical works of Joseph Crosfield & Sons, Ltd., with its vapour-wreathed towers and expanses of glass windows, must be familiar to countless railway travellers through Bank Quay station, Warrington. Many millions more make daily use of the powders and detergents produced there in vast amounts, while industrial firms of many kinds consume the chemicals which, in increasing quantity and variety, are being manufactured in this rapidly developing factory of the Unilever U.K. Chemical Group.

Lever Brothers absorbed this firm in 1919, and the works which the Crosfields founded has undergone great changes. Little is left of the original buildings: modern structures of steel, brick, and glass have risen on their foundations. 'Perfection' soap and other former products are no longer manufactured there: the empirical skills of the old soapmakers have been replaced by the scientifically applied techniques of industrial chemistry, while soap has gradually given way to chemicals. But a business comprises much more than the buildings which house it: it is a human institution, an organic structure, whose present and future are largely determined by its earlier evolution.

Some firms, no doubt, may cling too nostalgically to the past and become outdated; but others, while taking pride in former achievements, find these an inspiration for future progress. The history of a firm can also provide some insight into the sources of economic growth, the interactions between technological and commercial changes, the evolution of business organization, the influence of human personalities, the motives of business behaviour, and the social consequences of industrial development.

Private enterprise was the driving force of the Industrial Revolution. The great majority of firms were family concerns and partnerships, growing from small beginnings by ploughing back profits. Many of the industrial pioneers came recently from

3

the land, attracted into the towns by the prospects of expanding trade and industry. This is how the Crosfield business began.

The Crosfields originated from Cumberland, where the name occurs in late medieval documents. But the family tree can be traced back with certainty no farther than Thomas Crosfield, buried at Kirkby Lonsdale on 14th June 1613, whose descendants are revealed by seventeenth-century parish and Quaker registers, and also by wills, as yeomen or copyholders of Beetham, Preston Richard, Stainton, and other places in the Heversham–Kendal area. From the later part of that century, Joseph Crosfield's direct forebears held freehold and 'customary' (copyhold) land at Low Park and Stainton, about four miles south of Kendal.

The records of the Society of Friends, or Quakers, show that Crosfields were among the earliest followers of George Fox. They attended the meeting-house at Preston Patrick and were being persecuted for their sectarianism immediately after the Restoration of 1660. In the eighteenth century the Quakers became a respectable and rather exclusive 'connection', and played a remarkably enterprising part in the development of English trade and industry. Membership of this Society undoubtedly contributed a great deal both to the Crosfields' eventual economic success and to their social principles, not only because of the moral qualities it engendered, but also through the business links thereby formed.

Joseph Crosfield's grandfather, George Crosfield (1706–84) married Jane Rowlandson, daughter of James Rowlandson of Frith in the parish of Cartmel, a remarkable woman, who became a minister of the Society of Friends and made extensive journeys on religious service not only in the British Isles, but also, during 1761–2, in the New England colonies. A few surviving letters of this George Crosfield show that he was no unlettered yeoman. He appears to have been a man of moderate substance. The farm at Low Park, End Moor, which remained in the Crosfield family until 1825, was then stated to comprise between twenty-three and twenty-four acres of freehold and just over fifty-four acres of customary land, nearly seventy-eight acres altogether. Described as including 'an antient family residence of great respectability', it was offered for sale at £2,850, with the wood growing thereon at valuation.

Nearly half a century earlier, however, George Crosfield's younger sons, George (1754–1820) and Joseph (1756–1830), had left the parental roof for occupations outside farming, although their elder brother, James (1752–1808), remained at Low Park and the Crosfields long retained their links with the Kendal–Lancaster area. Joseph became a schoolmaster, eventually settling at Hartshill, Warwickshire. George junior went into the grocery trade at Warrington, where he was to lay the basis for the commercial and industrial fortunes of his descendants.

This George Crosfield was the father of Joseph, founder of the Warrington soapmaking firm.[1] We would know much more about him if the diary which he kept for many years had come to light. It was still in existence just before the first World War, when John Dymond Crosfield used it in writing some notes on the early family history, but present members of the family do not know its whereabouts. Fortunately, however, some extracts relating to his son Joseph have been preserved.

George Crosfield was born on 22nd May 1754. In his boyhood it is not unlikely that he attended the Friends' school in Stramongate, Kendal. The family had relatives there, apparently in the grocery trade, and after his schooldays were over young George was bound apprentice, at the age of sixteen, to Mary Kendal, a grocer in that town. When his term expired, he took a situation in Warrington, in the grocer's shop that had belonged to the Quaker, Samuel Fothergill (d. 1772). His removal thither took place in April 1777, when he was nearly twenty-three years old.

Fothergill has been variously described as a 'grocer', a 'tea-dealer', and a 'tea merchant and American merchant'. The trade was, in fact, both wholesale and retail. The Crosfields' Quaker connections made possible young George's entry into what was apparently a fairly prosperous business, of which he soon acquired the ownership, after first serving as an assistant. We find him writing to his father on 31st March 1779 that he was 'neither anxious, discontent nor unhappy. Trade flows much in the same Chanel it has hitherto done, probably it will

---

The same names—George, Joseph, James, and John—constantly recur in successive generations of Crosfields. See Appendix I for the Warrington branch of the family tree.

be sufficient for my own support, and since I have no other to be solicitous about I need not repine. . . .' Bailey's *Northern Directory* of 1781 shows 'Crosfield George, grocer', among the Warrington tradesmen. The shop was in Sankey Street.

Three years later, on 20th May 1784, about a month before his father's death, he married Ann Key (1765–1849), daughter of John (deceased) and Elizabeth Key of Warrington. By her he had a large family of six sons and seven daughters, two of whom died in childhood.[1] He and his family lived over the shop in Sankey Street.[2] Later he built himself a small cottage a few miles south of the River Mersey in Cheshire, which he called 'Low Park' after the ancestral home, but it seems to have been used more as a summer resort than as a residence. Its garden supplied fruit and vegetables for the household, which, besides the increasing number of children, included an apprentice and sometimes an assistant living with the family.

Unfortunately, there is very little surviving evidence about George Crosfield's business activities in Warrington. According to J. D. Crosfield's notes, he was 'a man of exact mind, keeping his accounts with care, even while an apprentice at Kendal, when his allowance was a penny a week . . . and the way in which he kept up his habit of writing in his journal shows him to have been a man of method and perseverance'. In connection with his business, he paid periodical visits to Liverpool for the purchase of stock. These journeys were generally on horseback, sometimes completed in the day, but more often involved a night at a Friend's house in Liverpool, where he had many acquaintances. His purchases were conveyed home up the river in small sailing barges or 'flats'. Some of his goods were carried on the Bridgewater Canal, for there survives a receipt dated July 1797 and signed by an agent of the Duke, for 3*d*. freight charge on '2 Casks 1 Empty Box'. Current accounts for the years 1793–5 with Parr's Bank (later absorbed into the West-

[1] George, b. 1785; James, b. 1787; Jane, b. 1789, d. 1790; John, b. 1790; Joseph, b. 1792; Elizabeth, b. 1794, d. 1806; Jane, b. 1797; Mary Ann, b. 1799; Margaret, b. 1801; Simon, b. 1803; William, b. 1805; Elizabeth, b. 1807; Hannah, b. 1810.

[2] These premises, where Joseph Crosfield was born, had been built in about 1755; they still stand today, though considerably altered, at 48 Sankey Street, the drapery shop of W. T. Williams. The present owner, Mr. H. E. Francis, very kindly showed the author over the premises and permitted him to examine the deeds.

minster Bank) provide evidence of the scale of his dealings. The debit side consists almost entirely of drafts and bills of exchange, the credit side of cash entries. For April to December 1793 the account was balanced at £1,196 15s. 3d.: for 1794 at £1,035 14s. 8d.: for 1795 at £1,177 14s.

George Crosfield became one of the leading Friends in Warrington. The minutes books of the Penketh Meeting reveal him as a very active member, first as a 'doorkeeper' and then serving on various committees, acting as scrutineer of accounts and trustee of various properties; he was also frequently chosen as one of the local representatives at the Hardshaw monthly meetings for the Manchester–Liverpool area, at the Lancashire quarterly meetings, and occasionally at the yearly meetings in London. The quarterly meeting's 'Record of Sufferings' shows that he abided staunchly by Quaker principles in refusing to pay tithes, Church rates, etc., for which he suffered distraint of goods, such as coffee, loaf sugar, and candles.

He was a man of very sociable disposition, enjoying good company. His diary referred to attendances at a weekly 'Club', maintained at 'The George', perhaps the 'Amicable Club', whose surviving minutes show that he was a founder member in 1788; it was originally held at the 'Old Coffee House' and seems to have been mainly a dining and wining club. Warrington, with its famous Academy, was at this time a centre of literary and philosophical culture. The Academy records reveal no trace of George Crosfield, but he became a member of the committee of the Circulating Library in 1781 and in most of the later years of his residence in Warrington. (The membership included such eminent scholars as Dr. William Enfield and Dr. John Aikin.) He was clearly a man of wide literary tastes: he often mentioned books in his diary, and took an interest in scientific lectures.

He seems to have enjoyed the esteem and confidence of his fellow townsmen and was often engaged in the duties of arbitrator and executor, both within and without the Society of Friends. There is little evidence of his participation in affairs of local government. The surviving records of the Warrington manorial court do not include his name, but his signature appears at the end of a constable's account book of 1783.

The wholesale grocery trade in tea, coffee, sugar, and other commodities,[1] and the close relations thereby established with Liverpool merchants, eventually led him into a new business venture, as revealed by the following extract from his diary dated 18th August 1799:

About this time I formed a new connection in business with A. Carson & James Atherton, of Liverpool, viz., the purchase of the sugar house at Lancaster, where we purpose carrying on the business of Sugar Refiners. I am to reside there and to have the principal management. My mind has been very deeply exercised on the occasion. The consideration of my large family and the great expense of living occasioned by the high price of provision [due to the French Revolutionary War] have in a great measure determined my judgment in this important matter: ambition or the love of money have had very little influence over my heart or mind, having always preferred content and peace. Sincerely believing this change of residence would be for the best I trust and hope we shall witness the favor of Providence.

By this time, Joseph, the fourth son, in whom we are mainly interested, had reached the age of seven years. His birth had been noted in his father's diary under the date 5th October 1792: 'At half past one (p.m.) my dear Nancy presented us with another fine lad to the great joy of us all. We mean to name him Joseph. In the evening we were cheerful on this happy event.' In Spring of the following year, young Joseph caught smallpox, but being 'a fine healthy, pleasant lad', he survived.

The removal to Lancaster took place in October 1799. Two years later a great disaster occurred, on 9th October 1801: 'Memorable for an event which was truly awful and alarming to us all, which was the Sugar House being burnt down to the ground . . .' It was rebuilt by the following January, but 'the loss is estimated at between 2 & 3000 pounds, exclusive of the sums insured'.

Despite this setback, and the disrupting effects of the French Wars, the sugar-refining business was successfully maintained. According to George Crosfield's will, dated 5th March 1818, the premises were situated on the north side of St. Leonard

[1] He supplied Peter Stubs with oil for whet-stones and for treating files before packing. T. S. Ashton, *An Eighteenth Century Industrialist. Peter Stubs of Warrington, 1756–1806* (1939), p. 50, n. 1.

Gate, Lancaster, and comprised a sugar-boiling house, ware-house, dwelling-house, cottage, and stables; he also owned three dwelling-houses 'lately built' on the south side of St. Leonard Gate. In July 1809 the partnership with Carson and Atherton was dissolved and the sugar house, etc., became George Crosfield's property solely. He then formed a new partnership with Thomas Giles, of Lancaster, who had a one-third share in the business. After the end of the war in 1815, however, Lancaster declined as a trade centre, and the sugar-refinery shared in the general stagnation. The firm found it necessary to resort more and more to Liverpool, where they did so much trade that in 1818 they decided to open a branch.

The family's removal to Lancaster at the end of 1799 had not severed the links with Warrington. George Crosfield had retained the grocery business there, which he left in charge of his assistant, Joseph Fell, aged twenty, and his eldest son, George, aged fourteen. This arrangement lasted till 1805, when the senior withdrew and gave the concern to the two young men in equal shares. So it appeared in Pigot's *Commercial Directory* of 1814–15 as 'Crosfield & Fell, Sankey-street'; they were listed as liquor merchants as well as grocers.

George Crosfield junior remained at Warrington until 1813, when his father thought it would be more advantageous for him to join the Lancaster firm, which he did in May of that year. His place at Warrington was filled by his brother John, who remained there two years. During those years John was joined by Joseph, who, after schooling and apprenticeship, founded the Bank Quay soapworks in 1814–15.

CHAPTER II

THE FOUNDING OF THE BANK QUAY
SOAPWORKS

NOTHING is known of Joseph Crosfield's early life in Lancaster. He probably attended the local Quaker school. Then, in September 1807, when he was nearly fifteen years of age, he was taken by his father to Newcastle-upon-Tyne, where he was apprenticed for six years to Anthony Clapham, 'to learn the trade of Chemist and Druggist'. It is not clear why Joseph, unlike his elder brothers, George, James, and John, was not brought into the grocery business; perhaps it was not thought capable of supporting more of the sons.

Anthony Clapham, a Quaker, appears in the Newcastle directory of 1801 as a 'chemist and druggist, Pilgrim Street'. In 1811 and later directories he is also described, either alone or in partnership, as a soap manufacturer, of both Pilgrim Street and Ouseburn, and later still as an alkali manufacturer. An Excise Inquiry Report in 1836 reveals that he then owned one of the biggest soapworks in the country. Tyneside was one of the main centres of the growing chemical industry and allied trades such as soap-boiling and glassmaking. Here Joseph Crosfield gained the technical knowledge and business experience that were to enable him to establish his own soapery at Bank Quay, Warrington.

In July 1809 Joseph spent a few weeks' holiday with his parents: 'his disposition', wrote his father, 'is open and lively'. He was home again in 1811, when, together with his brother George, he visited 'our relations [Thomas and Sarah Goad and family] at Baycliff', across Morecambe Bay, on the coast a few miles south of Ulverston. He also went to his birthplace, Warrington. In 1813 he once more visited his parents, at the same time, apparently, as 'Cousin Thomas Goad's daughters Hannah and Elizabeth', whom his father described as 'tall genteel young women in the bloom of life'. Here, it would appear, was a promising relationship.

Joseph had now served his time with Anthony Clapham. His father noted that 'he looks thin, is lively and good tempered; he appears to possess a large share of good nature but still inclined to offer his opinion on almost every subject mentioned'. In December 1813 'Son Joseph returned to Newcastle to assist his late master in the books a few weeks'. In the following months he must have been seriously considering and discussing with his father the possibilities for his future. His decision was a bold one. This young man of twenty-one, just out of his apprenticeship, decided to establish his own soapmaking business at Warrington! He relied, however, for advice and capital upon his father, who travelled from Lancaster to Warrington on 11th and 12th May 1814 'to view some premises near Bankey [Bank Quay] suitable for a Soapery, which business our son Joseph seems to have a strong inclination to. I stopped at Warrington till the 15th, but made no positive agreement.' Very soon, however, he appears to have given his consent, for on 7th June he wrote: 'Son Joseph returned from Warrington having concluded a bargain for the Premises at Bankey; he continued with us a week and then proceeded to Newcastle [to Anthony Clapham, no doubt,] to obtain a knowledge of making soap.' On 10th July he returned from Newcastle and on 1st August went to Warrington, 'which place is to be his future residence'. On 7th April 1815 his father visited him and 'went to view the Soapery at Bankey where our son Joseph has commenced business'.

The family's long-established connection with Warrington was probably the main factor influencing Joseph's choice of location, but he could hardly have selected a more favourable spot on which to commence soapmaking. Merseyside was of growing importance as an area of chemical, soap, and glass manufactures. There was an increasing demand for chemicals—especially the alkalis, soda and potash, and sulphuric acid—and also for soft soap, in the bleaching, dyeing, and calico-printing branches of the rapidly expanding Lancashire cotton industry, while the growth of population in the north-west and the expansion of Liverpool's export trade created a rising demand for hard soap. Salt, the basic raw material for these chemical and allied trades, was being produced in ever-increasing quantities in the neighbouring Cheshire saltfields, while the coal resources around St. Helens and Wigan were being vigorously exploited for industrial fuel. The Mersey, the main trade artery of this region, had been linked by river improvements and canals to the manufacturing areas of south Lancashire and north Cheshire.

Warrington, 'the gateway to Lancashire', had for centuries been important as the lowest bridging point on the Mersey. Standing on the main road to Carlisle and Scotland, and midway between Liverpool and Manchester, it was a nodal point for road traffic. Edward Baines stated in his *History Directory and Gazetteer of the County Palatine of Lancaster* (1824) that between sixty and seventy coaches passed through Warrington daily. But road carriage, by cart and packhorse, was slow and expensive, despite turnpike improvements. Warrington had the immense advantage of cheap river transport. As John Aikin observed in *A Description of the Country from thirty to forty Miles around Manchester* (1795), 'Warrington may, in some measure, be considered as a port town, the Mersey admitting by the help of the tide, vessels of seventy or eighty tons burthen, to Bankquay, a little below the town, where warehouses, cranes, and other conveniences for landing goods are erected. The spring tides rise at the bridge to the height of nine feet. Upwards, the river communication extends to Manchester.' Baines stated in 1824 that the river traffic at Warrington was 'incessant, and the brick-dust coloured sails of the barges are seen every hour of the day on their passage, flickering in the wind'.

Thomas Patten had made the Mersey navigable from Runcorn to Warrington in about 1690; he had built wharves at Bank Quay, where he established a copper works, to which ore could be brought by water. Then, under an Act of 1721, the Mersey-Irwell Navigation Company made the river navigable to Manchester, thereby enabling 'flats'—small flat-bottomed sailing boats or barges—to reach the very centre of the cotton-manufacturing region. Toll-free navigation from the estuary to Bank Quay, however, was preserved for Warrington traders. At about the same time the River Weaver Navigation opened up the Cheshire saltfield.

In the second half of the eighteenth century, water transport facilities in this region were greatly extended by the building of canals. The first was the Sankey Canal, built in 1755–7 from the Haydock and Parr collieries, near St. Helens, southwards to the Mersey, passing only a mile and a half west of Warrington. This put cheaper coal on the town's doorstep. It was followed by the more famous canal built from the Duke of Bridgewater's coal mines at Worsley to Manchester by James Brindley in 1759–61, and then extended during the 'sixties through the north Cheshire plain to the Mersey estuary at Runcorn; it passed a few miles south of Warrington via Stockton Quay. This canal broke the water-transport monopoly of the Mersey–Irwell Navigation Company, which retaliated by building the 'Old Quay Canal', or Latchford Canal, under an Act of 1794, connecting Warrington (near Howley Quay) with Runcorn, to obviate the necessity of boats having to wait for the tide on the river.

These river and canal developments were vital to the industrial growth of Warrington and other Merseyside towns. During the eighteenth century the manufacture of sailcloth and canvas had become the town's most important industry, together with that of linens and fustians; but it declined rapidly in the nineteenth century. Various metal-working trades were also established in Warrington, including the making of files, tools, and pins: the firm of Peter Stubs was to become the most famous. In the nineteenth century wire-drawing became very important, associated particularly with the name of Rylands. Watchmaking was another Warrington trade. Aikin also stated that an iron foundry had been set up. The town had long been noted for its malt and ale; the local water was suited to brewing. Sugar-refining had once been important, but, according to Baines, had died out by the early nineteenth century. To these manufactures we can add tanning, shoemaking, flour-milling, and glassmaking; one or two soap-boilers and tallow chandlers had also established themselves there before Joseph Crosfield came. It was in Warrington, moreover, that the first Lancashire cotton-spinning mill powered by a Boulton & Watt steam engine was built by Peel, Ainsworth & Co., in 1787, to be followed soon by other mills. Already, in fact, Warrington was becoming a 'town of many trades'. At the same time it still remained important as a market centre for the surrounding agricultural region. The township population in 1781 was given by Aikin as 8,791; by 1821 it had increased to 13,570.

The late eighteenth and early nineteenth centuries witnessed

13

a rapid development of soap-boiling on Merseyside, challenging the long-established predominance of London. Local resources of salt and coal, and availability of imported kelp (alkaline seaweed ash) from western Scotland and Ireland, of barilla from the Mediterranean, and of tallow and palm oil, through the port of Liverpool, gave this area considerable advantages. Merseyside soapmaking, described in the early 1790s as 'an Encreasing Trade not of many years' standing', expanded prodigiously in the following decades. By 1820 Merseyside was already the main centre for the manufacture of soft soap, producing nearly 3,000,000 lb., twice as much as London, and some 16,000,000 lb., of hard soap, two-thirds as much as the capital.

During the 1820s and 1830s the rapid development of the Leblanc process on Merseyside—based on Cheshire salt and south Lancashire coal—provided the local soap industry with increased supplies of cheap synthetic soda in place of kelp and barilla. By 1835 Merseyside's output of hard soap was approaching 48,000,000 lb., nearly half as much again as that of London. Palm oil was now increasingly used, in place of more expensive animal fats, especially in the manufacture of soap for export, which Merseyside almost completely dominated, as a London soap-boiler admitted in 1835: 'Liverpool is the great market now for the export of soap and there is the great consumption of palm oil and almost all the soap for exportation (certainly nineteen-twentieths) is made from palm oil exclusively.' By that date, in fact, about four-fifths of all soap exports were from Liverpool.

Joseph Crosfield thus made a very shrewd choice of site for his soapworks on the Mersey at Bank Quay in 1814. Imported raw materials such as tallow, palm oil, and kelp could be brought cheaply by water from Liverpool, together with salt from Cheshire, and coal from St. Helens, while manufactured soap could be carried by river and canal to the populous inland towns and, through Liverpool, to expanding export markets.

Bank Quay was at that time separated from urban Warrington by a stretch of fields. We get our first view of it in the map of the town by Wallworth and Donbavand in 1772. Its most striking feature, to anyone familiar with the present-day industrial concentration in that area, is its predominantly rural char-

14

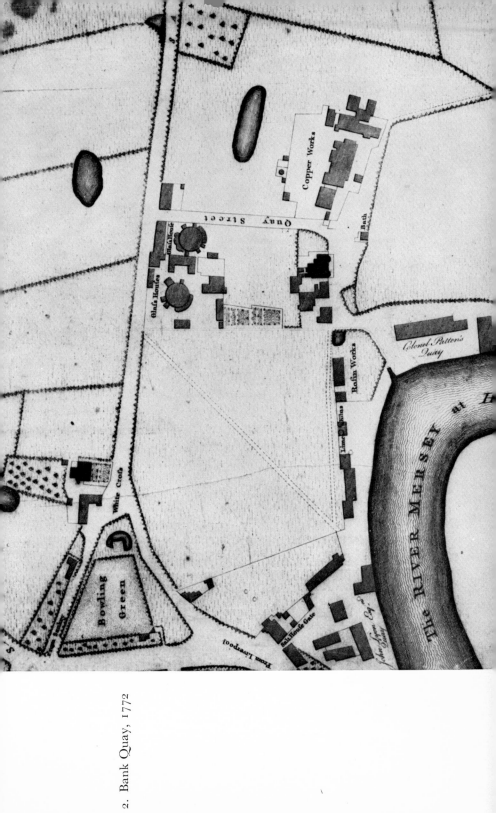

2. Bank Quay, 1772

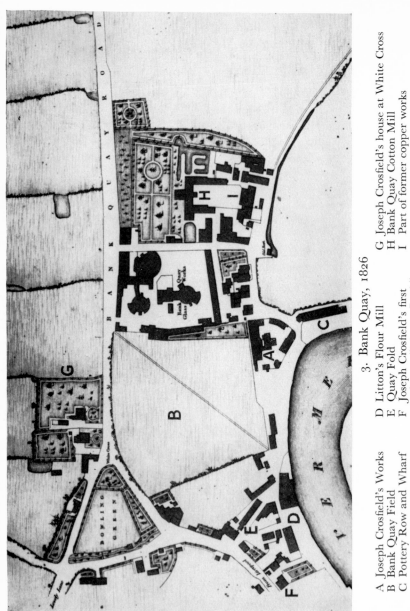

3. Bank Quay, 1826

A Joseph Crosfield's Works
B Bank Quay Field
C Pottery Row and Wharf

D Litton's Flour Mill
E Quay Fold
F Joseph Crosfield's first
  house ('Mersey Bank')

G Joseph Crosfield's house at White Cross
H Bank Quay Cotton Mill
I Part of former copper works

acter. The area north of the Liverpool road—the westward extension of Sankey Street, later called Bank Quay Road—where the White Cross wire-works was to be built many years later, was then entirely fields. Scattered industrial development had begun between the Liverpool road and the great northward loop of the Mersey, but this area too was mostly fields. The copper works established by Thomas Patten was connected to the main road by Quay Street, later to be renamed Factory Lane. 'Colonel Patten's Quay' and warehouses are also shown on the river bank. At the junction of Quay Street with the Liverpool road—now the north-eastern corner of Crosfield's works—a glassworks had been built in the late 1750s by Robert Patten, Peter Seaman, and Thomas Falkner, on land leased from Thomas Patten; by the early nineteenth century the works, called the Bank Quay Glass Works, belonged to Perrin, Geddes & Co.

South of the glassworks there appear to have been several large houses and gardens, to the west of which was a rosin works, some lime-kilns, and a building referred to in later deeds as having been a warehouse, then converted into a 'factory for weavers' (a handloom weaving shed), and finally into cottages. Further west still was John Lyon's quay. Lyon had a sugar house there, later converted, or rebuilt, to become the Littons' flour-mill, now Fairclough's. The name 'Salt House Gate', later to be known as Quay Fold, also indicates another use of some of the buildings there. The large area of open land west of the glassworks was referred to in deeds of this period as 'nearer Bankey (or Bank Quay) field'. Public footpaths or roads are clearly marked along its southern edge and diagonally across it.

At this time most of the land west of the Patten property was owned by the Lyon family, but in the early nineteenth century the glassworks company acquired the area between Patten's Quay and Lyon's sugar house. Of the various buildings erected thereon, the rosin works is of most interest to us. Surviving deeds reveal that this had been built in about 1768 by Roger Rogerson, an ironmonger, on land leased for 2,000 years from Matthew Lyon, and that after passing through various hands it was purchased in December 1802 by George Ainsworth, a Warrington coppersmith and brazier, for £252. Ainsworth, in partnership with John Stephens of Liverpool, proceeded to

15

convert and extend the rosin works into an iron foundry and wire-mill, called 'Mersey Works', which, however, proved a failure and had to be put up for auction on 5th January 1807. A sufficient sum was not then offered, but the works were put up for sale again on 31st May 1809, when they were purchased by Thomas Claughton, Esq., of Haydock Lodge, for £1,050.

These were the premises and leasehold land that Joseph Crosfield acquired in 1814, the nucleus from which the present-day works have been gradually developed. The original deed of sale, dated 9th July 1814, shows that he bought them from Thomas Claughton for £1,200. They comprised refining furnaces, forge, three-storied wire-mill, engine-house, annealing house, carpenter's shop and smithy, store-rooms, three-storied warehouse, and counting-house, with the main entrance facing the Mersey, so that 'vessels of one hundred tons burthen may be discharged at the gates', subject to the customary wharfage. They were 'capable of being converted into *any kind* of Manufactory, at a small expence'.[1]

It is probable that Joseph Crosfield was provided with most of his initial capital by his father. According to a speech by his son John, on the incorporation of Joseph Crosfield & Sons Ltd. in 1896, Joseph 'commenced with a capital of £1,500, and he lost every shilling of it the first year'. The latter statement was probably an exaggeration, but there is no doubt that Joseph experienced great difficulties at the start. The long wars with France were just ending: Joseph is said to have stood on a barrel in Sankey Street and read out the news of the Battle of Waterloo to the inhabitants of Warrington. It was in this same year that his first soap pan—scrapped fairly recently, though it had long ceased to perform its original function—came into operation. Several years of trade depression and social distress followed, during which Joseph was faced with the problems of converting the wire-works into a soapworks, acquiring more experience of soap manufacture, and developing markets for his products. In 1816, moreover, the duty on hard soap was increased from 2¼d. to 3d. per lb. Initial losses were almost in-

---

[1] There are no remains today of these old buildings, which were demolished at the end of the nineteenth century; the new buildings then erected have now, in their turn, been demolished in the present modernization programme.

evitable. Thus when, on 10th July 1815, his father went 'to view and inspect our son Joseph's Soap works at Bankey', he noted that they were 'very complete, but the Trade is a losing one'. Joseph had courage and resilience, however, and when he visited Lancaster in December 1816 his father remarked that 'he appears in good spirits notwithstanding his trade has been a very losing one'. By September 1817, when his father was again in Warrington, he had apparently surmounted the initial difficulties and was 'in good spirits, his trade being much better of late'. And when, in January 1818, he was next in Lancaster, he was 'in high spirits, his business has been profitable for about a year, by which he has regained his previous heavy loss'.

One way of reducing his overheads and of acquiring additional income was to lease part of his works, the whole of which was not required for soapmaking. A surviving deed, dated 1st May 1818, reveals that Joseph leased to Thomas Tipping, a Warrington Quaker and corn-dealer, 'All that new erected Edifice or Building now used, or intended to be used, as a Steam Mill for the Grinding of Corn, with the Engine House Outbuilding Offices and Appurtenances belonging thereto situate at or near Bank Quay . . . as the same Buildings and premises have lately been converted and set out from certain Buildings and premises of the said Joseph Crosfield at Bank Quay aforesaid used as a Sope-Manufactory.' The lease was for fourteen years at an annual rent of £110 clear of taxes, rates, etc. Moreover, Joseph would be permitted 'to use and employ so much of the power of the said Steam Engine as may be equal to one Horse power for the grinding of Kelp for the use of the said Soapery without paying any consideration for so doing'. This deed contains a plan and elevation of the soapery and cornmill, showing that more than half the premises had been converted to corn-milling.

Joseph now appeared to have established his business on a firm footing and to have weathered the worst of the post-war slump. He was thus in a position to think of marriage. On visits to his father's house at Lancaster in 1818–19 he regularly crossed the sands of Morecambe Bay 'to visit his love [Elizabeth Goad] at Baycliffe', and eventually, on 28th April 1819, shortly after Thomas Goad's death, the two were married at the Friends' meeting house at Height in Cartmel. The following

17

day they left for Warrington, where they were visited on 7th June by Joseph's father, who described their home, 'Mersey Bank', as 'a very pleasant residence'.[1] Joseph's wife brought him some additional capital. Surviving documents record payments by her brothers, totalling about £1,100, apparently out of her father's estate.

Marital happiness was soon clouded, however, by further business difficulties. On 25th February 1820 George Crosfield wrote in his diary of a visit by his son Joseph, 'to confer with me [about] the propriety of Joseph along with some other persons becoming the purchaser of the machinery &c. of the [corn] mill recently established by Thos. Tipping whose conduct has been scandalously fraudulent being deficient in the payment of his debts about £14,000; he has taken Joseph in about £800, which with his other recent losses has much distressed'. The minutes of the Hardshaw East Monthly Meeting, which appointed a committee to inquire into Tipping's affairs, reveal that the cost of the corn-mill and speculative trading had been beyond his capital resources. His property in the mill was put up for public auction at the George Inn, Warrington, on 3rd May 1820, when Joseph purchased it for £5,040. Out of this sum, however, as his private account-book indicates, he recovered over £800 owed to him by Tipping.

How did Joseph raise this large sum of money? His father's diary referred to 'some other person' assisting him in the purchase of the corn-mill machinery. Further evidence is provided by a surviving deed of 1st March 1821, whereby Joseph mortgaged both the corn-mill and the soapery as security for a loan of £4,500 from Mrs. Hannah Watt, widow, of Warrington. The loan and interest (at 5 per cent, varying slightly in later years) were also secured by a personal bond of the same date, entered into by Joseph 'in the sum of Nine thousand Pounds'. The transaction was arranged through the local bank of Parr, Lyon & Greenall.

Unfortunately, little information has been discovered about Hannah Watt, except that she was the widow of James Watt, of Warrington, and that she had been a Friend, but was apparently disunited after marrying outside the Society. She died, aged sixty-one, at Little Bolton, Lancashire, on 3rd June 1834,

[1] See below, p. 53.

and was buried at Penketh (Warrington). She appears to have been a close friend of Joseph Crosfield, who helped her in the management of her investments.

The deed of 1st March 1821 shows that the corn-mill was then occupied by Messrs. William and Thomas Wagstaff, who had previously been in partnership with the Littons as corn and flour dealers, and recently as corn-millers, apparently in Lyon's old sugar house at Bank Quay. This partnership appears now to have been dissolved, the Wagstaffs seizing the opportunity of Tipping's bankruptcy to set up an independent milling concern of their own. Joseph's private account-book shows that they leased his mill for fourteen years at an annual rent of £545 12s., their first payment being made in December 1820.

The mortgage loan from Hannah Watt was not enough, apparently, to put Joseph's finances on a firm footing. He appears also to have sought assistance from Joseph Fell, in return for a share in the soapmaking business. The mortgage deed of 1st March 1821 shows that the soapworks was 'now occupied by the said Joseph Crosfield and Joseph Fell'. We have previously seen that in 1805 George Crosfield, junior, and Fell had become partners in the Sankey Street grocery business, and that when the former went to Lancaster in 1813 his brother, John Crosfield, replaced him. John returned to Lancaster in 1815, but the firm of Crosfield & Fell continued to exist and it is probable that Joseph Crosfield took over the family interest in it.[1] It would therefore be natural for him to seek help from Fell in the crisis created by Tipping's failure, especially as they had become related by marriage—Fell's wife, Elizabeth (née Harrison), was Crosfield's first cousin—and were also associated as leading members of the local Quaker community. Entries in Joseph Crosfield's private account-book a few years later show Fell then holding a one-third interest in J. Crosfield & Co., which he probably acquired in 1820, when ownership of the soapery buildings appears to have been transferred to Crosfield & Co.

The assistance of local Friends thus enabled Joseph to strengthen his capital resources. He had been joined in 1820 by his younger brother, William, whose removal from Lancaster to Warrington is evidenced by Quaker records, and who was said

[1] See below, p. 39.

19

in the *Warrington Guardian* of 31st October 1885 to have, 'at the commencement of his business life, resided at Warrington, assisting his eldest [elder] brother, Joseph, who founded the Bank Quay Soap Works'. William was then aged fifteen and must have come to Joseph for business training.

Shortly afterwards, Joseph's father died at Lancaster. Joseph, William, and other sons and daughters had visited him, on account of his illness, in September 1820, and he had noted in his diary: 'Joseph is of an affectionate disposition, his company was pleasant.' This was almost his last entry. He died on 10th October. He had been a fond but strict parent, who had raised his children in Quaker habits of industry and honesty. These habits, together with his sage advice and financial assistance, contributed greatly to his sons' astonishing business successes. His estate and effects were valued at a figure somewhat below £14,000. His dwelling-house, sugar-refinery, etc., in Lancaster he left to his three eldest sons, George, James, and John, as trustees and executors, who were to make stipulated payments to his widow, sons, and daughters, including £1,500 to Joseph. This legacy must have been very helpful to Joseph at that critical period, though the loss of his father, of whom he was obviously very fond, must have grieved him greatly.

At this point we may refer briefly to the business careers of Joseph's brothers. In 1818–19 two of his elder brothers, George and John, had moved to Liverpool, where they established the wholesale grocery business of George Crosfield & Co. in Temple Court (or Place), while the other elder brother, James, remained in control of the Lancaster sugar-refinery. By 1829, or perhaps a year or two earlier, they were joined by William, who left his brother Joseph in Warrington to enter the grocery trade. Thus a great mercantile dynasty was established in Liverpool, which was to play an important role in the city's business and civic life. As their sons grew up they too entered the grocery business, and in 1843–4 Joseph Crosfield—son of George, the eldest brother of Joseph, the Warrington soap manufacturer— founded, with financial backing from his father and in partnership with relatives, D. and S. Harrison, the firm of Harrisons & Crosfield, wholesale tea and coffee merchants, still in existence today.

Simon, the other younger brother of Joseph Crosfield of

Warrington, also moved from Lancaster to Warrington in 1823, and may be the 'Crosfield, Simon, woollen draper, Horse-market-street', who appears in Pigot and Dean's directory of 1824–5. If so, he did not stay there very long, for he appears in Gore's Liverpool directory of 1829 as a partner in the tobacco-manufacturing firm of Field & Crosfield. He remained in this business until 1836, when he entered the chemical industry at St. Helens.

James Crosfield, who had married Hannah Goad, sister of Joseph's wife, remained in Lancaster until 1835. As a result of declining trade, the sugar-refinery was put up for sale in 1834— though not finally disposed of until 1840—and James removed to Warrington. He and Joseph are described in a deed of 18th March 1836 as 'both of Warrington . . . Soap Manufac-turers', but he does not, in fact, appear to have entered the soap business. He and Joseph were, however, as we shall see, partners in a chemical manufacturing firm then established at St. Helens, in which their brother Simon also joined them. He seems to have left Warrington at the end of 1840 and was re-ferred to in the following year as a merchant of Liverpool. Thus the Crosfields were making a striking contribution to the mercantile and manufacturing development of Merseyside.

CHAPTER III

JOSEPH CROSFIELD, SOAP-BOILER AND TALLOW CHANDLER

The art of soapmaking had been practised since ancient, pre-Christian times, and had developed in England hundreds of years before Joseph Crosfield was born, especially in London and Bristol. The raw materials were animal fats (tallow) and vegetable oils, which were boiled with alkalis obtained from the ashes of wood and plants, such as barilla (ashes of a plant growing on western Mediterranean coasts) and kelp (seaweed ash). The process was fairly simple, and crude forms of domestic manufacture persisted into the nineteenth century. At a much earlier date, however, soapmaking had become a specialized craft, though the great majority of soaperies were small.

In 1785, according to the Excise returns, there were 971 soapmakers in Great Britain, producing altogether just over 17,000 tons of soap. By 1814, when Crosfield bought the Bank Quay works, this number had been halved to 468, but total output had doubled to nearly 35,000 tons. This reduction in the number of firms continued in the following years—there were only 302 by 1834. Production was gradually being concentrated in the hands of the bigger firms: the average output of an English soapery in 1785 was a mere nineteen tons per annum; by 1851 it was 537 tons. At the same time, the demand for soap was expanding considerably, as a result of the rapid increase of population—that of the British Isles rose from about fifteen millions in 1801 to over twenty-seven millions in 1851—together with a rise in the standard of living and an increased need for soap in the growing, smoke-begrimed towns. Consumption per head rose from 3·6 lb. in 1801 to 7·1 lb. in 1851. The bulk of soap production was consumed at home—all save about 5 per cent in 1814—but exports were expanding; about 16 per cent was exported in 1834.

Traditional methods of soapmaking still prevailed in the early nineteenth century, but chemical science was beginning to be applied to it. The French chemist, Michel Chevreul, showed that 'saponification' was not, as had hitherto been thought, simply a mechanical mixing of fats and alkalis, but a chemical reaction: fats and vegetable oils, he revealed, are compounds of fatty acids (stearic, oleic, and other acids) with glycerine, and during the boiling process the acids combine with the alkaline caustic soda to produce soap (stearate, oleate, etc., of soda)—and similarly with caustic potash—leaving glycerine free in solution. These discoveries, however, appear to have had little or no effect on the practical art of soap-boiling at that time.

Numerous attempts were made in the late eighteenth century to produce artificial or synthetic soda from common salt, as a substitute for 'natural' alkalis such as barilla and kelp, and success was achieved in about 1790 by the French chemist, Nicholas Leblanc. Sodium sulphate (salt-cake) was obtained from the reaction of salt and sulphuric acid; this was converted to sodium carbonate (soda) by reaction with limestone and powdered coal. The Leblanc process was developed in Britain in the early decades of the nineteenth century. By the early 'forties, according to the *Penny Magazine*, it had almost 'driven kelp and barilla out of use' in soapmaking. The new alkali manufacture grew up in close proximity to soapmaking firms, the chief consumers of soda, especially on Tyneside and Merseyside; the latter, near to the Cheshire saltfield, became the most important area of soda and soap manufactures.

Soapmaking tended to concentrate on the main river estuaries because of the growth of imports of fats and oils. The home supply of tallow, the main raw material, was insufficient and increasing quantities had to be imported, chiefly from Russia in the early nineteenth century, but later on from Australia (mutton tallow) and from North and South America (beef tallow). The increasing use of vegetable oils led to an expansion in imports of olive oil from the Mediterranean, palm oil and palm-nut or kernel oil from West Africa, coconut oil and copra from the South Sea Islands, Ceylon, and the East Indies, and cottonseed oil from the southern states of the U.S.A. Liverpool was the main port for these vegetable oils. Pine resin, used in making yellow soap, was imported from Europe and North America.

Contemporary descriptions and engravings of soapmaking enable us to visualize the internal appearance and products of the Bank Quay soapworks. The two main categories of soap were hard and soft soap, the former being much the more important. Hard soap was made using soda; soft soap with potash. The output of hard soap was about twelve to fifteen times as great as that of soft soap, which was used mostly for washing operations in the textile manufactures. There were three main kinds of hard soap: 'white' or 'curd', the best-quality soap, made by boiling caustic alkaline liquors (lees, lyes, or leys) with pure molten tallow; 'mottled', made by combining them with tallow, 'kitchen-stuff' or grease, and oils; and 'yellow', in which a considerable proportion of palm oil and rosin were used. Fats and oils were quantitatively the most important raw materials. In the making of white soap, as much as three-quarters of the raw materials might be tallow, but for cheaper soaps less tallow and more vegetable oils, rosin, and water were used; the cheapest might be half or more water. The proportion of alkali used varied from about 5 to 10 per cent.

Tallow came into the soapworks either as masses of beef and mutton fat or, when imported, in barrels; the former had to be rendered and purified in melting coppers ('kitchen-stuff' was similarly treated), but imported tallow was usually pure enough for soapmaking. Palm oil was also imported in barrels; being solid in our climate, it had then to be melted, purified, and bleached. The alkali—whether barilla, kelp, Leblanc soda, or potash—was obtained by soapmakers in carbonate ash form, and had to be rendered liquid and caustic by steeping with lime and water in large vats or tanks. The lye so produced was pumped into the soap pans or boilers, where it was mixed with the appropriate amount of molten tallow or oil. These pans, originally made of copper—and still called 'coppers'—were now iron vessels, bricked or boarded round the sides; they were about eight to ten feet in diameter and four to five feet high (see illustrations facing p. 33). They were heated by a coal-fired furnace underneath, but in the first half of the nineteenth century steam heating was introduced, steam being piped to the various pans from a large boiler; only a few of the largest works, however, had adopted this by the early 1840s.

A large boiling-house contained a range of these huge pans

along one side, with alkali vats on the opposite side. The steaming contents of the pans were constantly stirred to hasten saponification; separation of the soap and spent lye was facilitated by adding common salt or brine, in which soap is insoluble and floats on the surface. Boiling was then halted, the spent lye (containing glycerine) subsided to the bottom of the pan and was pumped out as waste. This process was repeated several times, with lyes of gradually increasing strength, until saponification was complete. If white or curd soap was being made, it was now 'fitted', that is, boiled with a certain quantity of water or weak lye and then allowed to settle, when the black impurities ('nigre', mainly iron sulphide) fell to the bottom. In the making of 'mottled' soap, however, 'fitting' was dispensed with and the 'nigre' was left in the soap; sometimes strong lye, similarly impregnated, was also sprinkled on the surface, and the iron sulphide, percolating through the soap while cooling, left dark-coloured veins. Similar 'mottling' or 'marbling' effects were also produced by introducing colouring matter on a palette knife. The soap, in a semi-fluid state, was ladled from the coppers into buckets or pails and carried to the 'frame-room', where it was poured into wooden or iron frames forming a kind of cistern, to cool and solidify. The frames were then removed and the slabs of soap were cut by wires into bars, which were stamped and packed into boxes for sale.

White, mottled, and yellow soaps were the main sorts of hard soap—yellow being produced in greatest quantity—but 'toilet' soaps were also produced, though mostly, at this time, by specialist perfumery firms, who remelted and refined ordinary soaps and then added scents and colours to produce 'Windsor', 'cinnamon', 'almond', 'musk', 'rose', 'honey', and other varieties, sold in cakes or tablets.

Soft soap was produced mostly from whale, seal, or linseed oils and potash; the lye was not drawn off but combined wholly with the oil, and the product was not 'framed', but placed in casks or barrels, in which it was sent from the factory.

In addition to the boiling-house, frame-room, and packing-room, a large soapery would also have warehouses for storage of raw materials and finished products; a steam engine and boiler-house; a small laboratory for testing and experimenting; carpenter's and blacksmith's shops for making boxes, crates, and other equipment; sheds, stables, and yard for the carts and horses required for transport; and a counting-house or office.

Many soapmakers, including Joseph Crosfield, were also chandlers or candlemakers, tallow and palm oil being the materials most commonly used for candles. There were two methods of making tallow candles, by dipping and moulding. By the former, a number of wicks, attached to 'sticks', were dipped into a trough of molten tallow and then cooled, these processes being repeated till the candles were of requisite thickness. By the other method, the tallow was poured into cylindrical moulds, in the centre of which wicks were fixed; after cooling, the candles were pulled out of the moulds. Both these processes were still being performed manually in the first half of the nineteenth century, but in larger works they were becoming mechanized. Wax candles were also made by pouring molten wax on wicks suspended over a large pan, and then rolling them to a perfect cylindrical form.

Both soap- and candle-makers were severely restricted by Excise regulations. A duty of $1d$. per lb. was first imposed on soap in 1712. By 1816 it had been raised to $3d$. per lb. on hard soap—about equal to the cost of production—and $1\frac{3}{4}d$. per lb. on soft soap. This duty, of course, by raising the price, limited the sale of soap and was therefore denounced as a 'tax on washing' or a 'tax on cleanliness'; the similar candle duty was regarded as a 'tax on light'. Even more irksome were the controls imposed to prevent evasion of payment. Excise officers were continually on watch to check quantities of raw materials, to see these weighed into the pans, and to check the amounts of soap produced. Pans, frames, etc., had to be of specified types and dimensions, and pans had to be fitted with lids which were locked down when boiling was not being carried on. Due notice of intention to boil and to 'cleanse' soap from the pans into the frames had to be given to the Excise officer, who was to be in constant attendance during these operations; time limits were imposed for framing and cutting up. The officers could charge duty according to their gauge or estimate from materials used, regardless of the amount of soap produced therefrom; no allowance was permitted for any bad or spoilt soap. All these regulations, of course, necessitated the filling in of forms— 'specimens' and survey-books—and soap sent from the works

26

had to be accompanied by certificates, stating quantity, quality, and to whom sold.

These restrictions were a continual source of grievance to soapmakers, who insisted that they were utterly impractical and a hindrance to technical improvement. They were unequally enforced: some Excise officers carried out their duties laxly, winking at infringements, while others tried to impose the strict letter of the law. Evasion and smuggling were widespread, and all sorts of dubious practices were resorted to in order to baffle or weary the Excisemen. In 1833 the duty was reduced to 1½d. per lb. on hard soap and 1d. on soft soap and, as a result of the growing pressure for 'free trade', was finally abolished in 1853; that on candles had been removed twenty-one years earlier.

Joseph Crosfield, as we have seen, chose a very favourable location for soap-boiling and candle-making at Bank Quay, Warrington. He was able to import raw materials such as tallow, palm oil, rosin, and kelp very cheaply in flats on the toll-free Mersey from Liverpool: he could get coal from the near-by Haydock and Parr collieries, Leblanc soda from alkali works in the St. Helens and Widnes area, and salt from Cheshire.

The operations whereby these raw materials were converted into soap and candles at the Bank Quay works appear to have been on traditional lines. Joseph's chemical training was no doubt useful in this manufacture, but there is no evidence that he patented any improved processes. A report in 1837 by the Surveying General Examiners of Excise, still surviving among papers in the Customs and Excise Library, provides a most interesting account of the Bank Quay soapery:

This work contains 5 Coppers for the manufacture of Mottled and Yellow Soap, from Tallow, Stuff, Rosin, and Principally Palm Oil, which they work with Soluble [Leblanc] Alkali, made at their own works, at St. Helens;[1] but they make Black Ash [crude soda] at their Soap making premises, on which also are extensive works for the making of Candles.

The works are seated on the Banks of a Canal [a mistake for the River Mersey], which gives them facilities for receiving the materials

[1] See below, pp. 41–44, for an account of the soda works of Gamble & Crosfields at St. Helens.

27

and the disposal of their manufacture, to all parts of the Manufacturing Districts, into which the greater part is sent, at a very moderate cost for Transit. Their Stock of Soap was of middling and of very imperfect made quality. They found competition in disposing [of their goods], but not more than could be fairly expected, when capital and local advantages were considered. Their object was to get as good a price as they could, and they knew they had considerable advantages over the London supply. They had no wish to see the [soap] duties reduced, or taken off, having nothing to complain of in the charge thereof, as they found . . . the charge to be correct, both from weighing separate cleanses, and at their own stock taking, at the year's end, and they referred to the Books, and shewed clear results of it.

The average per week brought to charge, taken from the 2d. Quarter 1837, amounts to 15 Tons, produced by the labour of 16 Men, which is but very middling produce for the labour, compared with some other Manufacturers.

duties paid

	£	s.	d.	
1834,	12,667	10	1½	[Output in these three years there-
1835,	13,387	8	7½	fore averaged just over 900 tons per
1836,	12,057	9	0	annum.]
half 1837,	4,996	12	0	

In the three years [1834–6] the difference may be considered mere fluctuating. It [output] has fallen off for half of the year 1837. This was accounted for by the anticipated reduction of duty. [Trade had also become depressed.]

This House has not availed itself of the facilities afforded by the Soluble Alkali to save labour, as other manufacturers have done, as they do not produce quite one Ton per man in the week.

On a close examination of the premises, and inspection of the Survey Book, nothing arose to create suspicion of fraud.

Joseph's relations with the Excise authorities were not, however, anything like so happy as appears from this report. In April 1826 he and his partner, Joseph Fell, were prosecuted by the Attorney General in the Exchequer Court for breaches of the law relating to the manufacture of candles. Their alleged offences were that they had made candles without informing the surveying officer of their intention to do so and of the time when they would begin and of how many they intended to make; that they filled and drew more moulds, dipped more sticks, and thus made more candles than they had declared; that they removed candles before they had been weighed by the surveying officer; that they mixed candles which had not been weighed with those that had; and that they had hidden candles from the surveying officer—all these offences being committed 'with intent to deceive His Majesty of and in his duties upon Candles', whereby they had rendered themselves liable to penalties totalling £2,100. There is, however, no trace in the Exchequer Rolls of a judgment against Crosfield & Fell.

Similar difficulties arose in regard to soapmaking. Surviving letters in the Customs and Excise Library reveal Joseph complaining to the Excise Commissioner, in September 1837, of 'great annoyance' from a new surveying officer, John Bryant, in regard to the weighing of materials. Hitherto, it seems, 'for more than twenty years', with rare exceptions, there had been no trouble, but Bryant had recently instructed the assistant 'to weigh *all* the materials we put into the coppers and account for them to each copper separately'. This system had been 'rigorously and vexatiously pursued', by contrast with the former laxity. Bryant's aim, according to Joseph, was 'evidently to subject us to a charge of duty from materials, beyond the soap really made, or to subject us to a liability of being prosecuted for an evasion of the law with respect to the addition of materials to the copper'. There had been consequent trouble in regard to accounting for materials entered in the 'specimens'.

We do not make this complaint because of the trouble that the weighing [of] the materials gives us; though this is considerable (for he will not take even fluid oils by a gauge weight), but it is because we have to resort to expedients which we exceedingly dislike to avoid being charged with duty on an estimate of materials which we should inevitably incur to a large amount beyond the soap made— according to the practice now pursued of estimating the materials to each separate making of soap. We have told the officer Bryant candidly we will protect ourselves from this as we best can, or we must give up the manufactory.

On the other hand, Joseph defied Bryant or anyone else 'to adduce any grounds of suspicion that we defraud the revenue'. Joseph was convinced that Crosfield & Co. were being victimized, and he was infuriated on discovering a report by the assistant describing them as 'fraudulent traders'.

The other side of the picture is given in reports by the Excise officials. Bryant, in insisting upon seeing all the materials weighed before they were charged into the coppers, was acting according to the law and the rules laid down for surveying officers. But Crosfield objected to the strict enforcement of the letter of the law, considering that the officer had 'a discretionary power to weigh or not to weigh as he may think proper; and that the power to weigh should not be exercised unless there are grounds to suspect fraud'. Insistence upon weighing was vexatious and impeded manufacturing operations.

Some time ago [it was reported] Mr. Crosfield went to Mr. Bryant when on survey and said to him, 'Well Bryant, let thee & me understand each other. Dost thou intend to weigh all the materials?' Mr. Bryant answered, 'I do.' 'Well then', rejoined Mr. Crosfield, 'we'll give thee all the trouble we can, short of obstruction.' And in pursuance of this threat they have since weighed their materials in small quantities, viz. 3, 4, 5, 6, or 7 lbs. at a draught, for the purpose of detaining and annoying the officers. Mr. Crosfield states that they have a right to weigh the materials as they please, and they adopted this mode of weighing 'to give them enough of it'.

The surveying assistant also reported on various evasions by the firm. Tallow had been put into the coppers without weighing, even quite openly, Crosfield and his men laughing in the assistant's face.

On the other hand, as the Surveying General Examiners admitted, 'an opinion now pretty generally prevails of the inutility of weighing', which 'is sometimes but imperfectly performed . . . particularly at extensive works. It is generally admitted, that when materials are weighed into a clean copper for fine yellow soap, the Trader cannot cleanse [i.e. take out] so much [soap] as he is chargeable with by the presumptive charge from materials, which is an inducement to add materials clandestinely.' But the residue from the boiling enabled him to produce more than the required proportion of soap in succeeding 'cleansings'.

The Excise Commissioners were advised that this weighing regulation could not be efficiently enforced, that it was constantly causing trouble, and that therefore its abandonment was advisable. An order to this effect was therefore issued to the surveying officers early in 1840 and the regulation was not included in the consolidating Act of that year. Thus Joseph had won a notable victory.

Many years later his son, John Crosfield, recalled the difficulties the firm had with the Excise (*Warrington Examiner*, 25th July 1896):

When he went to the works in 1847, the soap duty had been reduced to £14 a ton [in 1833], and he remembered that every six weeks they had to pay £3,000 for soap duty.[1] The curse of the Excise was this that they could only make soap [of] a certain specific gravity. If it were more than that they were fined. The consequence was that some of the most valuable things that are used now in soap-making were then excluded. They dare not make any experiment in a 'boil' of soap for any improvement, because if the 'boil' turned out bad they had to send it back to the pan and lost £14 a ton on it . . . By the Excise law they could not open any pan any morning without giving notice to the Excise man that they wanted to do so. Every pan was locked down every night and they could take no soap out that did not pay duty. The Excise man could not leave the premises so long as there was any fire underneath any pan. They had an Excise man named Eastwood—a disagreeable fellow who plagued them in every way that he could—and his (Mr. Crosfield's) late brother, Morland, was so exasperated at the fellow that he was determined to pay him off. He made one of the men light a candle and keep it underneath the eighth copper a whole night, so that this miserable Excise man had to tramp up and down all night, for he could not lock the pan down.

Evidently Joseph's sons were as resourceful as their father in baiting Excise men!

Joseph was active in campaigning not only against the restrictive effects of the Excise regulations, but also against the duty itself, the root of all the trouble. He was present at 'a meeting of the soap trade' at Liverpool on 8th May 1835, when two representatives were chosen to give evidence before the Excise Inquiry Commissioners. The meeting was strongly of opinion 'that the weighing the materials before putting them into the coppers is unnecessary, and ought to be abolished—the fact being that it is in a great degree a dead letter, not being enforced except to annoy the trader, and that it has no effect to prevent smuggling'. A resolution was also passed urging 'the

[1] This would indicate a yearly output of about 1,860 tons, double that of the mid-thirties. Cf. above, p. 28.

total abolition of the duty'. Joseph continued to play an active role in the campaign that followed the publication of the Excise Report in 1836. He was responsible for proposing resolutions at the annual meeting of 'the London and Country Association of Soap Manufacturers' held in London on 8th February 1837 (reported in the *Morning Herald* of 17th February), which expressed considerable apprehension at 'the present declining condition of the trade, which is wholly attributable to the injurious operation of the Excise'. The duty, it was pointed out, was extensively evaded by smugglers, or dishonest traders; at the same time, it curtailed demand at home and damaged the export trade. Moreover, it was 'a tax on the health and cleanliness of all', especially of the poorer classes. The meeting therefore resolved 'to use every endeavour, both collectively and individually, to procure the repeal of this unjust tax'. The efforts of Joseph and his fellow manufacturers no doubt contributed to the eventual repeal of the duty in 1853.

The amounts of duty paid by Crosfield & Co. in the mid-1830s indicate that they were then producing around 900 tons of soap a year. Evidence as to their relative importance among soapmakers in England and Scotland at this time is provided by the Excise Report in 1836. In the year ended 5th January 1833 Crosfield & Co. paid £18,907 18s. duty. (This was substantially higher than the figures for the years 1834–7 given above, because of the reduction of the duties in 1833, from 3d. to 1½d. per lb. on hard soap and from 1¾d. to 1d. on soft soap.) The largest soapmaking firm in the country was that of Benjamin T. and W. Hawes, in London, which paid over £79,000 duty; Crosfield's came twenty-fifth in the list of 296 soapmakers in England and Scotland at that date.

The general appearance of Crosfield's works can be seen from Robert Booth's pen-and-ink sketch of about 1830, which depicts the manufacturing establishments at Bank Quay still in rural surroundings, with a number of small cottages clustered around them. The 1826 map (see facing p. 15) gives a similar impression. The glassworks had been extended, with a line of cottages—Glass House Row—along its southern boundary. Most of the old copper works buildings still stood, perhaps used as part of a cotton-mill built just to the north; the latter was probably that established by Thomas Ainsworth & Co. at Bank

32

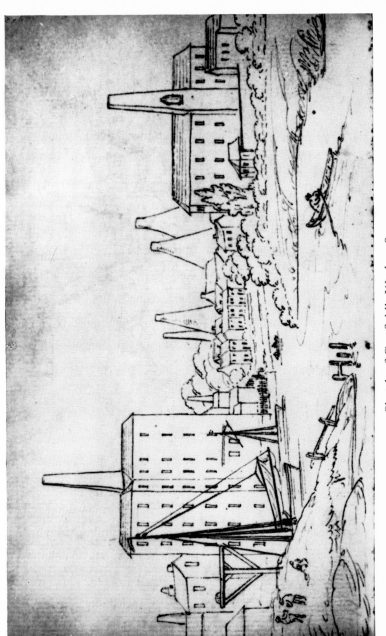

4. Sketch of Crosfield's Works, 1830

5 (a) Soap boiling, 1854

5 (b) Old soap pans, 1894

Quay in the late eighteenth or early nineteenth century, and later occupied by Thomas Barker & Co. Notice the ornamental gardens north and east of this mill!

A rough idea of the various parts of the soapery can be gained from an insurance policy upon them in July 1829: the west end of the main building (insured for £500), apparently containing the soap pans or coppers (utensils and stock insured for £900); a cottage near-by (£30); counting-house (£50); warehouse and candleroom on south side of yard (£300), with stock and utensils (£600); two cottages on east side of yard (£100); box-room and smithy (£50), with stock and utensils (£50); shed, with utensils, furnaces, and lye (alkali) vats (£80); shed and three steam boilers (£150). The total value insured was £2,810. From 1835 onwards, according to Joseph's account-book, Crosfield & Co. also rented the old 'Pottery Warehouse' at Patten's Quay from J. Wilson Patten.

Joseph's account-book shows what improvements and extensions were made to the soapery buildings during this period. The buildings were valued in 1827 at £2,036 10s. 9d. Further entries are as follows: 1831, cost of erecting new soap-room, £125; 1833, new joiners' rooms, £66 16s 6d.; 1836–7, new soap-room, £203 9s. 1d.; 1842, addition to candle-room and office, £228 6s. 2d. Capital improvements to the soapworks buildings between 1827 and Joseph's death in 1844 thus totalled only £623 11s. 9d., raising the valuation to £2,660 2s. 6d., without allowing for any depreciation.

This appears to have been a mistaken policy. Joseph should not have been short of capital in the late 'twenties and 'thirties, for, as we shall see, the soapery was producing substantial profits, and so was the corn-mill. Instead of ploughing back these profits and improving and extending the soapery, however, Joseph preferred to invest them in many other enterprises, including a chemical works, a plate-glass manufacturing company, a cotton-mill, railways, banks, and foreign government loans, on most of which he lost money.[1] He would have been wiser if, instead, he had done more to develop and improve his most profitable asset.

His account-book reveals that in 1827 the soapery buildings were transferred from Crosfield & Co. back to his private estate,

[1] See below, Chapter IV.

and that he was able to achieve this by means of capital accumulated in the grocery business of Crosfield & Fell.[1] From now on he charged the business a rent on these buildings, at 4½ per cent, as well as interest on his capital. The latter—his accumulating balance in J. Crosfield & Co., excluding the soapery buildings—was a mere £471 in August 1826, when these figures begin in the account-book, and it rose very slowly in the following years, to only £1,316 in 1835, because the bulk of the profits were being invested in other enterprises. We even find him borrowing further capital from relatives and friends: a short-term loan of £800 from Hannah Watt in 1825 (repaid in four or five years) to assist in buying a new house; £1,050 from Mary Goad, his mother-in-law, in 1834; £400 from the estate of Oliver Sibbern, for whose wife, Mary, Joseph was surviving trustee, in 1835; and, at the same time, £500 from Richard Ockleshaw, of the District Bank.[2] These loans, bearing interest at 4½ to 5 per cent, were all long-term: in 1843 he still owed £500 to Mary Goad and the whole of the other debts. Meanwhile he made regular interest payments to Hannah Watt on the corn-mill mortgage loan, and, after her death in 1834, to her son, Fitzjames Watt; in 1830 he repaid £500 and in 1831 £150, leaving an outstanding debt of £3,850.

On 9th November 1834 Joseph Fell died. Fell, unlike Crosfield, had left his profits and interest in Crosfield & Co. to accumulate from £1,168 in 1828 to £6,757 in 1835, far more than Crosfield's at this time. (The total value of his personalty approached £14,000). Payments to Fell's executors therefore put Crosfield under some strain and probably account for his further borrowings at this time. Moreover, he transferred to the soapmaking business part of his accumulated balance in the now-dissolved grocery partnership of Crosfield & Fell and the whole of his balance in the Bank Quay corn-mill.

These accretions of capital, and increased profits—he was now sole proprietor of the soapery—brought about an expansion of his balance in Crosfield & Co., to £12,025 15s. 3d. in 1841, but it declined to £11,180 15s. by 1843, mainly because of Joseph's speculation in a cotton-mill and other investments, but also due to his transferring £500 each to three of his daughters, Ann, Sarah, and Maria. His eldest son, George, was

[1] See below, p. 39.   [2] See below, p. 37.

given a quarter-share in the business in 1841, when its title was altered to Joseph Crosfield & Son. It is interesting to note the firm's first payment of income tax—introduced by Sir Robert Peel—in 1843: £27 7s. 1d.!

The soapery produced a fairly steady stream of profits, as the following figures indicate:

Year Ending	Total Profits	J.C.'s Share	Year Ending	Total Profits	J.C.'s Share
	£	£		£	£
Aug. 1826	600	400	Aug. 1835	2,219	2,219
,, 1827	2,010	1,340	,, 1836	1,900	1,900
,, 1828	1,500	1,000	,, 1837⎱	2,397	2,397
,, 1929	1,599	1,066	,, 1838⎰		
,, 1830	2,100	1,400	,, 1839	2,040	2,040
,, 1831	2,400	1,600	,, 1840	1,293	1,293
,, 1832	2,295	1,530	,, 1841	2,000	2,000
,, 1833	2,400	1,600	,, 1842	1,000	750
,, 1834	1,050	700	,, 1843	2,800	2,100

In addition to profits, Joseph received interest on his trading balance and rent for the buildings. Interest, however, was rarely more than £100 up to 1835, because Joseph was continually raiding the balance for other investments; thereafter it rose to over £500 per annum in 1842–3. The yearly rent was gradually raised from about £90 to £150.

Very little evidence has survived concerning Crosfield & Co.'s trading operations. There is a bald cash account covering the years 1819–21, which shows regular purchases from Liverpool merchants, but gives no indication of the nature, quantities, or prices of the goods. It also contains periodic payments to the Old Quay Company for carriage. Receipts are also shown from customers, without stating their trades or addresses, but occasional references to places such as Wigan, Belper, and Coventry, indicate that trade was fairly widespread. Crosfield & Co. were also able to vend some of their products through the wholesale grocery businesses of Crosfield & Fell (Warrington) and George Crosfield & Co. (Liverpool). Doubtless they shared to some extent in Liverpool's expanding soap export trade, though the Excise Report of 1836 states that most of their output was sent to 'the manufacturing districts' of the north-west and midlands.

Their turnover between June 1819 and April 1821 averaged about £2,700 per month, over £32,000 annually. The only surviving scrap of evidence on their prices is an invoice for a box of soap, delivered to one of the Greenalls in July 1830, containing 1 cwt. 9 lb. of 'firsts', costing £2 16s. 2d. (£2 12s. per cwt.) and 3 qrs. of 'white', costing £2 11s. (£3 8s. per cwt.).

Much of this trade was carried by river. The Old Quay Company (Mersey–Irwell Navigation) carried some of the firm's goods, but Joseph also acquired his own flats. The proceedings of his executors show that at the time of his death he owned several such vessels, which were used for carrying corn and flour, as well as in the soap trade.

Joseph's interest in the Mersey trade is evidenced by the fact that, together with other Warrington riverside manufacturers, he lent support to a proposal by J. Wilson Patten for improving the river navigation. They commissioned the eminent engineer, Sir John Rennie, to make a report in 1838. This showed that the largest vessels navigating the Mersey from Liverpool to Bank Quay were of eighty to one hundred tons, at spring tides only, and from thence to Manchester of about forty tons; navigation was made difficult by the shifting channel and sandbanks. The river could be considerably improved, but Rennie recommended instead a ship canal to Bank Quay, which might be extended to Manchester. Nothing came of this proposal, but it foreshadowed the Manchester Ship Canal scheme of the 1880s.

Joseph's trading operations could not have been conducted without the facilities and credit of local banks. Like his father before him, he at first banked with Parr, Lyon & Greenall, but this was a Tory institution, and in 1831, with the backing of local Radical manufacturers, a branch of the Manchester & Liverpool District Banking Company was established in Warrington. Joseph, as we shall see, became a large shareholder and local director of this bank, to which he naturally transferred his business. The records of the Warrington branch for this period have not been preserved, but a surviving letter of 18th March 1843 from Joseph Crosfield to Thomas Trueman, senior managing director and chairman of the Bank, fortunately provides us with a glimpse into his credit transactions. The bank set 'limits' to the credit it would allow its customers, according to their securities, and Trueman was apparently under the impression that Crosfield & Co.'s limit was £5,000. Joseph said he was surprised at this, 'as we have frequently exceeded this amount for short periods', without notice having previously been taken. He went on to state that the limit to their account was originally fixed by the local directors at £10,000 without reference to himself, and that he had caused it to be altered to £5,000, 'as being quite as much as we were then likely to want'. But 'when the corn mill came into my own hands and I had to work it myself, and our business was extended', he had obtained an extension of the limit to £8,000. 'This I think is 2 or 3 years since.'

They had not needed to avail themselves of this limit 'until 10 days since, when our account for 2 days exceeded it by a trifling amount'. This was 'in consequence of having £5,000 to pay Robinson & Hadwen for one parcel of Tallow before we removed it. . . .[1] On the 8th our balance was £8,227, on the 10th it was £7,563, on the 12th . . . it was £7,157, and today somewhere about £6,000. We could easily have kept it lower had it been desirable to do so.' He went on to point out that 'we have paid Robinson & Hadwen above £25,000 for Tallow [during] the last few months in cash before removing it'. He concluded by threatening to close his account: 'I would not continue my account where there is any want of confidence.' Matters were evidently smoothed over, however, for Joseph continued to bank with the District.

His connections with this bank enabled him to secure another long-term personal loan, similar to those obtained from Hannah Watt and others. A letter of 9th January 1835 by Joseph to Richard Ockleshaw, manager of the Stalybridge branch, together with information concerning the latter's account, reveals that Ockleshaw had loaned £900 to Joseph at 5 per cent interest. This, as we have seen, was probably occasioned by Joseph Fell's death. Joseph had a few months earlier helped Ockleshaw—previously at the Warrington branch—to obtain the Stalybridge managership by standing surety for him. Regular half-yearly interest payments appear in Ockleshaw's account. The loan was repaid by Crosfield & Son on 24th July 1844, just after Joseph's death. There is no evidence that Joseph obtained

[1] Joseph's writing of this firm's name is difficult to decipher, but it appears to have been Robinson & Hadwen, described in Pigot & Slater's Liverpool directory of 1843, as 'hide &c. brokers, 33, Tithebarn st. and 1 Bexteth st.'

any long-term capital, as distinct from short-term credit, from the District Bank itself.

The surviving remnants of the firm's early records—letters, invoices, and account-book—are all in Joseph's own hand. Like most small or middling manufacturers of that period, he did a great deal of the clerical work himself. He employed only one clerk, James McGowan, whom John Crosfield, Joseph's son, remembered as the 'forwarding clerk' when he entered the works in 1847, 'in the little soap room, with an inkpot in one hand and a brush in the other, marking and numbering the boxes'.

The original offices, overlooking the Mersey, together with the old candle-room and soap frame-room, were demolished when the Warrington–Garston railway line was built,[1] but a plan survives of these offices as they still existed in 1851. It shows two small rooms, each roughly twelve feet square; the first was for the partners, George and Morland, Joseph's elder sons, the second for two clerks, Anthony and James McGowan. Adjoining the office was a tiny laboratory, measuring about eight feet by five feet.

[1] See below, pp. 59–60.

CHAPTER IV

A MAN OF MANY TRADES

MOST men might have been satisfied with the foundation and development of the Bank Quay soapworks, but Joseph Crosfield actively engaged in a wide variety of other business enterprises. Warrington, the 'town of many trades', perhaps encouraged such versatility, but few entrepreneurs of his time can have been involved in so many economic activities.

The earliest of these—the original foundation, in fact, of the Crosfield commercial fortunes—was the grocery business of Crosfield & Fell in Sankey Street. We have seen that Joseph apparently took over from his brother John when the latter left Warrington in 1815, and that Fell also came into partnership with him in the soapworks. Crosfield & Fell were described in local trade directories as wholesale grocers, liquor or spirit merchants, and tea dealers in Sankey Street—at No. 48 according to Pigot & Co.'s directory of 1838.

Joseph's private account-book shows that Fell held a two-thirds share of the grocery business, and he was no doubt responsible for its management. Crosfield appears to have accumulated a trading balance in the business of about £2,300 by August 1827, but he utilized the whole of this, as we have seen, to purchase the soapery buildings for his private estate: he even incurred a debt to Crosfield & Fell of over £200. This was soon wiped out, however, by profits in the following years; his third-share thereof averaged around £210 a year, and though this was partially offset by a private grocery account of about £50 annually, his balance accumulated to £1,022 in 1834. Joseph Fell's death in November 1834 ended the partnership, though Crosfield & Fell continued for some years to appear in trade directories.

Another business in which Joseph became involved soon after setting up his soapworks was corn-milling. We have already seen how in 1818 he had leased more than half the Bank Quay premises to Thomas Tipping, for use as a corn-mill. We have

39

seen, too, that when Tipping went bankrupt two years later, Joseph bought the mill machinery for £5,040 and then leased the whole concern to William and Thomas Wagstaff for fourteen years at an annual rent (plus insurance) of £545 12s. Joseph had taken a considerable risk in this costly venture, following Tipping's disastrous failure. He had put far more capital into the corn-mill than the soapery, and he had been obliged to mortgage the buildings and contents of both as security for the £4,500 loan from Hannah Watt. But the risk paid off. The Wagstaffs evidently had better resources, business skill, and fortune than Tipping, and their regular rent payments not merely covered the interest due to Hannah Watt, but enabled Joseph to build up a substantial balance in his steam-mill account. By June 1834, when the Wagstaffs' lease expired, this balance amounted to £2,356, after allowing for repairs and improvements to the mill and machinery, and for repayment of £650 off the mortgage loan. In the following year he was able to transfer £2,503 from the steam-mill account to the soap-making business, to help overcome the difficulties created by Joseph Fell's death.

The Wagstaffs did not renew their lease, however, and Joseph had now, it appears, to operate the corn-mill himself. Crosfield & Co. are listed as both owners and occupiers of the mill in the Warrington rate-book of 1836, and Pigot & Co.'s directories of 1838 and 1841 refer to Joseph Crosfield not only as a soap-boiler but also as a corn-miller at Bank Quay. He appears to have experienced difficulties at first, and allowed for heavy depreciation in the value of the mill, but gradually he made the business profitable and built up a favourable balance of £1,152 by March 1839, despite trade depression.

Before his death, however, Joseph appears to have secured another tenant for the mill, since the executors of his will agreed that 'if E[dmund] Robinson & Co. elect to extend the time of the lease of the Mill we will agree to the same'. An obituary of Edmund Robinson in the *Warrington Guardian* of 30th June 1877 stated that he came to Warrington 'about the year 1847, as manager of Mr. Crosfield's flour mill at Bank Quay', but he must have come at least three or four years earlier and taken a lease of the mill.

The situation is complicated, however, by references in the

executors' proceedings to their negotiations with Robert Winstanley, 'with whom Joseph C[rosfield] was a partner in the
flour trade'. Local directories show that Robert Winstanley &
Co. were corn and flour dealers and cheesemongers in Sankey
Street, and Joseph's account-book reveals that he went into
partnership with Winstanley in August 1835, by investing part
of his assets from the grocery business of Crosfield & Fell, just
terminated by Fell's death. Doubtless he did so to facilitate
marketing of the products of his flour-mill. He acquired a half-
share in Winstanley & Co., which proved to be a fairly profitable
business, even during the depression of the late 'thirties and
early 'forties. By the beginning of 1843 his balance in this firm
stood at £1,612.

After Joseph's death, his executors decided to terminate the
partnership with Winstanley, but local directories and rate-
books show Winstanley, Hobson & Co. as tenants of the Crosfield corn-mill from 1844 onwards. It thus appears that this
new partnership took over the lease of the mill from Robinson
& Co.

Throughout this period it is interesting to note that the corn-
mill was valued in the local rate-books at a far higher figure than
the soapworks. In 1827, for example, the rateable value of the
corn-mill and its warehouse was £240, six times the soapery's;
in 1838 this figure was raised to £482, over three times the
revised soapery valuation.

Another of Joseph's ventures—into alkali or soda manufacture—was motivated by a natural desire to establish his own
supply of this essential raw material. At the time when he
founded the Warrington soapworks, kelp—shipped cheaply to
Liverpool from western Scotland and Ireland—was the main
source of alkali for the Merseyside soaperies.[1] (London soap-
boilers used barilla, which bore an import duty, but was richer
in soda and required less coal fuel.) In the late eighteenth century, however, as we have seen, the French chemist, Leblanc,
had invented a process for the manufacture of synthetic soda
from common salt. One of the earliest firms to apply this process
in England was William Losh & Co. on Tyneside, at the beginning of the nineteenth century, and Joseph Crosfield may have

---

[1] As we have seen (above, p. 17), Joseph was using steam power to
grind kelp in 1818.

41

acquired some knowledge of it while training as a chemist in Newcastle.

In 1822 the import duty on barilla was reduced, despite protests from the Liverpool soap-boilers that this would 'have the effect of wholly superseding the use of kelp in Soap Boiling . . . to the profit only of the London Soap Manufacturers and of Foreigners'. This factor, followed by the abolition of the excise duty on salt in 1825, made Leblanc soda an attractive proposition to Merseyside soap-boilers, who saw in it a means of maintaining their advantage over their London rivals. Cheshire salt and south Lancashire coal made this the most favourable area in the country for development of the Leblanc process.

The pioneers of the Merseyside alkali industry were James Muspratt and Josias Christopher Gamble,[1] and the soap industry was by far the biggest consumer of the soda they produced. Muspratt began the manufacture of Leblanc soda in Liverpool in 1823. In 1828 he was joined by Gamble in another chemical works at Gerard's Bridge, St. Helens. In 1830, however, Muspratt withdrew from the partnership and established a new factory of his own at Newton-le-Willows in 1831. Other firms also began to enter the now rapidly developing soda manufacture in the Merseyside area.

A number of soap-boilers built their own alkali works and Joseph Crosfield was among the first to do so, by acquiring an interest in a chemical works at St. Helens. This was originally an alum works, established in 1829 by Edward Rawlinson, a Lancaster solicitor, and Joseph Williams, his brother-in-law, at the Gerard's Bridge terminus of the Sankey Canal at St. Helens, but by 1833 the concern was bankrupt. When the works was put up for sale on 7th January 1836, surviving deeds reveal that Joseph Crosfield purchased it for £2,050 on behalf of himself, his brother James (who had just joined him in Warrington), and J. C. Gamble. At the same time the two Crosfields joined with Gamble in signing a new lease from Gilbert Greenall of the land on which Muspratt and Gamble's original works had been built. It seems probable that the alum works was continued as such for a few years, since it is thus referred to in the proceedings

---

[1] See D. W. F. Hardie, *A History of the Chemical Industry in Widnes* (1950) and T. C. Barker and J. R. Harris, *A Merseyside Town in the Industrial Revolution. St. Helens 1750–1900* (1954) for excellent accounts of these developments.

of Joseph Crosfield's executors after his death in 1844, which show that it was leased by the two Crosfield brothers to J. C. Gamble on 1st October 1840. It was subsequently developed by him as a soda works. Gamble, however, continued in partnership with the Crosfields at the other works. It is probable that Joseph Crosfield's younger brother, Simon, very soon came into the alkali business, for he is referred to as a manufacturing chemist in 1837 and appears as a partner in the late 1840s.

Joseph Crosfield's main interest in this new venture was the acquisition of cheap Leblanc soda for his soap works. Active management appears to have been left in the hands of his brothers, together with J. C. Gamble, and (after 1840) James Shanks. The last-named came there first of all in 1838, to erect three 'Gossage towers'—invented by William Gossage (later founder of the important soap and chemical works at Widnes), to condense the hydrochloric acid gas produced in the first stage of the Leblanc process. These 'noxious vapours' were a serious problem in the early days of the alkali industry. Muspratt was prosecuted by Liverpool Corporation in 1838 for creating a public nuisance. At the same time Sir John Gerard, lord of the manor of Windle, also took proceedings against the St. Helens alkali manufacturers, whose waste gases were inflicting serious damage upon the crops, trees, and hedges on his estate. In the later part of 1838 he preferred bills of indictment against Gamble & Crosfields, the main offenders, and other local alkali firms. True bills were found against them at the Kirkdale Michaelmas Sessions 'for creating a nuisance by permitting noxious effluvia to escape from their works', according to the *Wigan Gazette* of 9th November 1838. A settlement was reached, however, before the case reached Queen's Bench. The defendants would endeavour so to conduct their works that they would no longer be a public nuisance.

The firms were now faced with the prospect of unending litigation and heavy damages, unless they took steps to condense the damaging hydrochloric acid gas. At this critical juncture, Joseph Crosfield and Gamble quarrelled, as J. Fenwick Allen later explained in an article on Gamble in the *Chemical Trade Journal* of 1st March 1890:

Joseph Crosfield, dismayed by the demands made upon their firm for damage to trees, hedges, and crops, insisted on the immediate

43

adoption of Gossage's patents; to this Gamble was strongly opposed as he believed some plans he had himself conceived, would supersede Gossage's patents. Crosfield, however, was so impressed with the urgency of the situation and the value of Gossage's work, that on his own responsibility and in defiance of his partner's wishes, he concluded an agreement with Gossage to erect the necessary plant for them and put his process into operation. Gamble was very indignant . . . a quarrel ensued between the partners which was so serious that Joseph Crosfield never put his feet inside the works again.

He still remained a partner in the business, however, and the Gossage towers were erected at the end of 1838 by James Shanks, who two years later became manager of the works. Nevertheless, landowners and farmers continued to complain of damage, due mainly to the condensers being inefficiently operated. In 1840 Sir John Gerard and Samuel Taylor of Eccleston Hall brought actions at Liverpool Lent Assizes against Gamble & Crosfields and another alkali firm at St. Helens, as a result of which they obtained damages of £1,000 and £250 respectively, by settlement out of court, the defendants promising future amendment. Actions by other landowners were similarly settled.

These difficulties appear to have caused Joseph Crosfield's practical withdrawal from the firm. At the time of his death his share in the Gerard's Bridge alkali works was estimated by his executors at a mere £300, while his third share in the alum works property was put at £261.

Soda manufacture was not his only industrial interest in St. Helens. His private account-book shows that he purchased shares in the Manchester & Liverpool Plate Glass Company established in 1836, which built a factory at Sutton Oak, near the south-eastern boundary of the town, during the next year or two. Soda, of course, is an essential raw material for glassmaking as well as for soapmaking, and Crosfield's participation in the alkali trade probably led him into this further venture. It did not, however, prove a happy one. By 1841 he had invested £1,280 in it, but he then valued his total holdings of ninety-five shares (each nominally £25) at only £10 each. The company was unable to withstand the powerful competition of the old-established British Plate Glass Company and other glassworks during these years of serious trade depression. In September

1842 the Sutton Oak factory was put up for sale, but withdrawn as no one would bid enough for it. An effort was made to raise more capital in the following year, when Joseph purchased twenty-eight new shares at £9 each. Later that year, however, he valued his 123 shares at only £4 each, a further heavy loss. The works were again advertised for sale in 1844, just after Joseph's death.[1]

Joseph's continued purchases of the company's depreciating shares were apparently motivated by his personal involvement in its management, as evidenced by salary payments recorded in his account-book. In 1840 he was paid £150 as managing director, a position he may have held in previous years. That he had a strong technical interest in glassmaking is indicated by his taking out a patent for 'improvements in the manufacture of plate glass'. His specification, no. 8448, enrolled 23rd September 1840, describes his improved methods of fluxing the raw materials, and of grinding and polishing plate glass. But these did not save the company from heavy financial losses. Joseph's executors wrote the shares down to £2 each.

An even more disastrous venture was his partnership with John Clare and John Sowden in the firm of Clare, Crosfield & Sowden, owning and operating the Wharf Meadow cotton-mill, Warrington. A small private ledger has survived recording the capital, profits and losses of this firm. Joseph invested £3,008, Clare £2,273, and Sowden £633. The two latter had been engaged for some years in the cotton trade, and Sowden appears to have managed the mill. The capital was gradually paid up in the years 1830–2, probably while the mill was being built. After an initial loss in 1832, the business proved profitable during the prosperous mid-'thirties, and Crosfield's balance accumulated to £4,907 at the end of 1837; but in the subsequent trade depression he suffered repeated losses, so that by the end of 1842 his balance had shrunk to £2,214. In June 1843 he tried to bolster up his cotton business with a further £2,000, from his soapery assets, but this was pouring good money after bad, and he left his executors with a total loss (see below, p. 58).

Joseph was on somewhat safer ground when he invested in the new joint-stock banks that developed in the provinces following the Joint-Stock Banks Act of 1826. His first 'flutter' in this

[1] British Sidac Ltd. now use this factory.

45

field was the purchase of ten £100 shares in the Manchester Joint-Stock Banking Company in 1828-9, on which he paid £150, but he sold them in the following year for a small profit. In 1831, when the Manchester & Liverpool District Bank opened a branch in Warrington, Joseph was one of the first shareholders. He may also have been one of the first directors; he was certainly a director a few years later. He bought and sold a considerable number of this bank's shares, but at the time of his death he held 217. These shares, however, which were marketing at around £22 each in 1835, dropped heavily in the following trade depression and were valued by Joseph's executors at less than half this price in 1844. His consequent losses greatly exceeded dividends received, but, by way of compensation, his position as a director no doubt helped him in obtaining trade credit (see above, pp. 36-38).

Joseph also made a few speculative investments in other joint-stock banks. In 1834-5 he invested a total of over £600 in the Yorkshire District Bank and the Newcastle Bank, but soon sold out, at a modest profit.

After the successful opening of the Liverpool & Manchester Railway in 1830, many Lancashire business men became almost intoxicated by the twin possibilities of railway profits and commercial expansion. Joseph Crosfield was among them. His major interest was in the St. Helens & Runcorn Gap Railway, linking St. Helens with the Mersey and competing with the Sankey Canal, mainly for the transport of coal and salt. He bought fifteen £100 shares in this company in 1830, at more than £107 per share. In 1833 he sold five of them at £90 per share, and in the following years the value of the remaining ten depreciated rapidly. He sold five more in 1838 at £35 each, and a few months later valued the five he still held at only £10 per share. The company was evidently in serious trouble. The railway cost far more than originally envisaged and additional capital had to be raised by mortgage; not for many years were any dividends paid. Joseph loaned £150 to the company in 1836 at 5 per cent interest, and in 1842 he bought another £200 bond from Davies & Co., Warrington solicitors, for just over £100.

On 1st August 1836 he was elected a director of this railway company, a position he held until his death. The company's minutes show that he attended meetings regularly and took an active part in the business of the Board, serving on various committees. He was concerned with obtaining an Act in 1838 enabling the company to raise further capital by the creation of new shares, of which he himself bought ten for £50. These depreciated, however, as rapidly as the old ones, becoming almost worthless during the subsequent trade depression.

One way out of these difficulties was to amalgamate with the Sankey Canal, so as to end cut-throat competition. Joseph played a leading part in preliminary negotiations to this end in January 1838, but nothing was achieved. In January 1844 he was involved in further negotiations, which resulted successfully in an agreement for amalgamation. Before the Bill was passed, however, creating the St. Helens Canal & Railway Company in 1845, Joseph died.

During the railway promotional activity of the early 'thirties, Joseph had speculated in other local lines, such as the Lancashire & Cheshire, the Warrington & Newton—the first line into Warrington, connecting the town to the Liverpool & Manchester Railway—and the Liverpool & Birmingham. He had also bought shares in the London & Birmingham Railway. Altogether he invested about £1,600, but by the end of 1833 he had sold all these shares, at a loss of about £250, several of the schemes having proved abortive. His losses did not deter him, however, from further speculation during the railway boom of 1836. He invested a total of nearly £1,100, mainly in local lines, such as the Lancaster & Preston, the Chester & Birkenhead, and the Manchester & Birmingham Extension, but also in the Edinburgh & Glasgow and Cheltenham & Tring railways. The net result of his dealings was a loss of over £100.

Joseph was clearly obsessed with the excessive optimism of this early 'railway mania'. In the case of local lines, he was no doubt interested in helping to provide cheaper and quicker transport, which would benefit his own trading activities. In the St. Helens & Runcorn Gap Railway especially, he made a long-term investment and also participated in its management. But in most cases, particularly outside the Lancashire-Cheshire area, he was merely speculating—buying shares to sell again after brief intervals, in the hope of making capital gains. Though his experiences in this field were not very happy, they provide

47

evidence of the way in which Lancashire capital was helping to build Britain's railways.

Joseph also made various other investments. In 1826 we find him holding five £10 shares in the Manchester Insurance Company; he sold them in 1832 at a small loss. In 1833 he records purchases of £1,000 worth of raw cotton and over £700 of wheat, on which he obtained small profits. Perhaps he was utilizing the resources of Crosfield & Co. to purchase raw materials for the Wharf Meadow cotton-mill and the Bank Quay corn-mill respectively.

Joseph's speculations were not confined to Britain. He also invested in foreign government loans and industrial enterprises. He was involved in the speculative mania for Central and South American mining shares during the boom and crisis of the middle and later 1820s. After a mild flirtation with Colombian bonds, he went into Anglo-Mexican Mining Company shares, which he later exchanged for Brazilian mining ones. His investments totalled over £1,000, and he lost about £250. Undeterred, however, he plunged during 1833–5 into Brazilian and Spanish government bonds, investing over £2,000, but hardly breaking even on their sales. In 1839 he bought a few Assam tea shares, and in the early 'forties he was dabbling in Portuguese bonds, and suffering more losses.

All this forms an extraordinary catalogue of speculative investments. The resources for these operations came mostly from the profits of the soapery, which were to a very considerable extent frittered away in a variety of risky enterprises. Some of these ventures, such as the cotton-mill and the plate-glass company, proved disastrous, and on most he lost a good deal of money.

Why did Joseph behave in this way? Perhaps he wished to safeguard himself by placing his eggs in several baskets; there is no doubt that the profits of the grocery business and the corn-mill proved very helpful, while the chemical works provided him with cheap soda for soapmaking. The soapery, once firmly established, brought in fairly safe and steady profits; by the early 'thirties it was one of the two dozen largest in the country, and restrictions upon expansion were imposed by the Excise duty and regulations. There is little doubt, however, that he had sufficient resources and locational advantages to have expanded further, had he so wished. The conclusion seems inevitable that he preferred the excitement of new and speculative ventures, even though he so often suffered losses.

These losses were exaggerated, however, by the fact that his death, in February 1844, occurred when the economy was only just emerging from one of the worst trade depressions of the century. Had he lived a few years longer, he would have been able to turn some of his losses into profits, and the valuation of his property would have risen considerably.[1]

[1] See below, pp. 57–59, for the settlement of his estate by his Executors.

CHAPTER V

PUBLIC AND PRIVATE LIFE

PERSONAL details about Joseph Crosfield are very scanty. Except for a surviving silhouette (see frontispiece), we know nothing of his physical appearance. Remarks in his father's diary show that he was an affectionate son, lively, good-natured, enterprising, and spirited in the face of adversity. Occasional remarks by various Warrington people in later years indicate that he was long held in great respect. His son John stated, over forty years after his father's death, that 'the lasting memory which he left behind was of a great and good man . . . I do not think a worthier or nobler citizen ever lived in Warrington . . . His hand was always employed for the good of the people. He often neglected his business in doing public work, and would go to the office at eight o'clock at night to begin to write his letters. He shortened his life with hard work.'

That this was no mere expression of filial piety is proved by the testimony of others. Councillor Richard Kean, for example, who had known Joseph, said in 1872 that he 'was full of kindness and went about scattering his gifts where he thought they were most needed'. The *Warrington Guardian*, though a Tory paper, stated four years later that he 'is still remembered by living inhabitants of Warrington as one of the most able public men the town ever possessed'. J. G. McMinnies, who had been associated with Joseph in Radical politics from the late 1820s onward, and who was later president for many years of the Warrington Liberal Party and eventually became M.P. for the town between 1880 and 1885, recalled how Joseph took 'a leading part in politics in Warrington. Whoever was absent from the meetings, he was present; whoever was discouraged, he never was cast down; whoever shrank from labour, he never did. He brought to politics and to other matters of public and private usefulness a sagacity, an industry, an earnestness, which made him remembered to that day as the ablest public man Warrington ever had.'

50

Perhaps this was going too far. Unfortunately, there is little surviving evidence of Joseph's political activities. Warrington, at that time still under manorial administration, appears to have been dominated by Tory landowning and Church influence, combined with the commercial, banking, and brewing complex of Parr, Lyon & Greenall. Joseph, as a Quaker and rising manufacturer, was strongly opposed to monopoly of power by the Establishment. He appears to have participated actively in the campaign for the repeal of the Test and Corporation Acts in the late 1820s, for parliamentary reform in the early 'thirties, and for free trade in the later 'thirties and early 'forties. His private account-book reveals a subscription of £50 to the Anti-Corn-Law League in 1842. He was an ardent follower of the great Quaker Radical, John Bright, in his campaigns for political reform and the removal of fiscal restrictions on trade and industry. We have already noticed Joseph's activity in the movement for repeal of the Excise duty on soap.

In view of his Radical political activities, it is not surprising that his name does not appear in the records of Warrington manorial court. It is possible that he may have served as a Commissioner under the Local Improvement Act of 1813, but the records appear not to have survived. Throughout most of his life in Warrington he was one of the life governors and permanent committee members of the Dispensary and Infirmary, established in 1810 'for the relief of the Sick Poor'. (His brother George had been the first treasurer.) He also served on the Warrington Board of Health in 1832, which was set up to deal with the serious cholera outbreak at that time. His interest in public health is also evidenced by his purchase in 1836–7 of shares totalling £30 in proposed Warrington Public Baths, but the scheme appears to have been a complete failure.

Joseph, like his father and brother George before him, was a zealous and prominent member of the Penketh Preparatory Meeting of the Society of Friends. The minute books reveal him serving on committees, scrutinizing accounts, acting as clerk to the meeting from 1821 to 1826, and as trustee for various properties, e.g. for the meeting house and the school. He subscribed £70 towards the building of a new meeting house in 1830. He was also frequently chosen as a Penketh representative to the

Hardshaw East Monthly Meeting, held in Manchester or War-
rington, and was clerk to this meeting between 1833 and 1836.
The meeting's 'Book of Sufferings' shows him refusing to pay
Church tithes in 1836 and having to suffer distraint of goods.

Joseph played an active part in the development of local
education. He was concerned not only with the Quaker schools
at Penketh and Warrington, but with the founding of the Warrington Educational Society in 1838, 'for the purpose of . . .
extending education among the working classes of Warrington
without respect to religious distinctions'. This was doubtless a
reaction to the establishment a few years previously of the first
'National' or Anglican school in the town. The intention to provide non-denominational education, however, appears to have
weakened and the Educational Society's first school, opened in
Newton Street in 1841, became a 'British' or Non-Conformist
institution; eventually, in 1858, it was renamed the Warrington
People's College, and, as we shall see, Joseph's sons continued
to take an active share in its management.

Joseph also took an interest in the Warrington Mechanics'
Institution, established in 1825, 'for the promotion of useful
knowledge among the working classes'. He was a trustee at the
time of his death and doubtless had been concerned with the
Institution's activities in preceding years.

His educational and intellectual interests also led him, again
following his father and brother George, to active participation in the affairs of the Warrington Circulating Library. This
Library, founded in 1760, was to become in 1848 the nucleus of
the first municipal rate-aided library in the country. Joseph
was elected to the committee in 1817 and remained on it until
1841. From the minutes one can see what books he recommended for purchase and so discover his intellectual interests.
He evidently had a passion for books of travel and geographical
exploration, followed by historical works, especially political
memoirs and biographies; he also recommended a number of
philosophical or scientific books and journals, and evidently
had a liking for poetry, particularly of Byron, and also for
novels. One gets an impression of wide cultural interests.

Joseph's brother George had been one of the founding members in 1811 of the Warrington Auxiliary Bible Society, a
branch of the British and Foreign Bible Society. This was a non-

denominational body, including Anglicans and Dissenters, whose aim was to distribute copies of the Bible cheaply to the poor. Its minutes show Joseph presiding at the annual meeting of 1840 in the Friends' meeting house, and thereafter he served on the committee.

Like most manufacturers in the early Industrial Revolution, Joseph lived close by the works. After his marriage in 1819 he resided at 'Mersey Bank', which later maps show as a fairly large house, standing in its own grounds, on the Liverpool road, just west of Quay Fold, approximately facing the entrance to modern Thewlis Street (see map facing p. 15). His father described it as 'a very pleasant residence'; it was in mainly rural surroundings, overlooking the Mersey and the Cheshire countryside beyond. (The Garston railway was not built till a quarter-century later.)

In 1826, however, Joseph leased a plot of land on the other side of Liverpool Road, to the east of 'White Cross House', facing Bank Quay field. On this he built a new house (clearly marked on the 1826 map, facing p. 15), which his private account-book shows cost £1,070. Improvements in the 1830s brought the total cost to £1,344, a very substantial price for a house in those days. It had a 'gig-house', stables, and large gardens, and was surrounded by fields. Here he lived throughout the rest of his life, and his family remained there for some years afterwards, before selling the house and moving into Cheshire. Towards the end of the century the property was acquired by the Catholic Church and the present-day church building was erected in the grounds; Joseph's former residence became the priest's house, but was demolished some years before the second World War.

Joseph's growing family necessitated a large house.[1] George, the eldest son, was given a partnership in the business at twenty-one years of age. Part of his education was at the Quaker school at Penketh. His brothers Morland and John also went there for some years, followed by residence at the Quaker boarding

[1] His wife Elizabeth bore him ten children: George, b. 10th May 1820; Thomas Goad, b. 15th March 1822, d. 3rd Nov. 1822, aged 8 months; Ann, b. 7th Oct. 1823; Sarah, b. 7th May 1825; Morland, b. 17th March 1827; Maria, b. 30th Jan. 1829, d. 19th April 1844, aged 15 years; Joseph, b. 12th Jan. 1831, d. 12th April 1844, aged 13 years; John, b. 11th Feb. 1832; Jane, b. 22nd Nov. 1835; Harriet, b. 11th June 1841.

school at Lawrence Street and Bootham, York. The girls also were sent away to various private schools. Joseph's concern that his children should be well educated is evident from his will, in which he instructed his executors to provide 'the best education that can be obtained', and that they should 'not put my Sons to business too early lest they attach too much importance to matters of trade'.

Joseph's death occurred suddenly, in his house at White Cross, 'after a short illness of an inflammatory nature', on 16th February 1844, at only fifty-one years of age. His brother George wrote in a brief 'Memorandum' that Joseph's death was mourned not only by his family but by

a widely extended circle of friends and neighbours . . . for he was of a truly kind and affectionate disposition, given to hospitality, ever ready to assist the poor and others also with his aid in various ways as a friend and counsellor; possessed of talents of a superior order, good judgment, and a mind well stored, his advice was often sought and freely given. His remains were interred at Warrington on the 20th, a large assembly of relations, friends and neighbours attending, and manifesting the respect and esteem in which he was justly held.

Joseph's last words, written on a slate in the morning of the day he died, are also recorded: 'Brother George, my hours are numbered, a victim to self-doctoring. I cannot speak, every moment of existence nature unceasingly takes for respiration. Thou must address my children in my name. I look for very liberal aid to George [his son] in arranging with the Bank.'

Immediately after Joseph's death, his children were seriously attacked by what the doctors called 'gastric fever', and two of them, Maria, aged fifteen, and Joseph, aged thirteen, died about two months later and were buried beside their father. The three grave-slabs are still to be seen in the old burial-ground of the Friends' meeting house in Buttermarket Street, Warrington.

PART II

VICTORIAN GROWTH AND PROSPERITY, 1844–1896

CHAPTER VI

THE SECOND GENERATION

JOSEPH CROSFIELD's death at the early age of fifty-one, followed so tragically by the deaths of two of his children, Joseph and Maria, left his family in sad bereavement and business difficulties. The heaviest burden fell upon his eldest son, George, then nearly twenty-four years of age and already a partner in the soapmaking firm. His other two surviving sons, Morland and John, were aged nearly seventeen and twelve respectively, while the ages of his four remaining daughters were twenty (Ann), eighteen (Sarah), eight (Jane), and two (Harriet). Joseph's wife, Elizabeth, aged forty-nine, survived him for thirty-three years, but appears to have taken no part in business affairs.

Joseph's will, dated 14th November 1842, provided that his widow should receive an annuity of £250 per annum, to be reduced to £150 should she remarry, which she did not. Subject to this prior charge, his estate was to be divided equally amongst his children, whose shares were to be invested by his executors until they reached the age of twenty-one, the income therefrom to be used for their maintenance and education. He appointed his brothers George and John, both merchants of Liverpool, and his son George as executors and trustees. Their proceedings are recorded in a surviving note-book.[1]

Joseph's multifarious business activities left them with some knotty problems. At a preliminary meeting on 21st February 1844 they agreed 'that for the present the Manufactory of Soap & Candles carried on under the firm of Joseph Crosfield & Son should proceed as usual', until stocktaking at the beginning of July. They also agreed to accept new shares offered in the St. Helens & Runcorn Gap Railway Company.

During the following months they tackled, first, the affairs of the corn-mill, offering to extend E. Robinson & Co.'s lease. It appears, however, as we have seen, that this offer was declined

---

[1] Very kindly loaned by Mr. Eric O. Crosfield.

and that Winstanley, Hobson & Co. took over the tenancy,[1] though the partnership with Robert Winstanley in the corn and flour trade was wound up.

The executors' worst problem was the cotton-mill partnership of Clare, Crosfield & Sowden. They decided to wind up Joseph Crosfield's interest in this concern and, after hard bargaining, agreed that the Wharf Meadow mill and its machinery should be sold to John Sowden for £9,000. Eventually, however, they came to the dismal conclusion that though a large amount was nominally due from this business, 'yet it does not appear that anything is likely to arise from it, but all is lost that is embarked in it'. The whole of Joseph's nominal assets therein—reckoned at £4,372 at the end of 1843—had therefore to be written off.

The affairs of the soapery were settled after stocktaking in July. Profits for the previous year had soared to £5,193, more than double any earlier figure, but Joseph's interest in the business (excluding the soapery land and premises) was valued at only £11,434. This amount was left owing to his father's estate by George Crosfield, junior, who was to carry on the soapworks. He was to pay the estate £150 per annum rent for the premises and 4½ per cent interest on the shares of his brothers and sisters, which were left invested in the business.

Most of Joseph's other assets were also written down by his executors. His own valuation of the soapery premises was left unaltered at £2,660. The corn-mill was valued at £2,800, but the machinery therein, which Joseph had estimated to be worth £4,500, was put at only £1,700; his balance in the mill ledger (rent a/c), flats, etc., was given as £1,260. The next biggest item was £1,956 10s. for his District Bank shares. Joseph's other industrial holdings comprised £650 for St. Helens & Runcorn Gap Railway Company shares and loans; £226 for Plate Glass Company shares; £260 for one-third share in the Gerard's Bridge (St. Helens) alum works; and £300 for his estimated interest in Gamble & Crosfield's alkali works. His dwelling-house at White Cross, which had cost him a total of £1,344, was valued at only £750, and his furniture at £357. Finally, £500 was due on a life insurance policy with the Friends' Provident Institution. Debts of £3,850 and £500 were still outstanding to

[1] See above, p. 41.

58

Fitzjames Watt and Mary Goad, respectively; the executors at once paid £450 off the former. After deduction of these debts, Joseph's estate totalled £23,048; but just prior to his death he had given £1,500 to three of his daughters, Ann, Sarah, and Maria, and a small cottage at Latchford to his son George, thus leaving £21,488. His executors, however, affirmed his estate to be under £20,000, on which they paid £310 probate duty.

The family continued to live for some years in the house at White Cross, paying £60 per annum rent to their father's estate. These meticulous arrangements bear the strong imprint of George junior's financial exactitude, which is also evidenced by surviving documents in his handwriting, carefully recording income and expenditure (household, educational, travelling, etc.) on account of his mother and sisters. The accumulating surpluses became substantial and were invested by George on their account in London & North Western Railway stock.

Joseph's dying hope 'for very liberal aid to George in arranging with the Bank' was apparently fulfilled, for his eldest son quickly took his place as a substantial shareholder and local director of the District Bank. That the soapery prospered financially in the next few years is also evidenced by repayment of the whole remaining mortgage debt of £3,400 to Fitzjames Watt's widow in 1850. George's brother Morland was brought into partnership in 1848, when he reached the age of twenty-one, and the firm's name became 'Joseph Crosfield & Sons'. The third brother, John, after completing his education at Bootham School, York, and Glasgow High School, entered the works in 1847 and into partnership soon after his twenty-first birthday in 1853.

The soapery's survival had been thrown into serious jeopardy in the late 'forties by the plans of the St. Helens Canal & Railway Company for building the Warrington–Garston branch line. An agreement dated 1st June 1847 survives, between Joseph Crosfield's executors and Gilbert Greenall, Esq., chairman of the Railway Company, to the effect that 'whereas the said Branch to Warrington is intended to pass through a certain Soapery, Lands and Hereditaments belonging to the said Executors', the latter agreed to sell the land, soapery and candle-house (but not the corn-mill) to Greenall for £10,000. This agreement, however, did not come into effect, being superseded by another of 19th July 1848, whereby only a small portion of the works, on the south side, nearest to the Mersey, was to be sold to the Railway Company. Crosfield's eventually secured in return £2,161 10s. and two small portions of Bank Quay Field, north and west of the original soapery and corn-mill. On this land new buildings were at once erected—a large new soap and candle warehouse and offices, a 'black ash' shed, and a new melting-room and boiler-house.

The railway, which had threatened the soapery's existence, now provided excellent transport facilities. From the branch line, running alongside the works, private sidings were soon to be constructed, whereby boxes of soap could be loaded directly into wagons from the warehouses and distributed by rail throughout the country. Coal could be similarly brought into the works. Provision was also made, however, for crossings over the railway line, to maintain access to the riverside quays, and for a private right-of-way directly northwards to the Liverpool road. At the same time, the ancient public footpath along the north side of the original buildings was still preserved, forming a narrow passage—the 'Soapery entry'—between the old and new buildings.

At this point, with the future of the soapery now assured, and with its physical expansion beginning under the partnership of Joseph's three sons, we may pause to survey general industrial developments in the Bank Quay area, since these were ultimately to be of great importance in imposing restrictions upon Crosfield's expansion, and since, also, it is of interest to recall the former industrial uses of areas over which the huge modern soap and chemical works have gradually extended (see map facing p. 75). The story of Crosfield's expansion involves a great number of piecemeal acquisitions of surrounding land, a gradual absorption of neighbouring concerns, an immense complexity of deeds, agreements, tenures, and rights of way, which have been accompanied by an inevitably hotch-potch development of buildings and plant, though these are now rapidly disappearing in the modern programme of demolition and rebuilding.

Between Joseph Crosfield's foundation of the soapworks and corn-mill and his death in 1844, there had been little further industrial building in the Bank Quay area. To the north there was still the empty Bank Quay Field, east of which were the cottages of Quay Fold and the *Ship* and *Bowling Green* public houses, standing on the Liverpool turnpike road. Litton's flour-mill still stood on the banks of the Mersey east of the soapery. The Bank Quay glassworks had changed hands. Garven and Carruthers had owned it for some years, but were in constant financial difficulties and were probably glad to sell their free-hold land, including the Bank Quay Field and a small area on the south side, to the St. Helens Canal & Railway Company, when the latter was planning to build the Warrington–Garston line. In about 1851 the glassworks were taken over by Charles H. Cartwright, who operated them successfully for many years, manufacturing bottle-glass.

South of these works were the cottages of Glass House Row and several older, larger houses. The Bank Quay cotton-mill was still at work to the east of Quay Street or Factory Lane (as it was now called), with the cottages of Factory Yard clustered round it. By about 1860, however, the mill appears to have closed down. North of it were railway sidings, a coalyard and the small Bank Quay gas-works. Bordering Bank Quay on the east was the Grand Junction Railway line to Birmingham and London, built in the 1830s and absorbed in 1846 into the London & North-Western Railway.

At the time of Joseph Crosfield's death, the only buildings erected to the south and south-west of his works were Patten's warehouse, called the 'Pottery Warehouse', leased for some years by Crosfield's, and a number of cottages in 'Pottery Row'. Beyond these to the south-west lay enclosed fields. The first industrial development in this area was Edward Tayleur & Co.'s establishment, just after Joseph's death, of the Bank Quay Foundry, on the Mersey immediately south of Patten's Quay. This was also a shipbuilding firm, constructing both steam and sailing ships of iron. Another later industrial development, immediately south-west of Crosfield's, was the foundation in 1869 of the Mersey Flint Glass Works of Robinson, Son & Skinner.

Tayleur's shipbuilding venture, not surprisingly, proved short-lived. Warrington could not for long compete with Liverpool and Birkenhead. Tayleur sub-leased part of his land, near to the L. & N.W.R. line, for a cement works, and by the early

61

1860s the foundry had been abandoned, to be replaced by a spelter or galvanized-iron works and a chemical factory on the land sub-leased from Tayleur. The chemical works was operated by Julian Winser & Co., who also later established a soapworks, which was acquired in 1885 by William Lever and became the first Sunlight Soap Works.[1] The spelter works belonged to the Warrington Spelter Co., owned by the Ryland brothers, who acquired the whole of the leasehold land of the former Bank Quay Foundry in the early 'seventies. In the late 'seventies, however, the spelter works were apparently leased to Phillips, Bennett & Co., a Birmingham firm; then in 1893 these and also the chemical works were taken over by H. D. Pochin & Co., Ltd., chemical manufacturers of Salford, while in 1897 the southern portion of the Rylands' leasehold property was transferred to the Pearson and Knowles Coal and Iron Co., Ltd., in which the Rylands had substantial interests. An impression of this varied industrial build-up south-west of Crosfield's can be gained from the 1894 Ordnance Survey map.

Obviously expansion in this direction would be very difficult for Crosfield's, who found it much easier to push northwards into the vacant area of Bank Quay Field. The whole of this area, as we have seen, had been bought in 1848 by the St. Helens Canal & Railway Company (which was absorbed in 1864 by the L. & N.W.R.), but, after the building of the Warrington–Garston line, it became surplus to their requirements and was gradually acquired by Crosfield's. Their first acquisition has been previously mentioned.[2] Then in 1856 they obtained for £1,500 another, bigger piece, of two and a half acres, extending northwards right up to Liverpool Road. This was followed in 1869 by the purchase for £3,100 of the remaining part of the former Bank Quay Field, together with another plot of land adjoining it on the west, up to Quay Fold, totalling altogether about three acres. All this land was freehold.

These territorial acquisitions north of the original buildings provided them with a good area for future expansion. To these were soon added two further adjoining areas, to the south-west. The first of these, acquired in 1869, was near 'Crosfield's Crossing' over the Garston railway, at the south-west end of Factory

---

[1] See Charles Wilson, *The History of Unilever* (1954), Vol. I, pp. 30–3.
[2] See above, p. 60.

Lane, opposite the old soapery buildings. It was rather more than half an acre, sub-leased from Robinson, Son & Skinner, at a yearly rent of £37 15s. 9d., out of the land which they had just leased from J. Wilson Patten. The other acquisition, in 1872, was between one-third and one-half an acre, comprising Patten's Quay, 'Pottery Row', and the 'Pottery Warehouse', on the bank of the Mersey, between the old soapery and the former Bank Quay Foundry. The freehold was acquired for £2,506 6s. 10d.

Apart from some very small adjustments on their western boundary, Crosfield's made no further land purchases for over twenty years. They had, for the time being, ample room in which to expand. On their newly acquired land, as we shall see, they rapidly erected new buildings; already, by 1861, their works were referred to in Slater's directory as 'a large and extensive soap manufactory'. Business prosperity enabled the partners to make a cash settlement in regard to Joseph's estate. By an agreement of 17th December 1862, soon after Harriet, the youngest daughter, had reached the age of twenty-one, they paid £6,000 for the leasehold land, soapery and corn-mill buildings, steam-engine, boilers, and machinery that still formed part of their father's estate. This sum was divided among all the children, including the co-partners George, Morland, and John, in accordance with Joseph's will, 'ample funds' having been provided for the payment of their mother's annuity.

Until the early 'sixties part of Crosfield's buildings was still used as a corn-mill. For a number of years James Fairclough had been the tenant. (Later he acquired Litton's mill.) But soon after 1863 the mill was taken over for soapmaking, as the business was now rapidly expanding.

Economic and social factors in the third quarter of the nineteenth century—often referred to as the era of 'Victorian Prosperity'—favoured such expansion. Britain, as a result of her industrial leadership and liberal commercial policy, was expanding her manufacturing production and overseas trade at a high rate, while the continued growth of population, rising living standards, and improvement of urban water supplies led to a great increase in the demand for soap. National consumption had risen from about 24,000 tons in 1801 to about 87,000 in 1851, while annual consumption per head had doubled from

3·6 to 7·1 lb. This rising consumption was boosted in 1853 by Gladstone's abolition of the soap duty. John Crosfield still vividly recalled this event in 1896:

> . . . he remembered that night as well as if it were yesterday. The men had to work all night for a month previous. Of course, no grocer bought more than one cwt. of soap at a time, so that he might not have a pound on his premises when the duty came off. At Bank Quay they accumulated under bond 200 tons of soap . . . After it struck twelve o'clock the men set to work and loaded the [horse-drawn] lurries and carted the soap to Bank Quay goods station. [This was before the Warrington–Garston line was built.] They there loaded the train up with the 200 tons of soap for Manchester and it was delivered in the streets of Manchester before eight o'clock, and they were the first with it. They thought they had done wonders then, but it looks very small now.

The abolition of the Excise duty contributed to the striking expansion of the soap industry in the second half of the nineteenth century. The removal of import duties on raw materials was another stimulus; that on tallow, for example, was finally removed in 1860. National production of soap doubled between 1851 and 1871 to over 150,000 tons, and by 1900 had reached about 320,000 tons, while annual consumption per head rose from 7·1 lb. in 1851 to 17·4 lb. by the end of the century.

Crosfield's shared in this growth and prosperity. But expansion could not be achieved without heavy capital investment. Unfortunately, there is no surviving evidence as to the firm's capital and profits during this period. That profits were substantial is evident from the great increase in the wealth of the Crosfield brothers,[1] but they were apparently insufficient to meet all the heavy capital requirements of the 'sixties—for settlement of their father's estate, for buying land, and for erecting new buildings and plant. A new partner, George William Goodwin, was therefore brought in. He joined the firm sometime between 1863 and 1867; how much he invested is unknown. His brother, Peter, became Crosfield's representative in Manchester. But they did not stay long; G. W. Goodwin withdrew from the partnership in 1874. Soon afterwards Goodwin Brothers established their own soapmaking business in Ordsal Lane, Salford.

[1] See below, pp. 65 and 134–5.

Business ability was also required, as well as capital. The elder brother, George, was mainly responsible for Crosfield's expansion in the third quarter of the century. Contemporary references, and obituary notices, bear witness to his great skill in commercial affairs, and to his industry and determination. His niece, Mrs. Gaspari (née Gertrude Crosfield), now in her eighties, who still remembers him from her childhood, states that he always had the reputation of being very clever and the most able of the three brothers. A few surviving documents in his clear and precise handwriting show that, like his father, he at first did a good deal of the firm's clerical work himself, and that he had a very detailed knowledge and sound grasp of the soapery's affairs. His abilities were also evident in other spheres. He became a director of the District Bank. He was a director and vice-chairman of the Warrington Wagon Company, established in 1860. He was a prominent shareholder and auditor of the Warrington & Stockport Railway, built in the early 'fifties and absorbed in 1859 by the L. & N.W.R. In the latter railway he invested very heavily and in 1869 he became a director; soon he was serving on numerous committees of the Board. His L. & N.W.R. responsibilities became, in fact, so great that he left Warrington in 1875 and went to live in London. From now on he appears to have played a decreasing part in the affairs of Joseph Crosfield & Sons and eventually, at the beginning of 1881, he withdrew entirely from the partnership. What his share in the business then amounted to, however, is not known.

The second brother, Morland, is a very obscure figure, about whom little information has survived. Even the local obituary notices, often so fulsome in this period, are terse and uncommunicative. He appears to have played a subordinate role in the business. He died, at the end of 1875, at the early age of forty-eight. He left an estate valued at nearly £90,000. When it is remembered that the business was divided between the three brothers, yet Morland left a fortune between four and five times as great as his father's, some impression is gained of the growing prosperity of the firm.

His death, occurring at the same time as George's removal to London, left the business mainly in the hands of the youngest of the three brothers, John, then nearly forty-four years of age. After George's retirement in 1882—followed by his death in

1887—John became sole proprietor. George had no sons, while those of Morland—Ernest Morland (b. 1857) and Sydney Morland (b. 1861)—though brilliant sportsmen, apparently had no capacity or interest in business and spent most of their days shooting, fishing, and cricketing. John therefore remained in sole command, but from the middle 'eighties onwards his sons, Arthur Henry (b. 1865), Joseph John (b. 1866), and George Rowlandson (b. 1877), entered the business and began to relieve him of responsibility.

CHAPTER VII

GROWTH AND TECHNICAL
DEVELOPMENT

SOAPMAKING processes changed much more in the second half of
the nineteenth century than in the first. The removal of the
Excise duty, the rapidly growing demand for soap, and the
applications of science brought about many technological
changes. Nevertheless, old-fashioned methods still lingered on.
Some of the old coppers or pans were still being used at the
end of the century, though many new ones had been installed.
The 1815 'Waterloo' pan, for example, was still in use at
Crosfield's, in the same buildings, which were then a hundred
years old. Soap-boiling was still, to a considerable extent, an
art or craft handed on from generation to generation. It is
doubtful whether William Lever would have succeeded with
'Sunlight' soap had he not enticed Edward Wainwright, the
soap-boiler, from Crosfield's. Members of the Wainwright
family had long been employed at Bank Quay and had acquired a great fund of practical experience. 'Ted' Wainwright
was a typical Lancashire working-man, devoid of scientific
training, yet a master of the art of soap-boiling. Lever got not
only him but also his brother and three sons, by paying higher
wages, and the Wainwrights, as Professor Wilson has pointed
out, 'pretty well monopolized the knowledge of practical soapmaking of Lever Brothers'. When Wainwright, offended over a
staff appointment, threatened to remove himself, his family, and
his secrets elsewhere, Percy J. Winser, Lever's works manager,
himself a trained chemist, wrote to Lever: 'There is no one in
his Dept. (except his *son* and his *brother*) who has *any idea* of
soapmaking, and a change would be very awkward.' Lever was
therefore obliged to smooth matters over. This illustrates very
clearly that at this time practical know-how still counted for a
good deal more than scientific theory in the processes of soap-
boiling.

Nevertheless, applied science and technology were making

67

important contributions to soapmaking. *The Grocer*, reporting on a visit to the soapworks of William Gossage & Sons at Widnes early in 1863, remarked that 'since the removal of the obstructions presented by the former Excise regulations', soap-making 'has been greatly advanced by the application of chemical science; in fact it has become a chemical manufac-ture, and its success as a commercial pursuit must be greatly dependent on the amount of practical science applied' to it. Gossage's soapworks, started only in 1855, were an outstanding example of successfully applied science: Gossage had numerous patents to his credit in alkali manufacture, soapmaking, etc. Like Joseph Crosfield, he had been trained originally as a chemist or druggist. His works soon became the biggest in the north of England and Crosfield's most powerful rival.

None of the Crosfields could rival William Gossage in applied science, but George Crosfield was strongly interested in it and in technical education.[1] There still survives at Crosfield's works a copy of the *Elements of Chemistry, Including the Application of Science in the Arts* (1842), by Thomas Graham, F.R.S., Professor of Chemistry in University College, London: it has George Crosfield's signature in it and is dated 'Warrington, 1843'. Markings in this book reveal his interest in the chemistry of soda and potash and their compounds, especially the silicates— a very early foreshadowing of their important part in Cros-field's future. Many patents were taken out for improvements in soapmaking and allied processes during this period, and al-though the Crosfields do not appear to have been inventive themselves, they were usually quick to appreciate the advan-tages of new techniques and to secure licences to use them.

The application of steam, both for heating and power, had already begun in the first half of the nineteenth century. It was utilized in both ways by Crosfield's. Joseph had used steam power for grinding kelp, but did not apparently use piped steam for heating the pans. His sons certainly did; they also used steam for melting and purifying tallow and oils, and for causticizing soda by heating the liquor together with lime in deep cylindrical iron vessels. They used it similarly, as we shall see, in the silicate plant. Steam power was also applied to 'crutching', i.e., mixing scents and colours with soap to produce

[1] See below, pp. 122–3.

68

6 (*a*) Soap pan, 1896

6 (*b*) Soap agitators, 1896

7 (a) Soap frame-room, 1896

7 (b) Bar soap department, 189[

what were called in the early 'forties 'toilet' or 'fancy' or 'perfumed' soaps. In 1860 these processes were still stated by J. S. Muspratt, in his *Chemistry, Theoretical, Practical, and Analytical*, to 'belong more properly to perfumery than to the soap manufacture', but they were increasingly introduced into soapworks in the second half of the century. The ingredients were generally mixed together by hand with wooden 'crutches' or paddles, but at the beginning of January 1870 John Crosfield entered in his note-book, 'Crutched 1st soap by Steam'.

Steam power was also utilized for pumping water or brine, melted tallow and oils, and alkaline lyes into the pans, for pumping away spent lyes, and for pumping the liquid soap from the pans into the crutching vessels or to the frames for cooling. This increasing use of steam required more boilers and engine-houses, and more coal fuel; the works tended to become a maze of pipes, while many of the old manual operations, such as ladling soap into buckets, etc., tended to disappear.

One of the most important developments in the second half of the nineteenth century was the increasing use of sodium silicate as both a detergent and a 'filler' (or 'builder') in soap. The method of producing this 'soluble glass' was described in Thomas Graham's *Elements of Chemistry* (1842), of which George Crosfield had a copy, i.e. 'by fusing together 8 parts of carbonate of soda (or 10 of carbonate of potash) with 15 of sand [silica] and 1 of charcoal'. It was stated in C. Tomlinson's *Cyclopaedia of Useful Arts* (1852) that 'silicated soap . . . is an excellent article. It is a mixture of silicate of soda with hard soap to the extent of one-fifth . . . the additional quantity of alkali increases the detergent properties of the article'. But there was an obvious possibility of adulteration, by increasing the proportion of silicate and by mixing Cornish clay, fuller's earth, etc., with it to act as a 'filler'. Filled soaps might also contain a high proportion of brine or water, being termed 'liquored' or 'run' soaps. An article in *The Queen* in May 1866 referred to the increase in such adulteration, which had been condemned by the Manchester Chamber of Commerce. But there was an increasing market for cheap 'filled' soaps, especially in the export trade.

The use of sodium silicate was stimulated by the shortage and high price of Russian tallow during the Crimean War. It was at this time that William Gossage entered soapmaking, by patenting in 1855 a process for the production of good cheap soap from palm oil and silicate of soda. Firstly, he prepared the silicate, or 'soluble glass', by fusing nine parts of soda ash with eleven of fine white sand in a reverberatory furnace. The molten silicate was then 'tapped' into moulds (see illustration facing p. 205). After cooling and solidifying, it was broken up, ground to powder, and dissolved in boiling water in a large iron pan or cistern, into which steam was injected. The solution was then concentrated in an evaporating pan or boiler, after which it was ready for addition to soap in a special mixing vessel; the mixture was crutched either manually or mechanically.

It is very probable that Crosfield's acquired from Gossage a licence to use this process. A new rating valuation of Warrington in 1863 provides evidence that they then had a 'silica works', and a report on an accident in these works in December 1872, when one man was killed and another injured, gives a few details of how the silicate solution was prepared. There were

two large [iron] cisterns or pans used for dissolving silicate of soda. Each of them was about 9 ft. in height, and about the same in diameter, and were built in an upright position upon a foundation of brick, one or two feet from the ground. The silicate with which they are charged is placed in a number of wire baskets, and by means of water and steam, the latter supplied from the boilers, the silicate is reduced from a hard substance resembling glass into a liquid. . . . Only one cistern or pan is used at a time, the second being charged whilst the first is being run off.

The pans were apparently fitted with mechanically operated 'agitators'. John Crosfield stated at the Coroner's inquest that the pans used to be open-topped, but that to save steam and coal fuel, and to dissolve the silicate more quickly, they were fitted with covers and steam was injected under pressure.

Silicate was increasingly used by Crosfield's in the making of soap. Very brief statements in John Crosfield's note-book show that in August–October 1878 they were using 'no hydrate', but a certain proportion of silicate liquor, to produce mottled soap of 45 per cent fatty acid content. This and previous mentions of 'hydrate' probably refer to another method of producing cheaper soaps, patented by James Blake and Francis Maxwell, of Liverpool, in 1856–7, by addition of 'hydrated' soap— saponified matter not deprived of its water, the alkaline lyes being fully combined, i.e. the fats or oils and alkali were exactly proportioned so as to be neutralized. This patent also included a process for enabling larger quantities of resin to be used in making soaps. Crosfield's paid Blake and Maxwell £1,000 in 1857 for an exclusive licence to use these patented processes.

Applied chemistry had revolutionized the production of soda in the first half of the century, and Joseph Crosfield had been one of the first soapmakers to appreciate the possibilities of the Leblanc process. His son George took over his interest in the alkali manufacturing firm of Gamble & Crosfield's at St. Helen's.[1] J. C. Gamble withdrew from the partnership in 1845, when it became Crosfield Brothers & Co.; control was mainly in the hands of Joseph's two brothers, James and Simon. The Warrington soapery no doubt continued to obtain most of its soda supplies from this source. James Crosfield died in 1852 and George withdrew from the business in 1857, leaving it in the hands of Simon (d. 1864) and his son Alfred, together with James Shanks (d. 1867). They had one of the biggest chemical works in St. Helens, but eventually, after Alfred Crosfield's death in 1877, it had to be put up for sale and passed out of the control of the Crosfield family.

It is not clear what arrangements Joseph Crosfield & Sons made for soda supplies after George withdrew from the St. Helens partnership. Possibly, as had been reported in 1837, they still made some of their own soda ash. But they were evidently unable to produce all their requirements and continued to obtain supplies from Crosfield Brothers & Co. or from other alkali firms in the St. Helens–Widnes area. John Crosfield's note-book contains a list of salt-cake (sodium sulphate) and soda ash (sodium carbonate) prices for the period 1863–72, and refers not only to Crosfield Brothers but also to the Mersey Chemical Company (William Pilkington & Son) of Widnes, with whom, apparently, his firm had dealings.

Since the prices of salt-cake are on several occasions quoted as

---

[1] Prosecutions against this and other alkali firms continued on account of damage caused by hydrochloric acid gas, e.g. in 1846 Sir John Gerard was awarded £1,000 against Muspratt, £400 against Crosfield's, and £300 against Gamble's.

'delivered here', Crosfield's appear to have been buying the half-processed material from alkali firms and evidently had their own furnaces for completion of the process. At the same time they were also contracting to buy soda ash, and must have had plant not only for causticizing white ash, as previously explained, but also for refining black ash, by lixiviation with water, followed by evaporation. But the product still contained sulphurous impurities. In 1854, therefore, they had obtained for £300 a licence from Gossage to use his process (patented the year previously) for 'oxydizing black ash liquors'—ridding them of these impurities—'by exposing such liquors . . . to the action of atmospherical air' while trickling through coke in a high tower, like the Gossage towers used to condense the hydrochloric acid vapours produced in the Leblanc process. They were allowed to use this 'for the purpose of their said Manufacture of Soap but not for any other purpose', i.e. they were not to compete with Gossage in the alkali trade.

In 1864 Crosfield's obtained a licence to use another Gossage process, patented in 1857, for recovery of sulphur from Leblanc alkali waste. John Brunner referred in a letter to Ludwig Mond of 17th March 1865 to Crosfield's working such a process. Though this proved unsuccessful, the attempt indicates that they still had their own soda ash furnaces. This is confirmed by surviving records of the weights of 'black ash balls' produced at the works in 1877.

A new development in the firm's methods of soda manufacture is evident from an entry in John Crosfield's note-book in April 1877 that they now had a 'Revolver at work'. This must have been a 'black-ash revolver', which mechanized the 'balling' process at Leblanc furnaces, by placing the materials (saltcake, coke, and limestone) in a large cylindrical iron furnace, lined with fire-brick, and rotated by steam power (see illustration facing p. 204).

In 1881, however, a new era began for the firm when John Crosfield became the first chairman of Brunner, Mond & Co., Ltd. The German Jew, Ludwig Mond, and John Brunner of Widnes had successfully introduced the Belgian Solvay or ammonia process for production of soda into Britain. In this process, ammonia is absorbed in brine and the liquid is then carbonated in tall 'Solvay towers' by injection of carbon dioxide produced from calcination of limestone; the sodium bicarbonate thereby produced is then heated to form sodium carbonate or soda ash. In 1873 Brunner and Mond established chemical works at Winnington, Cheshire, conveniently situated for salt and coal supplies, and today the headquarters of the I.C.I. Alkali Division.

In 1880–1 the firm was converted into a limited company. According to the private diary of A. W. Tangye, later a director of Brunner, Mond & Co.,[1] Ludwig Mond had hoped to get one of the big Leblanc makers as the first chairman, but failed to do so, and was therefore very pleased to get John Crosfield, who, as a leading soap manufacturer, would be valuable in helping to develop the market for ammonia-soda in that industry. At the same time Crosfield provided additional capital. There is a tradition that in their early days Brunner and Mond were so hard pressed that John Crosfield at one time had to provide them with cash to pay their workmen's wages. The reminiscences of his third son, George R. Crosfield, reveal that he originally invested £10,000 in Brunner, Mond & Co. At the time of his death he held 17,500 £1 Ordinary shares (fully paid up except for 1,750, on which 10s. had been paid) and 337 £10 Preference shares. He was Chairman of the company until 1891 and a director till his death ten years later. His investment proved extremely lucrative, dividends on Ordinary capital varying between about 20 and 40 per cent during this period. By 1901 the Ordinary shares had quintupled in value and his total interests in Brunner, Mond & Co. were estimated at over £89,000. At the same time he was able to secure purer soda on favourable terms and, according to his own statement in 1896, Crosfield's became Brunner, Mond & Co.'s biggest customer (see below, p. 82). It is probable that they soon ceased to produce their own soda ash, though, as we shall see, they extended their caustic plant.

The links forged with Brunner, Mond & Co., were of immense importance to Crosfield's future. One of the earliest and most striking effects was an infusion of stimulating new scientific ideas. But before considering these, we will take this opportunity of looking at the works as they existed in the middle

[1] Tangye's diary was made available by courtesy of the I.C.I. Alkali Division.

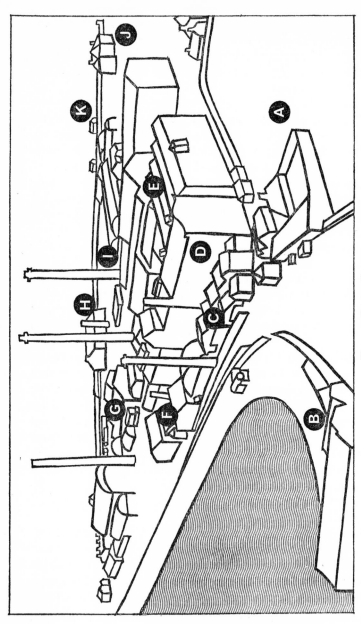

KEY TO PLATE 8

A Tallow yard
B 'Pottery' yard
C Raw materials
   (melting out)

D Soapery
E Cooling, crutching,
   cutting, packing,
   and warehousing

F Engineers' shops
G Caustic plant
H Glycerine plant
I Silicate plant

J Offices
K Joseph Crosfield's
   old house

8. Bank Quay Works, 1886

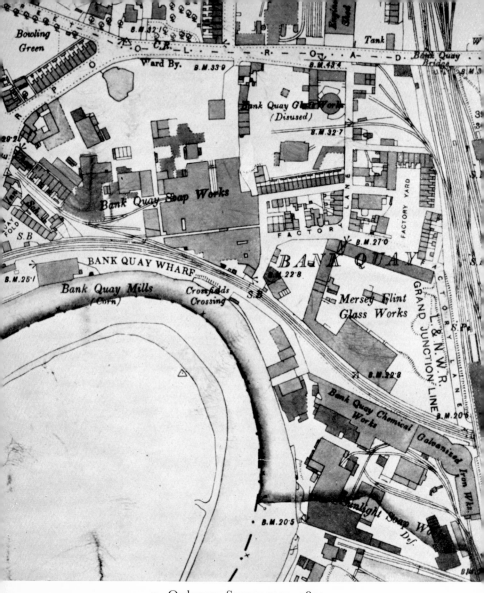

9. Ordnance Survey map, 1894

'eighties, on the threshold of a new era. We are able to do so with the fortunate aid of a description, accompanied by engravings, in the *Illustrated London News* of 13th November 1886, which referred to the Bank Quay factory as 'one of the oldest and largest soap works in the world'. The most striking illustration, a bird's eye view of the whole works, is taken from an advertising lithograph of about that date, a copy of which still survives: we have reproduced the original.[1] This shows very strikingly the firm's locational advantages, on the bank of the Mersey, with ships berthed alongside, and on the Garston railway line, with private sidings running into the works.

Here we see palm, olive, cocoanut, and many other kinds of oil arriving in casks, containing, as a rule, from 5-cwt. to 15-cwt. each; and there are some beside them containing the purest fat melted in England; but the great bulk of the casks and barrels shown in our Illustration are filled with tallow, made from the fat of sheep or oxen, brought from the remotest cattle farms in Australia, or in North and South America.

The tallow yard, full of barrels, in the right foreground, was the piece of land sub-leased from Robinson, Son & Skinner in 1869, adjoining their glassworks.

The four-storied building immediately opposite the tallow yard, near to 'Crosfield's Crossing', at the western end of Factory Lane, with a cottage or two attached, was the original soapery. (The nearest end was the former corn-mill.) It still contained soap pans. Immediately behind it were more boiling-houses, mixing, crutching and cooling rooms, and warehouses. John Crosfield's note-book reveals the gradual increase in the number of pans or coppers. In August 1870 the sixteenth copper was charged for the first time; in September 1872 the seventeenth; in April 1874 the eighteenth; and in August 1879 the nineteenth and twentieth. The *Illustrated London News* stated that there were now (1886) twenty-three pans.

Another illustration showed the raw materials being melted out of the casks by means of a steam pipe. The molten fats or oils were then pumped to the pans, one of which was illustrated.

---

[1] We have also preferred to reproduce contemporary photographs of the firm's manufacturing operations, rather than the engravings in the *Illustrated London News* (see facing pp. 68–69 and 204–5).

Into this pan are also pumped quantities of pure soda, dissolved in water. This liquor is obtained from Messrs. Brunner, Mond and Co.'s famous soda ash, the purest in the world. Messrs. Crosfield have only recently adopted its use, and, having been one of the first to do so, have thereby wonderfully improved the colour and quality of their soap.

The report went on to describe how the tallow and alkali liquor were mixed in the pans to form soap. In these 'enormous cauldrons', it was stated,

more than a hundred tons of boiling soap are worked by the single 'hand' (an old one) who stands by the valve, and controls, with a turn of his handle, the whole of this vast liquid mass. With any carelessness or inaccuracy on his part, the contents of the pan might be hurled into the air by the steam which, introduced at the bottom of the pan agitates the whole of its contents. In due course the soap, when somewhat cooled, is pumped into the frames, when it gradually becomes quite cold, and is then cut into slabs, bars, and tablets ready for packing.

Another sketch was taken in 'one of Messrs. Crosfield's eight frame-rooms; each frame being capable of containing about 12-cwt. of soap'. The next illustration showed 'a portion of the box-making department'.

Here one of the most remarkable features is the absence of hammers, the amount of hand-labour in the making of the packages being wonderfully small. The timber is sawn by machinery, and, when cut into the requisite lengths and sizes, is branded by machinery, and is actually nailed by machinery; the nails being only touched by the boys, who are required to drop them into the holes so that they take, of themselves, the position in which they are to be driven into the timber; a clever invention by Mr. Myers, a well-known American gentleman.

A plan of the works in 1853 shows that steam-powered saws were being used then, and probably earlier, in box-making, and John Crosfield's note-book refers to the starting of a new saw-mill in August 1871. He also noted in August 1881 'Myers box making machine at work' for the first time.

Finally, the *Illustrated London News* portrayed the stamping and packing processes.

. . . we see a number of lads engaged in stamping the smaller tablets of soap; but in this, as in many other things, steam is rapidly taking the place of hand-labour, and works all the machines used in stamping the famous Perfection Soap; the tablets of which are afterwards wrapped by numerous boys specially employed for this purpose.

Crosfield's were evidently progressive in utilizing steam-powered mechanization in all departments. The smoking chimneys shown in the general view of the works provide evidence of the increasing use of steam for heating and power. An internal view of the boiler shed showed a row of Lancashire boilers.

Space, unfortunately, did not admit of a verbal description of the alkali plant, but a glimpse of it was shown in a sketch. This depicted the 'black-ash revolver', for making soda, which we have previously mentioned (see illustration facing p. 204). The alkali and silicate plants can be seen in the general view of the works, to the west and north of the soapery buildings. Another interesting feature is the office building, then just erected (later to be converted into the general laboratory, and now engineering offices). John Crosfield stated in 1896 that since he first went to the works he had seen 'five or six offices built', an indication of the growing volume of clerical work.

The most important new development in the 'eighties, how-ever, was the building of a glycerine plant, bordering on Liver-pool Road. The recovery of glycerine from the soapmaker's 'spent' lye, which had hitherto been run to waste, was first developed industrially by the Frenchman Victor Clolus, who was reported in the *Warrington Guardian* of 22nd June 1881 to be manufacturing 'about three fifths of all the glycerine made in Europe and America'. After establishing glycerine works at Billancourt, near Paris, and Marseilles, he had come over to England to exploit his patent recovery process and was putting up a glycerine plant at Runcorn. (He was building another at Glasgow and was also proposing to go to the United States.) He had contracted with the soapmaking firms of Hazlehurst's at Runcorn, Gossage's at Widnes, and Crosfield's at Warrington for the purchase of their spent lye. This waste liquor consisted of a mixture of salt, glycerine, and a small quantity of soda in solution, also gelatine and albumen. The recovery process was described as follows:

The [spent] lye is concentrated by evaporation until the salts contained in it begin to crystallize. The liquid is then cooled to free it from gelatine and albumen. It is afterwards made to absorb carbonic acid, until bicarbonate of soda is precipitated and separated from the liquor. After the completion of this process, hydrochloric acid or 'spirit of salt' is passed into the liquor so as to convert any carbonate of soda which has escaped separation into chloride of sodium (common salt); this chloride of sodium is separated from the liquor by [evaporation and] crystallization.[1] This liquor then contains glycerine and a little free hydrochloric acid; after freeing it from the acid the glycerine is purified and concentrated [by distillation] . . . Glycerine is much used, not only in the manufacture of explosive compounds, but also in the preparation of toilet soaps, also for sweetening sour wines.

Crosfield's were not long content to dispose of their spent lye to the Runcorn works of M. Clolus. Within a few years they erected their own glycerine recovery plant. John Crosfield was reported in the *Warrington Examiner* of 25th July 1896 as saying that 'that was about twelve years ago'. In this new development his eldest sons—Arthur Henry and Joseph John, both then under twenty years of age—played a leading part. When their uncle George, who had recently retired from the business, saw the new building, 'he asked what it was for. They told him it was to recover the glycerine out of the spent lyes. "Well," he said, "you are two foolish lads. You have wasted £2,000 and it will be a lesson to you." ' By 1896, however, the glycerine plant had become 'the most lucrative of any part of the business'.

Another direction in which Crosfield's kept abreast—or even ahead—of the times was in the installation of electric lighting. In the late 'seventies the incandescent (carbon filament) electric light bulb was invented by Edison in America and Swan in England and the new form of illumination began to be adopted in this country in the early 'eighties. Crosfield's were among the first firms to install it. The *Warrington Guardian* reported on 10th February 1883 that their works and offices had just been 'lighted by electricity' for the first time. The earliest electric-lighting plants were mostly private ones—in the days before public power stations were built—and Crosfield's was operated by a 5 h.p. steam engine driving a dynamo, which generated

---

[1] The salt thus recovered could be used again as brine in the soap pans. See Appendix III for a flow diagram of soap and glycerine manufacture.

electricity for two to three hundred lights. These Swan incandescent light-bulbs had been installed throughout the works and offices, replacing gas lighting.

An even greater stimulus to scientific progress at Crosfield's came in about 1890 from the transfer of the German chemist, Dr. Karl Markel, from Brunner, Mond & Co. Markel, originally from Stuttgart, with a German father and an English mother, was brought over by Ludwig Mond in 1883 as a tutor to his sons, Robert and Alfred, but soon rose to an important position in the firm's laboratory. According to some notes by John Crosfield's third son, George R. Crosfield,[1] Markel had prospects of becoming a professor in one of the German universities when he was persuaded to come to England, and A. W. Tangye refers to Markel in his private diary as a 'very well trained chemist'. But there was, says Tangye, 'no trace of the Hun' about this 'vivacious charming Italian type', who was apparently something of a lady-killer as well as a clever chemist. After carrying out valuable research on various projects at Brunner, Mond & Co.'s he was sent to work on a caustic soda process at Crosfield's in 1890. John Crosfield, according to Tangye, was delighted with Markel's personality and chemical ability, and 'begged him off Dr. Mond'. Eventually Markel was appointed Works Manager and, as Tangye put it, 'completely reorganized the old fashioned and decadent Firm and made it a *great* success'.

Tangye's comments upon Crosfield's are exaggerated. The firm, as we have seen, had expanded very considerably and had become one of the biggest soapworks in the country; its products had a deservedly high reputation; it had been progressive in introducing steam-powered mechanization in many departments, and in installing electric lighting; it had been among the first soapmaking firms to develop silicate production and, more recently, glycerine recovery; it had been fairly quick to utilize improvements in the manufacture of soda ash and caustic soda, and John Crosfield was not only among the first to recognize the possibilities of Mond's ammonia-soda process, but had sufficient courage and foresight to invest a good deal of capital in Brunner, Mond & Co. They had also recruited some

---

[1] MS. 'Notes on some of the happenings at Jos. Crosfield & Sons between 1895 and 1914' (1948).

scientific personnel, for there is a reference in the *Warrington Guardian* in June 1880 to a Mr. H. B. Gurney, who was a chemist at Crosfield's works.

On the other hand, there is little doubt that some of the buildings and plant were old and out-of-date, and that although the firm had been progressive in developing production of silicate, caustic soda, and glycerine, its efforts were handicapped by inadequate scientific knowledge. Yet whereas some firms might have continued along traditional lines and have gradually gone downhill, John Crosfield and his sons were intelligent and adaptable enough to realize their shortcomings and to take steps to remedy them, by recruiting Markel and other scientists and by acquiring more capital to permit the scrapping of outdated plant, the erection of new buildings and development of new processes.

George R. Crosfield's 'Notes' provide further insight into these developments:

> The competition from Lever Bros. [who had started up in Warrington in 1885 and removed to Port Sunlight at the beginning of 1889] was at that time bearing down heavily on Crosfields' soap trade and it was decided therefore, with the help of Markel, to develop the chemical side, confining ourselves to those products which were naturally linked up with the soap manufacture, namely, caustic soda, silicate of soda, glycerine in all its branches, and later on, edible fats.

This shift from soap into chemicals was not new, but it was to become increasingly important. By the 'nineties Crosfield's were describing themselves as 'soap makers and chemical manufacturers'.

In John Crosfield's obituary in the *Warrington Guardian*, 28th December 1901, it was stated that from about 1890 the works had been put 'on a thoroughly scientific basis'. Several laboratories were built to analyse and test raw materials and finished products. A works plan of 1896 shows the main laboratory in some converted cottages at Quay Fold. Each production department was said to have been 'placed under the charge of a trained chemist'. At this time Germany was ahead of England in many branches of applied science, and Markel, according to George R. Crosfield, 'was obsessed with the idea that no good chemist came out of England, and the consequence was that we began to get an overdose of German scientists in the Works'. Moreover, 'Markel's knowledge of scientific development on the Continent made him emphasize the importance of Crosfield's getting into touch with oil and soap firms overseas, and this factor accounts for the frequent visits which our representatives made to the Continent.'

These continental links were, as we shall see, to be extremely important—in the development of the Sabatier-Normann hydrogenation process for fat-hardening, for instance, and in the agreement with the German firm of Henkel for production of 'Persil'. One of the earliest examples of Markel's influence was an agreement of 30th June 1890 with Dr. Eugen Schaal, chemist, of Stuttgart, in regard to the development of a process (for which he had filed patent specifications in 1884–5) 'for converting petroleum and other hydrocarbons into acids soaps and compounds analogous in constitution to resins and ethers'.[1] Crosfield's acquired sole and exclusive use of this process for three years, during which they were to test it in their works and try to render it a commercial success; if it was successful, they would have the monopoly of its use and sale during the period of the patent; Schaal was to have 25 per cent of the net profits from it. Crosfield's were not, however, successful in this venture into the then comparatively undeveloped field of petroleum chemicals. It is indicative, nevertheless, of their growing interest in developing new and cheaper sources of oils, etc. for soapmaking, which was soon to lead them to the successful development of the hydrogenation process.

In a speech celebrating the conversion of the firm into a limited company in 1896, John Crosfield gave full credit to Markel for modernizing the works. Indeed he was inclined to depreciate too much the firm's earlier and inevitably cruder pioneering efforts. He referred to the 'new period' which began with Markel's arrival:

He set to work to apply scientific knowledge where they had been merely common practical manufacturers without any chemical knowledge. The first thing he did was to pull down all their old Lancashire steam boilers about seven feet in diameter and put in new ones all eight or nine feet in diameter constructed with proper flues and so saved the combustion of fuel. When Dr. Markel came

[1] See R. F. Goldstein, *The Petroleum Chemicals Industry* (1958), pp. 62–3.

they evaporated 4 lb. of water to every pound of fuel and today they evaporated 9 lb.[1] from the same quantity of fuel . . . They then worked at 40 lb. pressure in their boilers; now they worked at 90 lb. pressure . . .

When Dr. Markel came he . . . transformed the whole manufacture of glycerine . . . and he has succeeded . . . in manufacturing absolutely pure glycerine which no firm in the world except themselves had done out of spent lyes. The demand for it was so great that they were beginning to double the plant.

Well, then, Dr. Markel attacked the manufacture of silicate of soda . . . He (Mr. Crosfield) began to make silicate of soda about 35 years ago, and a 'bonny mess' he made of it. But they kept on doing it in a crude kind of fashion until Dr. Markel came, and he thought he could say it without any boasting that they are now the finest makers of silicate of soda in this kingdom or the next.[2]

Dr. Markel also began the manufacture of caustic soda [i.e. pure caustic soda for sale, as distinct from caustic lyes for their own soap-making] and he believed their caustic soda ranks higher than any in the market. It is a most beautiful manufacture. They were the largest consumers of Brunner Mond's pure alkali in the world; they were using 10,000 tons a year.

It seems that in the late 'eighties, even before Markel's arrival, Crosfield's had been developing a new process, using ferric oxide, for causticizing soda, in addition to the older lime process. This process was referred to in a Crosfield patent of 1887 for an improved machine for mixing granular materials, which was 'designed especially for mixing soda ash and oxide of iron for caustic making'. When the Society of Chemical Industry visited Bank Quay in July 1906, they made particular mention of this 'Loewig or Ferrite process', which was

first successfully carried out in these works . . . visitors from all parts of the world having come to see it in operation. Iron Oxide 'Blue Billy' and Soda Ash are mixed and heated in a gas-fired revolving furnace [like the black-ash revolver] for several hours; carbon dioxide is given off and Sodium Ferrite is produced, which is treated with water in lixiviating tanks, producing a solution of Caustic Soda

---

[1] This is either an exaggeration or a misprint for 6 lb.

[2] In November 1893 they secured from F. Siemens & Co. a licence to use an improved regenerative gas-fired furnace for this manufacture. In 1894-5 J. J. Crosfield and Markel patented a process for evaporating silicate of soda solutions in a vacuum, instead of in open vessels as previously; thus they obtained a product in solid form.

of high strength. The Ferric Oxide is again used in the revolver with fresh Soda Ash, thus making a 'circular tour'.

The firm's plans for expansion during the 'nineties were restricted, however, by shortage of land and capital. Most of the land acquired in the third quarter of the century (Bank Quay Field, etc.) was now covered with buildings, and all the adjoining areas—once open fields—between the river and the main L. & N.W.R. line were by this time in the occupation of other industrial firms (see map facing p. 75). Shortage of land for expansion in this area had made Lever Brothers move to Port Sunlight, and it caused the building congestion at Crosfield's which William Lever remarked on in a letter after visiting their works in November 1900:

> I went through Messrs. Crosfields' works at Warrington last week, and while I may say their Managing Director [in charge of production], Dr. Markel, has done all a man possibly can do with works crowded into the middle of a town, and with cottages on all sides, and actually a right of way to the Public through the very centre of the Works, still the working conditions are enough to damp the ardour of the most enthusiastic. Buildings are piled storey upon storey, departments interlace and overlap, some are badly lighted owing to the impossibility of getting daylight into them, and in the frame room they actually have to have an arrangement by which they can take up the flooring from certain sections as soon as the frames are emptied, in order to let light into the floor below.[1]

The land shortage was eased to some extent by the acquisition of the leasehold land and property of the Bank Quay Glass Works in 1893. After the death of Charles Henry Cartwright in 1884 this bottle-making business soon collapsed, and Crosfield's acquired the land and buildings in September 1893 for £3,000. In addition to the glassworks site in the corner formed by Liverpool Road and Factory Lane (but excluding the cottages of Glasshouse Row), they obtained a small area on the other side of Factory Lane, with a private railway siding from the L. & N.W.R. line.

The derelict glassworks were knocked down, but most of the

---

[1] According to the manuscript reminiscences of the late A. Tilling, the flooring was removed 'to enable the frames to be built up to a greater height from the ground floor, thus conserving space and helping the circulation of air to dry the soap'.

land was undeveloped and used only as a yard in 1896. Some new buildings had, however, been put up on the southern portion. Of these the most interesting was that for increased production of toilet soaps. The great bulk of Crosfield's trade had always been in household or washing soaps, though they had produced scented tablets for some years. Rising standards of living, however, were now combining with manufacturing improvements to increase the importance of the toilet trade. For this, the soap base was reduced to shreds, dried in hot-air stoves, and then 'milled' by being passed several times through massive granite rollers, to make it thoroughly smooth and ready for mixing with specially blended perfumes and colours. The soap, now in 'ribbons', saturated with scent, was next passed through a 'plodding' machine—akin to a sausage-making machine—from the nozzle of which it was extruded in a continuous bar, which was then cut and stamped into tablets, which were wrapped and packed for sale (see illustration facing p. 176).[1]

Crosfield's various 'Erasmic' soaps—'La Belle', 'Duchess', 'Countess', 'Peerless', and 'Herb', registered between 1886 and 1889—were now being vigorously developed, in addition to the older 'Honey', 'Castile', and 'Windsor' scented soaps, and the firm was extending its milling and other departments. They also begun to develop a trade in perfumery and other toilet requisites.

The growing numbers of wrappers, cartons, and boxes, and the expansion in advertising, with posters, show-cards, hand-bills, etc., led to the establishment of a letterpress and litho-graphic printing department on the former glassworks land, together with a new saw-mill and box-making department, and timber and box stores.

Another interesting reference in the key to the works plan of 1896 is to the production of 'dry soap', or soap powder, in the old soapery. How long Crosfield's had been making this it has been impossible to discover; it was not produced in any great quantity, as Hudson's dominated this field, but it pointed the way to 'Persil' and their other modern washing powders.

On 15th November 1894 the leasehold land on which the original soapery was built was made freehold by deed poll.

[1] See Appendix III for a flow diagram of soap manufacture at this period.

Immediately afterwards, on 21st December 1894, John Crosfield transferred all his freehold and leasehold land at Bank
Quay to his sons, Arthur and J. J. (as he was usually called).
He had been gradually withdrawing from active control of the
business, and this transfer was preparatory to the conversion of
Joseph Crosfield & Sons into a limited company, whereby more
capital could be acquired to finance new developments (see
below, Chapter X).

During the preceding half-century Crosfield's production of
soap had risen very considerably, but much more rapidly in the
third quarter than in the last. John Crosfield recorded weekly,
monthly, and yearly output or 'delivery' figures very conscien-
tiously in the early part of his note-book. In 1855 and 1856,
years affected by the Crimean War, annual output was about
3,200 tons, but rose rapidly after the war to 4,096 tons in 1857
and 4,759 tons in 1858. Expansion continued in the generally
depressed years of 1859 (4,985 tons) and 1860 (5,250 tons), and
then rose even more swiftly, despite the American Civil War
and the 'Cotton Famine', to 6,004 tons in 1861; 6,485 tons in
1862; 7,638 tons in 1863; 8,275 tons in 1864; and 8,918 tons
in 1865. In 1866, a year of economic crisis, production fell to
8,801 tons and was still only 8,985 tons in 1867.

Unfortunately, these regular entries now ceased and only
occasional figures were henceforth recorded. Nevertheless, we
are able to see how production continued to grow in the last
quarter of the century. It rose substantially in the boom years of
the early 'seventies: in June 1871 monthly output was 969 tons,
'the largest we ever made', and annual output reached a peak
worthy of record in 1873, when it was 11,450 tons. Thereafter
no yearly figures are available; only sporadic weekly or monthly
deliveries are given, usually when new high levels were reached.
The year 1876 was evidently a very good one: a weekly output
of 303 tons was noted at the end of June, followed by 310—the
'largest yet'—for the second week in September. In the week
ending 2nd May 1877 a new record of 343 tons was achieved,
which stood unbroken for a number of years.[1] It was closely

---

[1] This was considerably below the output of Gossage's, who, at the time
of William Gossage's death in 1877, were reported to be 'the largest manufacturers of soap in the kingdom, if not in the world, turning out no less than
500 tons a week' (*Warrington Guardian*, 14th April 1877).

approached in 1885: in two of the weeks during May deliveries of 332 and 325 tons were recorded. In autumn of that year monthly output was above 1,000 tons: 1,003 tons in September and 1,019 tons in October. In the week ending 19th November 1886 a new record delivery of 348 tons was established, but output apparently fell in 1887: for the week ending 13th May it was 253 tons. No more figures appear until 1893: in the week ending 25th February the weekly record of 348 tons was equalled, and the total February output was 1,219 tons; in the week ending 4th March, a new record of 361 tons was noted.

One must be cautious in estimating annual output from these intermittent and exceptional figures in the last quarter of the century. Output often fluctuated very greatly from week to week and from month to month; the peak figures of weekly output were a good deal higher than the average. It would appear, however, that yearly production had reached about 15,000 tons by 1893.

Several interesting conclusions can be drawn from these figures. Firstly, the third quarter of the century, the era of 'Victorian Prosperity', was undoubtedly more buoyant for Crosfield's than the last quarter, the period of the 'Great Depression'. Between the middle 'fifties and 1873 production had increased between three and four times (though one must remember that in the former years output was depressed by the Crimean War, while in the latter year it was at a peak). Between 1873 and 1893 it rose apparently by no more than one-third: the peak of 1,219 tons for February 1893 was only just over one-quarter higher than the earlier peak of 969 in June 1871. During most of the 'eighties production was increasing very slowly. This is confirmation, incidentally, of A. W. Tangye's view.[1]

This falling-off in the firm's rate of growth cannot, however, be attributed to the so-called 'Great Depression', since population growth and rising living standards were causing soap consumption to increase rapidly. The national production of soap, which had risen from about 90,000 tons per annum in the early 'fifties to about 150,000 tons in 1871, reached about 260,000 tons by 1891. Crosfield's had increased their share of this expanding total output from about 3 per cent in the early 'fifties to about 7 per cent in the early 'seventies; but by the early 'nineties it

[1] See above, p. 79.

had fallen to not much more than 5 per cent. There was clearly need for Dr. Markel's radical changes.

Another feature of the output figures is that their fluctuations do not coincide with those of the general trade cycle. Indeed, they usually—though not always—display a marked contra-cyclical tendency, rising most rapidly during periods of general slump and more slowly in booms. Thus output increased more substantially during the depression of the late 'fifties and the 'Cotton Famine' of the early 'sixties than in the boom of 1865–6. The boom of the early 'seventies, by contrast, coincided with a rapid growth of production at Crosfield's. But in the slump of the late 'seventies output rose to new heights. There are no figures for the general recovery of the early 'eighties, but during the deep depression in the middle of that decade Crosfield's again broke production records. And these were once more shattered in the slump year of 1893. The main reason for this output behaviour was the steadily rising demand for soap, even during the so-called 'Great Depression', combined with the sharp decline in prices of raw materials during slumps.[1]

There are no surviving statistics of Crosfield's output of chemical products for this period, but there is no doubt that in the later part of the century they were producing growing quantities of silicate of soda, caustic soda, and glycerine, not merely for their own soapmaking, but increasingly for sale. Surviving freight-rate quotations show that from the 'seventies onwards they were sending silicate to places as far apart as London and Glasgow, and exporting it to Ireland and the Continent; there are also a few references to carriage of soda and glycerine from Warrington.

Their manufacture of candles had apparently ceased many years earlier. They were listed among the tallow chandlers in the Warrington directory of 1861, but not in that of 1871. The only surviving piece of evidence about this manufacture is a book in George Crosfield's handwriting recording output between late 1852 and early 1859, which clearly shows that this side of the business was relatively unimportant and was being run down. Output declined from nearly 82,000 'dozens' (lots each of a dozen pounds) in 1853 to about 31,000 'dozens' in 1858, while the number of chandlers employed dwindled from

[1] See below, p. 105.

four to one only by 1859. The candles were all 'dipped', made by means of manually-operated dipping 'machines'; a small proportion of mould candles were supplied by other chandlers. The trade was a very seasonal one: output rose to a maximum in the darkest months between November and February, when candles were in greatest demand, fell off rapidly in the spring, and ceased entirely in the summer.

The decline of candle-making was insignificant within Crosfield's general expansion. This growth is evident not merely in buildings and output, but also in numbers employed. Although steam-powered mechanization effected labour-saving economies, the great increase in the scale of production necessitated a growing labour force. According to the Excise report of 1837, there were then sixteen men in the soapery. A considerable increase occurred in the second half of the century. During the municipal elections in October 1871 John Crosfield spoke of 'the 120 workpeople whom they employed', and by the mid-'eighties the number had risen to about 250. Expansion was even more rapid in the next few years, so that by 1896, according to the company prospectus of that year, there were over 800 employees.

Personal testimony to the firm's growth and technical development during this period is provided by the recollections of John Willett,[1] who came to Bank Quay in 1866 and retired in 1922:

> When I started at Crosfields' it was a very small place, in fact the Works were in a field. There were very few hands employed; we knew every one by name . . . Mr. Tom Wainwright was the manager of the Soap Running Department . . . My first job was running lurries from the cutters to the cutting machines. All soap was cut by the hand-box—we had no patent cutting machines . . . We had to carry all the runnings to the frames and mix them in by hand crutch—we had no mixers in those days. When we were crutching stiff ones it was hard work, I can assure you . . . We did not make many varieties, only three—pale, brown, and blue mottle. I cannot possibly remember all we make today. A public entry ran through the works into Quay Fold, and it divided the soap rooms from the pans, or the 'stage' as it was called then. The soap was pumped down spouts, some we carried in pails on our heads . . .

---

[1] In *Crosfield's Flag*, Spring 1922.

All the pans were on the ground floor, and the soap was boiled by fire, no steam then. The manager of that Department was Jacky Long, a man who always 'thee'd and thou'd' everybody [in Quaker style][1] . . . There were only nine pans then . . . Numbers 1, 2, and 3 we made blue mottle in, so it only left six pans for pale and brown. Then the Firm began to increase and [before long] they put down the sixteenth and seventeenth copper. We had started to make 'Perfection'. [He remembered how Arthur Crosfield came to the works in 1882, 'put on the white slop and apron and learned the trade', how later he went out travelling and 'built up the export trade'.] Orders came in splendidly, especially for 'Blue Mottle'. They had to set to work and make more mottle frames. All the rooms upstairs were full. Then they had the room built which is now the toilet room, and filled that with mottle frames . . . Then they began to extend and took in a piece of land that ran along the Works, which belonged to Major Cartwright. That was not enough, so they took the Bank Quay Bottle Works, and have gone on increasing ever since. Looking 56 years back and then looking at today, it is marvellous how the Works have grown. There was no glycerine plant in the old days, and we were glad to get rid of the spent lyes as best we could, and today . . . Crosfields' glycerine is known all over the world, as well as 'Perfection', 'Pink Carbolic', and 'Golden Pale'.

[1] According to Sir Arthur Crosfield, 'Jackie' Long had begun to work in the firm 'at something like seven years of age, and therefore had worked for many years under my grandfather'. He retired on a pension in the 1880's, when 'the old-fashioned era of the soap trade' was drawing to a close (*Crosfields' Flag*, Jan. 1921).

CHAPTER VIII

TRADE AND TRANSPORT

TECHNOLOGICAL developments, important though they were, did not take up so much of the partners' time as the commercial side of the business. Since the cost of raw materials formed a large part of the total cost of production—upwards of 60 per cent[1]—it is not surprising that their purchasing was a constant preoccupation. At the same time, the marketing of soap products, in what was still a highly competitive trade, also required much attention. John Crosfield's note-book, to which several references have already been made, is devoted almost entirely—except for very occasional and brief remarks on technical innovations—to recording prices and purchases of raw materials, prices and sales of products, and output figures. It covers the period from 1854 to 1893. The figures become very scrappy from 1886, but until that date he wrote down in great detail, at intervals of only a few days, the prices of all the varieties of animal fats, vegetable oils, and rosin in Liverpool, London, Hull, and other markets; less frequently the prices of salt-cake and soda ash; and regularly the prices of the main kinds of soap.

The two main raw material markets, on which John Crosfield kept constant watch, were Liverpool and London. Liverpool was the firm's chief source of supply, but London was especially important for tallow. Purchases were also made in Hull, particularly of cottonseed and linseed oil. Tallow was still their main raw material, and many varieties were purchased: in addition to home supplies, beef and mutton tallow came from Russia, Australia, and North and South America, and also lard, bonegrease, and horse-grease. Palm oil, obtained from the flesh of the oil-palm fruit, came mostly from Nigeria, in several varieties according to local origin—Lagos, Benin, Bonny, and Old Calabar—and also from the Cameroons. Palm-nut oil was also purchased in considerable quantity. Coconut oil came mainly

[1] See below, p. 178.

from Ceylon, Cochin, and Sydney (the South Sea Islands); copra, the dried flesh of the coconut, from which the oil or fat had to be pressed, was also quoted, but probably not purchased. Increasing amounts of cottonseed and linseed oil were bought in the later decades of the century. Rosin was regularly in demand; American varieties tended to displace French. Alkali or soda supplies we have already examined.

Prices of all these raw materials varied considerably. That of tallow, for example, varied according to whether it was beef or mutton tallow, or low-grade bone-grease or horse-grease; whether it was home-produced 'town tallow', or from Russia, or North or South America, or Australia, and also according to local qualities in these main markets; whether new or old; whether 'finest', 'good', 'medium', or 'common'; whether 'bracked' or 'unbracked' (i.e. whether or not sorted and graded); whether bought 'on spot' or 'to arrive', i.e. for future delivery (often expressed as either 'for consumption' or 'on contract'); whether bought in London or Liverpool; and whether or not delivered in Warrington. Similar variations occurred in other fats and oils. There were also marked fluctuations in the prices of all raw materials according to the rise and fall of the trade cycle—the pattern of boom and slump—but the amplitude of these swings varied as between different commodities. Moreover, these cycles were irregular and complicated: at this distance one can discern long-term trends, perhaps covering a quarter-century, together with trade cycles varying from about seven to eleven years; but all the time there were shorter-term seasonal or speculative changes, from month to month, or week to week, or even day to day.

John Crosfield's attention was mainly concentrated on the short-term fluctuations. We have not space here, however, to consider either all the variations in different raw materials, or price movements over short periods. A brief outline of the main trends in the 'spot' price of London Y.C. (Yellow Colour) tallow will serve as a guide to those of fats and oils generally.

When John Crosfield began his note-book, the price of tallow had risen very high as a result of the Crimean War, since Russia was at that time the main source of imports. It averaged about 63s. per cwt. in 1855, but fell, fluctuatingly, in the post-war years. In the late 'fifties it fluctuated between 50s. and 60s.; in the 'sixties and early 'seventies between 40s. and 50s.

During the last quarter of the century, there was a 'Great Depression' of prices, and tallow dropped to a much lower level. In the slump of the middle 'eighties, and again in the middle 'nineties, it fell as low as 21s. This great fall was due not merely to the general factors producing the 'Great Depression', but also to the greatly increased supplies of tallow following the immense development of cattle-rearing and sheep-farming in the Americas and Australia.

The cyclical fluctuations and long-term trends in the prices of other fats and oils corresponded generally with those of tallow. But there were some variations worth noticing. The price of palm oil, for example, which Crosfield's also bought in great quantity, was not liable to such sharp and large fluctuations as that of tallow, though it tended to follow roughly the same cyclical pattern. It was generally about 10s. per cwt. below that of tallow, but in a boom tallow sometimes rose 20s. or more above palm oil, while in a slump it fell to within 3s. or 4s. of it. Moreover, looking at prices over the whole period, palm oil did not fall to the same extent as tallow, i.e. there was a long-run tendency for the gap between their prices to narrow. Coconut oil, on the other hand, fluctuated much more in price than palm oil and was generally somewhat dearer; on occasions it rose considerably higher than tallow. This no doubt accounts for the fact that from the late 'sixties onwards prices of coconut oil were less frequently quoted by John Crosfield, whereas cottonseed and linseed oils, which were generally from 5s. to 10s. per cwt. cheaper than palm oil, were recorded more and more often. Thus Crosfield's and other soapmakers benefited greatly both from the generally declining trend in the prices of traditional raw materials such as tallow and palm oil and also from access to these cheaper oils. John Crosfield had to keep a sharp eye, however, on the relative prices of these various commodities, which were continually changing.

Similar variations occurred in the prices of rosin. Increasing supplies from North America made it very much cheaper. From being but a few shillings per hundredweight below the price of palm oil in the early 'sixties, it fell to only a third or even a quarter of the latter.

Prices of salt-cake and soda also fluctuated. They do not occur in John Crosfield's note-book until the early 'sixties, perhaps because the firm was not dealing in the market, but obtaining supplies from Crosfield Brothers at St. Helens. Average prices are listed, however, for the years 1863–72. These show a gradual rise in the price of soda ash from 7s. or 7s. 6d. per cwt. in the slump of 1863–4 to 12s. in the boom year of 1866, followed by a fall in the subsequent trade depression to just over 7s. in 1870–1; they then began to rise again in the following boom. Thus there were very considerable fluctuations—prices at the peak of a boom might be nearly double those at the bottom of a slump—but the changes appear to have occurred more gradually than those in fats and oils.

All these raw materials were bought in considerable and increasing bulk. Single purchases of up to 1,000 pipes or casks of tallow, and of up to 1,000 tons of palm oil, are recorded. Amounts varied, however, not only according to manufacturing requirements, but also according to the partners' view of future supplies and prices; stocks, of course, similarly varied. John Crosfield's note-book shows that the firm followed a fairly successful policy of buying heavily and sometimes on long-term contracts during periods of generally depressed trade, when raw material prices were at their lowest, and of trying to hold off from the market or to purchase smaller quantities in periods of generally booming trade, when raw materials were high; they would then live off their accumulated fat, stocks of which might be run down to low levels. Examples of this policy are their very large purchases of fats and oils in the general depressions of the early 'sixties, the late 'seventies, and middle 'eighties, when prices were at extremely low levels. Similarly, if a boom was developing and raw material prices looked like rising sharply, large purchases might be made, as in February 1872, when John Crosfield bought 1,000 casks of tallow at 42s. to 43s. per cwt., just before the price shot up by more than half.

Examples of long-term contracts made in slump periods are their agreements towards the end of 1878 for obtaining sixty tons of palm-nut oil per month at 35s. 6d. per cwt. during 1879, and for fifteen tons of cottonseed oil per week at 26s. 3d. per cwt.; a similar contract for palm-nut oil was made a year later. A six months' contract for soda ash at 8s. 3d. per cwt. was made in June 1867, and a year's contract for salt-cake at 47s. 6d. per ton in August 1880, covering 1881. But such long-term contracts appear to have been unusual: the partners were evidently unwilling to bind themselves in such a fluctuating market.

The River Mersey remained very important to Crosfield's throughout this period for transport of raw materials from Liverpool. When the London & North-Western Railway proposed in 1860 to build a bridge over the river below Warrington at Fidler's Ferry, Crosfield's strongly opposed the Bill before a Parliamentary Select Committee, together with other local traders and Warrington Corporation, on the grounds that it would seriously impede the river traffic. Not merely did they engage counsel, but George Crosfield and the captains of some of his flats gave evidence. They pointed out that almost all their raw materials came on the river from Liverpool, by means of their own sailing flats. According to George Crosfield, 5,000 tons a year came from Liverpool and 1,000 tons from Wales (probably lime). 'The cost by their own vessels was 1s. 3d. a ton, including interest on capital, or 1s. not reckoning the interest. . . . The cost by railway would be 4s. 3d. per ton, and 6d. per ton cartage. . . . The cost by hired boats was 2s. 6d. per ton.' The L. & N.W.R. had previously charged 5s. 6d. per ton, but he had beaten them down. 'Their firm only used the railway in cases of great emergency.' It would cost them £900 a year more to have their goods carried by rail instead of by water. He maintained that the flats could work on 200 days out of the year, in which they made fifty or sixty trips to Liverpool and back. Perhaps these statements were exaggerated—it was pointed out that the river was often only navigable at the spring tides and that the shallow channel and sandbanks made navigation difficult—but the river was nevertheless a great asset to Crosfield's and other firms, who strongly disliked this prospect of a railway monopoly. Mainly as a result of their evidence, the Bill was thrown out.

The Mersey continued to be the main route for import of raw materials in the later part of the century. A good deal of London tallow came by water, though more perhaps came by rail. Cottonseed and linseed oils from Hull, Selby, and Leeds were mostly carried by rail. It was mainly through Liverpool, however, that Crosfield's still obtained the bulk of their imported fats and oils. Salt from Cheshire and soda from Widnes also came, for the most part, by river. Crosfield's followed Fairclough & Sons' example by putting a 'screw-steamer', called the *Ada*, of 140 tons burden, on the river in the early 'eighties, in addition to a number of flats or barges, which could now be towed by the steamer. A newspaper account of a mishap during a gale early in 1886 reveals that the *Ada* was valued at £1,800 and that she had brought a cargo of tallow and resin worth £1,000; a flat, the *Mayfly*, was valued at £450 and was loaded with salt worth £20. The engraving of the works at about this date shows the steamer, together with a sailing coaster and a flat, at the quays alongside the works (see facing p. 74). The river also provided Crosfield's with water for soapmaking and, at the same time, with an easy means of disposing of waste effluents.

These valuable advantages were threatened, however, in the early 'eighties by the proposed Manchester Ship Canal. This, as originally planned, would have run much closer to Warrington than it eventually did and would have been connected to the river below Bank Quay. Crosfield's and other riverside manufacturers feared that they would lose the existing toll-free river navigation, owing to diversion of water into the canal and consequent silting-up, and that the river would be contaminated by salt water and so rendered unfit for manufacturing purposes. For these and other reasons they and Warrington Corporation sought to secure amendments in the Ship Canal Bill of 1883.

At this critical juncture John Crosfield was Mayor of Warrington and played a leading role in negotiations with the Ship Canal promoters that eventually resulted in an agreement. The Ship Canal Bill was rejected, however, in 1883, and another Bill in 1884, but a third Bill was passed in 1885. Considerable modifications were made to the original scheme to meet Warrington's objections. One of the most important obligations laid upon the Ship Canal Company, from Crosfield's point of view, was that they were to keep the river dredged, at their own expense, so that at all times there would be a depth of eight feet at low water of spring tides between the western boundary of Monks, Hall & Co. and the eastern boundary of Warrington. Moreover, Warrington vessels were given specially favourable rates on the Ship Canal, which they would be able to use during

95

neap tides. Thus Crosfield's preserved their precious river navigation, though, as we shall see, the Ship Canal Company never properly fulfilled its dredging obligations, which were to prove a long-lasting source of dispute. The prospect of improved water carriage, however, encouraged the firm to acquire more steamers, in addition to the *Ada*—the *Constance*, the *Gertrude*, and the *George*, all between 100 and 200 tons burden, and named after children of John Crosfield. The Ship Canal was opened to traffic at the beginning of 1894.

Crosfield's soap products became increasingly diversified during this period, as new raw materials and processes were developed. John Crosfield's note-book begins in the middle 'fifties with three main types: 'XX', pale yellow household soap; 'CY', Curd Yellow apparently; and 'Mottled'. There may have been other varieties at that time, but an increasing number were produced in the following years. Better-quality soaps were developed, both household and toilet; in July 1871, for instance, John Crosfield first listed 'Golden Pale', a more highly priced soap than 'XX', and soon afterwards a 'Skin' or toilet soap. These soaps contained a high proportion of tallow, while the attractiveness of toilet soaps was improved by scents and colours; many types of mottling were also produced. At the same time, soaps were made at much lower prices by using cheaper oils and rosin and by 'filling' with silicate, etc.

One of the firm's price lists (p. 97), dated 2nd January 1872, has fortunately been preserved (now at Unilever House). It enables us to see the wide variety of soaps produced at this time.

All these prices were 'Per Cwt. at Warrington, or Free Alongside in Liverpool'. A discount of $2\frac{1}{2}$ per cent was allowed for cash payment. John Crosfield's note-book indicates that a similar or bigger discount was also given on large orders of several tons. Most of their soap was sold in bars, but the scented or toilet soaps were produced in the form of stamped tablets. An advertisement in the *Co-operative News* of 26th November 1874 shows that Golden Pale and Brown Windsor were also sold in tablets.

Crosfield's built up a strong reputation for their mottled (or marbled) soap. Muspratt's *Chemistry, Theoretical, Practical, and Analytical* (1860) particularly mentioned that 'a very superior

PALE SOAPS

1. Crosfield's Golden Pale . 35/-
[2. Is Missing]
3. Crosfield's XXX Pale
   Genuine 33/-
4. Crosfield's XX Pale . . 31/-
5. Crosfield's Tallow Crown . 30/6
6. Crosfield's Double Extra
   Pale 30/-
7. Crosfield's X Pale . . . 26/6
8. Crosfield's Extra Pale . . 25/6
9. X Pale 24/-
10. Primrose. 22/6
11. Crosfield's XL Pale . . 22/6
12. Crosfield's Crown . . . 28/-
13. XX Crown 27/-
14. Extra Crown 22/6
15. Thirds, Pale 21/-
16. Common. 19/-

CURD AND MOTTLED

21. Curd, White. 41/6
    White 31/6
    Seconds, White . . . 23/6
22. Crosfield's Finest Blue
    Mottled 25/6
23. Crosfield's Blue Mottled . 24/-
24. Grey Mottled 24-6

SCENTED

25. Honey, 1-lb., ½-lb. & ¼-lb.
    tablets in 56-lb. boxes . 40/-
26. Brown Skin, 1-lb. bars, in
    28-lb. boxes 32/-
27. Brown Skin ⎫ 1-lb., ½-lb. &
28. Almond   ⎬ ¼-lb. tablets in
29. Household ⎭ 28-lb. & 56-lb.
               boxes . . 32/-

BROWN

17. First Brown 29/-
18. Mottled Brown 28/-
19. Seconds Brown 22/-
20. Economic 13/6

30. XXXI Pale 22/6
31. XXI Pale 21/6
32. XI Pale 20/6

and beautiful marbled soap is manufactured by Messrs. Crosfield of Warrington', and the *Illustrated London News* referred in November 1886 to their 'world-famed blue mottled soap', as well as to their manufacture of toilet soaps and household pale soaps. The latter were the bread and butter of Crosfield's trade. According to the *Warrington Guardian* of 23rd June 1886, 'pale yellow household soap' was 'the most important branch of Messrs. Crosfields' manufactures'.

To sell their soaps, Crosfield's gradually built up a sales force of travellers and agents. There is little evidence, however, about their activities. At the celebration of the firm's incorporation in 1896, they and the departmental managers were brought together for the first time. Several of the travellers had been selling Crosfield's soaps for twenty years or more, one apparently for as long as fifty years. C. F. Huffam, who entered the firm as a traveller in 1877, was placed in charge of the commercial staff six years later. The firm had export agents in London, Liverpool, Glasgow, and perhaps in other ports. Local agents were also employed abroad. According to the *Warrington Guardian Year Book* of 1901, Arthur Crosfield took over responsibility for the commercial side of the business, after an initial training from the age of seventeen (i.e. from 1882) that included 'the practical art of soap-making'. He was said to have been 'in constant touch with some 16 travellers in the home trade, and nearly 60 agents and correspondents for the export all over the world'.

Most interesting evidence regarding the distribution of Crosfield's products in the home market is provided by a large volume of railway and shipping freight-rates for carriage of soap from Warrington to hundreds of other towns during this period. Professor Wilson has stated in his *History of Unilever* that: 'The outstanding feature of the industry was the very limited and local nature of the markets. A series of conventions, almost medieval in their parochialism, maintained a system of zones, so that Northern soapmakers held the markets in the North of England, Norwich makers held the East Anglian markets, while London makers held London and the South . . . Preserves were respected and poaching was kept to a minimum.' So far as Crosfield's were concerned, however, these statements are exaggerated. The freight-rates repeatedly supplied to Crosfield's on request by many railway companies during the years 1862–88 demonstrate that, although the bulk of their trade was undoubtedly in the North, they also sent soap to a great many towns all over the rest of England and also in Wales, Scotland, and Ireland. Railway rates were not, of course, directly proportional to distance. In the middle 'sixties, for example, the rate per ton of soap from Warrington to Wigan was 5s. 10d., Blackburn 10s., Newcastle 17s. 6d., Worcester 16s. 8d., Holbeach 24s. 2d., and Abingdon 24s. 2d. These differences were not so large as to prevent Crosfield's from distributing goods outside the Northern area, and they were counterbalanced by proximity to the main sources of soda and salt and to the port of Liverpool. Cheap water carriage (e.g. 7s. 6d. per ton to Dublin) enabled them to carry on trade with Ireland, and soap was also sent by steam-packet, as well as by rail, to Glasgow and other ports in Scotland and also to London and English provincial ports, especially in the south-west. John Crosfield's note-book shows that he kept a careful eye on the prices charged by 'the London makers', as well as by neighbouring firms such as Gossage's. The *Illustrated London News* perhaps exaggerated when stating in 1886 that Crosfield's 'Perfection' soap 'may be had from Grocers, Chandlers, and Italian Warehousemen throughout the United Kingdom', but there is no doubt that by that time the firm was building up a national market for its leading products.

Although water carriage was, as we have seen, of prime importance for import of raw materials, the distribution of Crosfield's soap products was—with the exception of the Irish and foreign trade—mainly by rail. As George Crosfield stated before the Select Committee on the L. & N.W.R.'s proposed bridge at Fidler's Ferry in 1860, 'most of their goods went to Manchester and eastwards, and were sent by rail'. Four years later the firm made an agreement with the L. & N.W.R. that, in consideration of the Company laying down a siding to their soap-warehouse, they would 'continue to forward by their [the Company's] Line, the whole of our traffic to all and every town or place to which they convey, save and except such portion of it as we may be instructed by our Customers to forward by other means of conveyance; provided always, that the Rates charged by the London & North Western Railway Company are not higher than the Rates . . . charged by other Carriers to the same places.' The book of freight-rates shows that in future years the L. & N.W.R. carried the bulk of Crosfield's soap, but that the services of other railway companies were utilized. George Crosfield's eventual directorship of the L. & N.W.R. may have helped the firm to get better terms. Some hard bargaining went on to secure preferential rates for regular bulk traffic.

In addition to the siding on the Garston branch line, the firm acquired another, on the main L. & N.W.R. Preston–Crewe line, in 1893, when the former Bank Quay Glass Works were bought. Track was laid throughout the works, and by 1896 Crosfield's owned two locomotives and forty-six wagons. But although most of the home trade was by rail, the Bridgewater and Old Quay canals were still occasionally used for trade with Manchester and Liverpool. For the export trade, the River Mersey was most important, while the building of the Ship Canal provided Bank Quay with a double connection by water with Liverpool.

There is little surviving evidence about Crosfield's export trade at this time. The *Illustrated London News* stated in 1886, that 'Perfection' soap was sold 'throughout the World', and 'Erasmic' soaps were also exported—to India, for example, in

99

1893 or a little earlier—but most of their exports were cheaper 'filled' varieties, and mainly bar soaps. At the Liverpool Exhibition in 1886 the *Warrington Guardian* reported that 'some of the most brilliantly coloured samples are not prepared for or offered in the English market. They are intended for export', and were designed to 'take the native fancy in the foreign bazaar'. And again at the Royal Jubilee Exhibition in Manchester in 1887 it was reported that these strongly coloured soaps were 'special manufactures for China, Java, India, the Cape, West Coast of Africa, South America, the West Indies, Canary Islands, and others of less importance'. The comparative cheapness of sea transport made it no more costly to send soap to Bombay or Rio de Janeiro (20s. and 30s. respectively, plus 10 per cent primage, in 1885–6) than to the other end of England. By 1896, in addition to their United Kingdom trade marks, Crosfield's had registrations in many other countries, including Denmark, Switzerland, Spain, United States, Brazil, Cape Colony, New South Wales, South Australia, and Tasmania. They sold their soaps through British export merchants and commission agents in the countries concerned. By the end of the nineteenth century they were undoubtedly among the leading soap exporters, though still a long way behind Gossage's.

Crosfield's, like other soapmakers, did very little advertising before William Lever's time. They relied mainly upon their travellers and the quality of their goods. John Crosfield's eldest son, Arthur, stated in 1896 that the main cause of their success was the rule laid down by his uncle George: 'He said, "Whatever you do use good materials and put plenty of them into your soap." That rule they had faithfully adhered to . . .' They had endeavoured 'to maintain throughout the country a good name . . . Their business had not been built up by cutting down the profits of their friends nor had it been built upon bunkum.' Here, perhaps, was a kick at Lever's brash advertising, which was alien to traditional marketing methods in the soap trade.

Lever's success, as explained in the *History of Unilever*, was based on heavy advertising of a proprietary branded soap, sold in tablets, as distinct from the traditional bars of 'Tallow Crown', 'XX Pale', etc. Professor Wilson appears, however, to have overlooked the fact that long before Lever's time perfumers and soapmakers, including Crosfield's, had been producing tablets of *toilet* soap, stamped with fanciful names, such as so-and-so's 'honey', 'primrose', 'musk', or 'almond' soap. Lever extended these methods to *household* or laundry soaps and used a distinctive brand—'Sunlight'—different from the traditional names, which were not proprietary and usually had reference to colour, scent, or quality. 'Sunlight' was purely and simply a trade mark. At the same time Lever began the practice of wrapping household soap—at first in imitation parchment only, but later also in cartons—to preserve the appearance and scent of the tablets, and adopted high-pressure advertising to create a national market.

Lever's first factory, as we have seen, was established in Warrington in 1885, next door to Crosfield's, who, being an old-established and much bigger firm, tended to regard him as an upstart, using dubious and ungentlemanly marketing methods. But, as Lever's 'Sunlight Self-Washer' soon began to compete seriously with their own soap, they quickly swallowed their pride and were apparently the first to imitate his selling techniques. They had already, in 1877 (after the first Trade Marks Act of 1875), registered a brand name—'Perfection Pale'—which they had used for a few years previously. But this was for a traditional bar soap, sold as 'Crosfield's Perfection Pale'. In 1885, following the appearance of Lever's 'Sunlight', they dropped the word 'Pale' and gave great prominence to 'Perfection' on a new household tablet soap which they then introduced.[1] (Joseph Watson's 'Matchless Cleanser' and Gossage's 'Magical' appeared about the same time.) They also began to wrap 'Perfection' and to push its sale by flamboyant advertising.

It was given great publicity at the Liverpool International Exhibition in 1886. Crosfield's do not appear to have participated in earlier exhibitions—certainly not at the Great Exhibition of 1851 or that in 1862—but they now put on a very impressive display. Laudatory reports appeared in local newspapers and a lengthy feature article, with a description of their works, was published in the *Illustrated London News* of 13th

[1] 'Perfection' was usually preceded by the word 'Crosfield's', though in much smaller letters. Lever Brothers successfully opposed Crosfield's application in 1886–7 for registration of the sole word 'Perfection', on the ground that it was a commonly used word of description and commendation. They did likewise in 1907–9 (see below, p. 190).

November 1886. Similar publicity was given to their exhibit in Manchester a year later. The *Warrington Guardian* considered that Crosfield's had 'inaugurated a new departure in the artistic and effective display of their many colour productions, as against the old style of never varying obelisks'. They produced a beautiful Oriental mosque, 'composed entirely of soap, and mainly of different kinds of mottled soap, while the "Perfection Soap" is used for the corner cupolas'. There was also a kiosk containing 'a beautiful display of Toilet Soaps, and of many-coloured mottled soaps, exquisite in tint and manufacture'. Crosfield's obtained two gold medals at the Liverpool Exhibition, one for 'Perfection' and one for general excellence in the manufacture of all soaps. The *Warrington Guardian* gave 'Perfection' a lengthy 'puff', describing it as 'superior to anything of the kind that has hitherto been put on the market':

Whilst containing no free alkali whatsoever, and incapable of injuring the most delicate fabric or the tenderest skin, it yields a splendid lather, and is in every respect what a good soap should be, combining both luxury in use and the greatest economy in results. This combination of recommendations and the fact that it is made from the purest materials and on the most scientific principles of manufacture give it an irresistible claim on the public favour; and we understand that already its sale is increasing with the rapidity that, from its unequalled value, might be anticipated.

The *Illustrated London News* similarly pointed out that 'it combines the most *extraordinary* lathering powers with absolute PURITY and NEUTRALITY'. The soap's general-purpose qualities were emphasized: it was 'equally good in Hard or Soft, Hot or Cold, Fresh or Salt, Water' and could be used in the 'Household, Laundry, Bath-room, or Nursery, for Washing Anything and Everything'.

Crosfield's Perfection Soap is offered as the outcome of long and most expensive scientific experiments; for cleaning floors, paint, kitchen, and other rough household work, it cannot be excelled. Its greatest victory will be obtained in the laundry, where it will indeed prove itself a 'wonder worker'. Its great lathering and dirt-extracting properties will lighten the toil of the user, make clothes cleaner and whiter, and save its cost to the purchaser, for no soda or dry soap need be used with this wonderful washing soap. Against disease and infection it is all-powerful, being a pure disinfectant, and, as a *skin soap*, it is *invaluable*.

In this combination of superlatives we have—apart from the exploitation of sex—practically all the characteristic appeals of modern advertising phraseology. 'Perfection' was certainly a very good soap and did, no doubt, in the words of the *Illustrated London News*, 'speak for itself'. But Crosfield's could no longer rely on mere quality. They had to promote sales by vigorous advertising. In November 1886, the *Warrington Guardian* reveals, they took advantage of 'the fashionable craze of the hour', word-forming competitions, by offering 45 guineas in prizes for the greatest number of words to be formed from 'Perfection'. Then they engaged four llamas, recently exhibited at Liverpool— 'beautiful and highly trained animals . . . lately the property of the King of Italy'—to make a tour of the provinces, drawing a carriage attended by natives, commencing at Liverpool on 23rd December 1886 *en route* for Glasgow and then visiting all the main towns throughout the country.

This 'stunt' provided the theme in January 1887 for another word-forming competition, based on 'Crosfield's Llamas'. Many prizes, ranging from £40 to £1, were offered, with further prizes for guessing the number of entries, while boxes of soap, containing tablets of 'Perfection' and of Brown Windsor and Honey toilet soaps, were given to all competitors. The object was simply 'to bring before the public the excellent quality of Messrs. Crosfield's Soaps', and at the close of the competition the profits, to be determined by a public accountant, would be given to charitable purposes.

Another advertising device adopted at this time was the issue of a small pocket-diary for 1887. This was interspersed with page advertisements of 'Perfection', while little homilies about it appeared at the top of every page. It also contained testimonials from a professor and a lecturer in chemistry, one in London the other at Manchester University. These verified that 'Perfection' contained a high proportion of fatty materials, a low proportion of water, no silicate of soda, only traces of insoluble matter, and no free (uncombined) alkali. Thus it was a good economical soap, safe for the most sensitive skins or fabrics. Its attractiveness was increased for toilet purposes by 'its very fragrant scent'.

Expenditure on advertising 'Perfection' totalled £7,000 in 1886 and grew in the following years.[1] Later advertising schemes included more prize competitions (e.g. for silver watches in the early 'nineties), thousands of picture posters, handbills, circulars with rhymes or songs, show cards, and glass plates for shop-window display. As a result, sales of 'Perfection' increased rapidly and for many years it was to remain the pride of Crosfield's soaps. It was, however, only one—though the most outstanding—among an immense variety of soaps produced at Bank Quay. An indication of this variety is provided by the increasing number of the firm's trade marks, registered after the first Trade Marks Act of 1875. By 1896, when Crosfield's became a limited company, they had well over 300 on the Register, about nine-tenths of them for soaps and the rest for chemicals. (Some marks were used for both soap and chemicals, e.g. 'Pyramid', first registered in 1886.) A great many, however, were variations on a similar theme (e.g. various designs for 'Perfection') or different names, wrappers, and cartons for the same soap, sold in different markets. The best known, together with 'Perfection', were the various toilet soaps sold under the 'Erasmic' trade mark, first registered in 1886, but there was a host of others, as the practice developed of substituting brand names and emblems for what were called in 1896 the 'old-fashioned' pale, brown, and blue-mottled bar soaps, though the latter were still selling well both at home and abroad, together with the long-established 'Honey', 'Castile', and other non-branded scented tablet soaps. Some well-known Crosfield 'specialities' in household tablet soaps, in addition to 'Perfection', at this time and in later years, were 'Rainbow', 'Good Judge', 'Uncle Toby', 'Miracle', 'What Next', 'Defiance' (brown and carbolic), and 'Gipsy' (brown).

These soaps, as we have seen, were of many different qualities and prices. Prices differed mainly according to composition— the dearest were the 'pure' tallow soaps, the cheapest the 'filled' variety. John Crosfield's note-book records the prices of the firm's main soaps between the 1850s and the 1880s, but, since all tended to move together, we need only consider one—'XX' Pale—in order to gain an impression of their trends. The note-book begins during the Crimean War, which produced an

[1] See below, p. 189.

extraordinary series of price fluctuations due to interruption of Russian tallow supplies. Between October 1854 and May 1856 'XX' prices ranged from 43s. to 33s. per cwt. They then fell— fluctuating with the trade cycle—to between 27s. and 30s. by the early 'seventies. The 'Great Depression' in the last quarter of the century, however, produced a much smaller decline in soap prices than in those of raw materials. During the slumps of the late 'seventies and middle 'eighties 'XX' dropped to 24s., but in more prosperous years it was nearly as high as in the boom of the early 'seventies.

Soap prices were not merely better maintained in the long term, but were much less affected by short-term cylical fluctua- tions than prices of raw materials. This was partly because variations in the latter were 'absorbed' to some extent by stocks, partly because other costs, such as wages, interest, and rents, were more stable, partly because of manufacturers' agreements, but mainly because of the relatively steady demand for soap. The industry was affected in a contrariwise kind of way by fluctuations in general economic activity. In a boom, when raw material prices rose sharply, demand for soap did not expand very greatly, soap prices rose by a relatively small amount, profit margins were therefore narrowed and there was a keener struggle for business among soapmakers; but in a slump, when the prices of raw materials dropped considerably, demand for soap was relatively well maintained, prices did not fall very much, profit margins were thus improved, and there was a generally happier atmosphere among soapmakers.

Taking a longer-term view, however, one can see that these cyclical fluctuations were what Sir John Clapham called minor 'ripples on the broad heave of historical change'. Over the whole half-century, as we have seen, the demand for soap rose remark- ably, due to the rising population and living standards; soap prices fell much less than those of raw materials, and so, despite relatively small and temporary set-backs, this was a period of generally expanding business and good profits, even during the so-called 'Great Depression'.

There are, unfortunately, no surviving figures of Crosfield's turnover or profits during this period. A rough indication of the former, however, may be derived from their dealings with the District Bank. The minutes of the Warrington branch directors' meetings show that on 10th February 1845 the 'limit' on the firm's credit still stood at £5,000. On occasions, however, they were allowed to exceed this, as Joseph had done. Thus on 22nd November 1845 'Messrs. Jos. Crosfield & Son having purchased a large quantity of Tallow which must be paid for in February, wish to know if they may be allowed to overdraw for 1 month or 6 weeks from 2,000 £ to 3,000 £ beyond their limit of £5,000. [This] was considered, when it was resolved that as Messrs. Crosfield & Son are highly respectable & Mr. Geo. Crosfield [is] a proprietor of 650 of our Shares, this Board hopes the Managing Directors will sanction the advance.' On 20th January 1847 George Crosfield was elected a local director, and his signature regularly appears on the Board's minutes in the 'fifties and 'sixties.

Crosfield's 'limit' was still £5,000 in the early 'seventies, but their business with the Bank continued to grow. Large customers such as Crosfield's were permitted to commute the Bank's percentage commission to a lump sum, at a rate (in 1873) of 10s. per £1,000 passing through the account. Crosfield's first requested this privilege on 17th February 1845, when they asked 'whether the Bank would transact their business for £50 a year', indicating an annual turnover of about £100,000. By 1873, when the charge was £150, the turnover had apparently trebled to £300,000. In 1877 the charge was raised to £200, indicating a turnover of £400,000. Unfortunately, no later figures have survived. It is interesting to note, however, that on 10th November 1885 the Bank agreed to transact Lever Brothers' business, then just starting in Warrington, 'at a fixed Commission of £20 a year. The turnover will be about £30,000. . . .'

CHAPTER IX

COMPETITION AND COMBINATION

Lever's phenomenal rise was to show how open to competition the soap trade still was in the late nineteenth century, despite efforts at combination. Professor Wilson and Mr. Reader have previously examined the records of the Soap Makers' Association (S.M.A.), established in 1867,[1] but they have exaggerated the national character of the Association and do not seem to have appreciated the extent to which there existed a division between northern and southern makers. This division is clearly apparent from an examination of Crosfield's part in the various efforts at trade association. The Soap Makers' Association of 1867 was not the first such effort. The above authors have pointed out a previous association—the 'North of England Soap Association' in the 'fifties—but this had been preceded by an even earlier one, the 'London and Country Association of Soap Manufacturers' of the late 1830s,[2] and there are examples of local associations for particular purposes some years previously. Joseph Crosfield had played a prominent part in this earlier Association, which appears to have been mainly concerned with agitating for repeal of the Excise duty on soap, but which may also have considered soap prices.

This was certainly the main motive of the 'North of England Soap Association', which met several times in Liverpool between March 1852 and October 1854. Its secretary was George Crosfield and its membership included some of the leading soap-making names in the North, such as Tyson (Liverpool), Hazlehurst (Runcorn), Hodgson & Simpson (Wakefield), and Hedley (Newcastle). The rules indicate that their object was purely the fixing of prices, at a time of great instability due to 'existing political difficulties', leading up to the Crimean War, which

---

[1] Professor Wilson in the *History of Unilever*, Mr. Reader in an article, 'The United Kingdom Soapmakers' Association and the English Soap Trade, 1867–1896', *Business History*, June 1959. This title, however, is a misnomer: the 'United Kingdom' Association was not formed till many years later.

[2] See above, p. 32.

interfered with the supply of Russian tallow. The Association was unable, however, to prevent wide fluctuations—despite its penalties, 'solemn declarations', and 'honourable pledges'—and faded out of existence in the middle 'fifties.

After the war, more stable conditions returned. Stability may have been reinforced to some extent by informal agreements between various firms. John Crosfield's note-book refers to a 'Mott^d. [Mottled] Agreement', which was terminated, however, at the end of 1865. The difficulties of the 1866 economic crisis —notable for the collapse of the great London banking and discount house of Overend, Gurney & Co.—soon led soap-makers to form a new Association. In December of that year John Crosfield noted that they had 'sold several big lots XXP at 30/-. This is a price never taken before.' Falling prices and profits led to the founding of the Soap Makers' Association in July 1867. This Association was to continue, in one form or another, for upwards of sixty years. Crosfield's still possess the original subscription book, which shows that most of the chief soapmaking firms throughout England, including Crosfield's, became members.

The minutes of the Association before 1886 and most of the early annual reports appear to have been lost, but a review of its achievements in the ninth annual report (1877) reveals its main objects. Overt price-fixing would have been too shocking for contemporary economic orthodoxy, and had to be clothed in a decent veil of language. 'Although the Association repudiates any attempt to fix prices, much good has been done in enabling the whole Trade to obtain an advance immediately on the rise of the market [for tallow], by the issue of a circular announcing the agreement to advance.' They had also agreed to abolish 'booking forward'—arranging long-term contracts with customers at fixed prices, instead of selling for immediate delivery—and had attempted to restrict credit or discount.

Crosfield's and other northern makers did not, however, participate to any great extent in the affairs of the S.M.A., which, despite its national membership, was in fact dominated by the London makers and was often referred to by Northerners as 'the London Association'. There remained a great deal of competitive rivalry between northern and southern firms, and very soon the former re-established their own regional association. John Crosfield's note-book reveals that on 22nd March 1871 there was a meeting of the chief northern makers in Liverpool, which agreed on 'terms of payment', i.e. discounts, etc., and also agreed 'to do away with all contracts after April 30th'. But signs of a rift soon appeared. On 26th September 1872, 'We advanced £1 per ton, other makers professed £2 per ton advance'. Early in April 1875, after the London makers had advanced £1 per ton, 'We advanced £1—H & S. [Hodgson & Simpson] & G's [Gossage's] refused to advance'. Crosfield's therefore returned to the former prices almost immediately.

Alterations in prices were mostly recorded by John Crosfield without any explanatory note, so that it is impossible to tell whether or not they were agreed. Crosfield's kept a very keen eye on the London prices. In September 1876, for example, the London makers advanced £1 per ton, and so did Crosfield's. But on 2nd February 1878, when 'Gossage & H. & S. advanced Tallow soaps & skin [soaps] £1 per ton, we did not advance anything but Mottled. The advance was a farce.' And less than two months later 'G & S. [Gossage & Sons] & H. & S. reduced £1 per ton not having got the advance. Trade in the country very bad.' On 21st May, therefore, 'Gossages reduced Pales 20/– & Mottled 10/–', and Crosfield's followed suit. A few months later the roles were reversed. On 2nd September, 'We advanced Mottleds £1 per ton', but 'G. & S., H & S. refused to advance', so on the 30th 'We reduced Mott^d. as Gossages & Simpsons refused to advance'.

The differences between these neighbouring firms were temporarily settled, however, on 8th February 1879: 'I met Timmis [of Gossage's] & Simpson in L'pool & fixed price of Mot^d.' When Gossage's reduced their soaps by 10/– per ton all round at the end of April, Crosfield's followed them. At the end of October trade improved, so 'Gossages and we raised XX Pale £2' per ton. On 24th January 1880, however, when 'H. & S. reduced Mottled £1 per ton in a pet', Crosfield's did not.

The surviving reports of the S.M.A. reveal similar differences in trade policy among London makers. The agreement for abolition of 'booking forward', for instance, was frequently violated. The twelfth annual report (1880) stated that 'a very serious competition was being carried on by houses in the North, who had for some time refrained from holding any meetings, and in consequence of which much ill feeling existed'. Eventually, however, in the spring of that year the 'Northern Soapmakers' Association' (N.S.A.) was resuscitated and agreement was reached with the S.M.A. regarding abolition of contracts and of the practice of taking further orders at old prices after an advance had been agreed on. John Crosfield's note-book reveals that he attended several of the meetings in Liverpool, London, and Manchester whereby harmony was restored.

Affairs seem to have run smoothly during the next few years. The minutes of neither Association have survived, but the S.M.A.'s annual report for 1882–3 refers to an attempted 'arrangement of prices between the Makers in the North and South'. In the spring of 1883, however, John Crosfield referred to a quarrel between Hodgson & Simpson and Gossage's, as a result of which the former left the N.S.A., which subsequently broke up

Towards the end of 1885, however, meetings were again held in Manchester and Liverpool and the N.S.A. was reconstructed. The prices of raw materials had fallen, as the S.M.A.'s seventeenth annual report noted, to 'unprecedentedly low' levels, and though industry in general was very depressed, the soapmakers were prospering and displaying a more co-operative spirit. Crosfield's and other northern makers still remained members of the S.M.A., but their most active interests were in their regional Association. This included all the important northern firms previously mentioned and others such as Joseph Watson & Sons (Leeds), D. C. Keeling & Co. (Liverpool), and Christopher Thomas & Bros. (Bristol). John Crosfield and his sons rarely attended even the annual meetings of the S.M.A., which they and other northern makers obviously regarded mainly as a convenient body with which they could try to arrange agreements mitigating competition between north and south. A close watch was kept on London prices and upon the competitive activities of London makers. Correspondence early in 1886 'as to the desirability of united action in changing prices between the Northern & the London Associations' came to nothing. Prices were reduced on several occasions, either generally or in particular areas to meet London competition. Similar action was also taken in Scotland, where the makers also had their own Association.

The main concern of the N.S.A., as revealed by the surviving minutes of 1886–8, was to get agreement on prices and to prevent underselling. The Association was obliged, however, to adopt a very flexible policy. It was agreed, at its 'reconstruction' in January 1886, that 'when any member desires a change in prices, he shall communicate with the Secretary, who shall call a meeting of members for the first Wednesday following, to discuss the matter'. This agreement was clarified in the following August, after Thos. Hedley & Co. had reduced prices 'without giving adequate notice'. This firm was informed 'that you are quite within your rights as Members of this Association in taking any action with regard to prices that you think best. But it is expected of you that you will (1) give such timely notice that the other members may have opportunity of consulting, and, if necessary, remonstrating with you before you carry the change into effect. And (2) that you will give such notice that all the other firms can be put in a position to make *the same changes at the same time.*'

Differences continually occurred between members. Some often wished to advance or reduce prices, while others did not, and accusations of underselling were constantly being made. More subtle means of 'unfair competition' were also employed to win customers: by giving excessive discounts, rebates, bonuses, or credit; by giving extra allowances on large orders; by the old practices of 'booking forward' and 'taking orders at old prices'; by letting customers know that an advance in prices was impending, or by sending them telegrams immediately after such an advance, so that they could put in orders at old prices, before the new lists were received; by permitting travellers to make illicit allowances to customers out of their commission or expenses; by cash gifts; by supplying soap overweight; and by selling the same soap, under different names, at lower prices. Indeed, it is extraordinary that the Association could survive when its members were constantly accusing each other of treachery, double-dealing, and fraud, and when evasions of the agreed rules were so frequent. There is evidence, however, that the Association did reduce, even if it could not abolish, cut-throat competition, and that agreed changes in prices were sometimes achieved. But it only needed one firm to break away, and all would go back to the competitive jungle.

John Crosfield and his sons, Arthur and J. J., played a very active part in the Association, regularly attending its monthly meetings in Liverpool; from September 1886 onwards Arthur Crosfield was its secretary. On some occasions, however, there is no doubt that their firm was deliberately undercutting, though they were certainly not alone in doing so. On 7th April 1886, for example, it was reported that Crosfield's were selling mottled soaps for export at 1s. per cwt. below the agreed prices, 'without giving notice to any of the other parties to the agreement'. Their conduct was strongly condemned, and they agreed to raise the prices, but not on orders already received; at the next meeting on 5th May, therefore, Gossage's stated that they would have to reduce their prices accordingly.

Further differences with Gossage's, their biggest rivals, occurred later that year. On 6th October Gossage's complained that Crosfield's were copying the brand on their Prize Medal Mottled Soap, and on 3rd November that Crosfield's were underselling them in Glasgow and elsewhere; but both these charges were denied. At this same meeting, Gossage's and Hodgson & Simpson joined 'in condemning Messrs. Crosfields' action in commencing to wrap "Perfection Soap" '. But Crosfield's were supported by Hazlehurst's, similarly producing 'Sun', who 'pointed out the necessity of competing with the "Sunlight", a marked feature of the latter being the preservation of appearance and scent, due, of course, in a great measure, to every Tablet being wrapped'.

On other occasions, Crosfield's were the complainants. Thus on 2nd February 1887 they accused Goodwin's (Manchester) of underselling them in mottled soap in south Lancashire. Goodwin's undertook to remedy this. Crosfield's would play the game provided that others did likewise: they 'agreed to discontinue their second quality of cheap mottled branded "Demon" whenever Messrs. Keeling would give up the "Surprise", and not sell at less than 12s. per cwt. for any cheap mottled'. They and others strongly opposed Gossage's proposal, at this same meeting, to reduce branded 'specialities' such as 'Perfection' and Gossage's 'Magical', that were not usually included in price agreements. Gossage's 'were in favor of keeping down the price of Soaps all round, in order to stamp out the increasing quantities of Soaps now sold by small local makers', e.g. Lever

Brothers. The other makers, however, including Crosfield's, while willing to make a reduction in ordinary soaps, were not prepared to reduce the 'specialities', pointing out that 'such a reduction was not justified by competition on the part of London or Glasgow Soapmakers, and that as regards competing with Messrs. Lever Bros., the result would rather be to play into their hands than anything else'. Gossage's decided to reduce 'Magical' against the general opinion. Lever's rapid rise was obviously causing discomfiture and division among soapmakers.

On 6th May 1887 Gossage's threatened to resign from the Association on account of the excessive allowances, discounts, etc., given by certain firms or by their travellers, and 'it was generally admitted that the rules of the Association had been broken'. At the next meeting, on 18th May, John Crosfield 'admitted that his firm was the first to take 1/6d. [per cwt.] off the List [prices] to ton buyers', i.e. for large orders. On 3rd August, moreover, 'complaints were made against Messrs. Crosfield for sending out Soap overweight', and they were also accused once again by Gossage's of having 'taken less than the agreed price for Mottled for Export', without giving due notice to other makers; but Crosfield's declared that they had been driven to this by the underselling of Messrs. Keeling and other firms.

Gossage's raised the matter again at the next meeting, on 7th September, when Crosfield's retaliated by complaining that Gossage's Glasgow agent had underquoted them in Scotch XX Pale; Gossage's denied it. At meetings in early October, when prices were raised, both Crosfield's and Gossage's emphasized that the advance should be 'clean and sharp', and that 'no orders should be accepted at old prices'. If this rule were broken, said John Crosfield, 'he saw little use in the holding of any more meetings'. On 2nd November he accused Hodgson & Simpson of having informed customers beforehand that prices would be advanced. Similar accusations were made by and against other firms; the usual excuse was that the travellers had merely been exercising their own judgment. At a meeting on 4th April 1888, Gossage's complained of Crosfield's allowing excessive discount on certain export soaps, and Crosfield's agreed to reduce their terms.

These constant recriminations appear to have resulted once

more in the collapse of the Northern Association. The minutes now ceased and at a General Meeting of the S.M.A. on 1st February 1889 Edward Simpson stated that 'they had now no Association in the North, their meetings had not been agreeable and had been suspended'. Christopher Thomas and Frederick Gossage agreed that now 'every one would have to fight his own hand', i.e. they were back to a free-for-all. The S.M.A., though it still survived, was an almost utterly ineffective body, unable even to attempt any control over prices in London and power-less against the practices of 'booking forward', etc. Another in-creasingly important factor, mentioned by one of the Knights, the biggest London soapmakers, on 22nd February 1889, was 'the large amount of soap thrown on the market by Messrs. Levers and other makers of new sorts'. Lever had for some years been deliberately excluded from the Association, because of his objectionable advertising and undercutting, but, having grown too powerful to be ignored, had been finally admitted on 1st February, doubtless with the idea that he would be more likely to conform if he were in rather than out.

Some kind of co-operation appears very soon to have been revived in the North, for Simpson informed the S.M.A. on 8th March that, at a recent Liverpool meeting, 'the Northern makers were determined to sacrifice trade rather than reduce prices', provided that they were supported by the London makers. A special general meeting of the S.M.A. was therefore held on 5th April, attended by one of the Crosfields, and resolu-tions were passed to prohibit 'booking forward' and the taking of orders at old prices after an advance. Subsequently, however, it proved impossible to get general agreement and the negotia-tions fizzled out.

Another similar effort was started in March 1891, when a special committee was appointed to regulate prices in London and the South, with the idea of eventually having an 'arrange-ment for rise or fall with the Northern Association'. But by the beginning of 1892 this, too, had collapsed; Knight's reduced their prices independently, owing to the general prevalence of 'booking forward', undercutting, the competition of northern makers, and 'excessive advertising' of certain soaps.

The S.M.A.'s twenty-fifth anniversary meeting on 10th June 1892 was attended by Arthur Crosfield and several of the

COMPETITION AND COMBINATION

northern makers. Timmis (of Gossage's) said that the Northern Association 'had ceased to exist', but that 'they now agreed to *terms* [of payment] in the north but not prices', i.e. as in London. On 5th August 1892, however, the S.M.A. secretary reported that he had received a letter from Arthur Crosfield, still secretary of the Northern Soapmakers' Association, urging the London makers to reconsider their recent reduction in prices, as the northern makers had not reduced theirs. But the Londoners decided that, 'in view of the falling Tallow market', they could not comply.

Further negotiations between north and south followed in the early months of 1893, in which Arthur Crosfield, as secretary of the Northern Association, took a prominent part. The Northerners urged co-operation against the perennial evils of 'booking forward' and acceptance of old prices after an advance, which they had once again decided to abolish. Obviously this would entail simultaneous price-fixing throughout the country. A general meeting of the whole trade in April 1893 appointed a joint committee of northern and southern makers, including Arthur Crosfield, to bring about united action, but, as so often in the past, this proved impossible.

The Northerners still persisted, however, and at the end of November 1895 Arthur Crosfield again wrote to suggest renewed efforts to achieve simultaneous alteration of prices by northern and southern makers. Unfortunately, there was 'no arrangement amongst the makers in the South for altering the prices of soaps'. Nevertheless another joint committee was set up, again including Arthur Crosfield, but, inevitably it seems, their efforts proved in vain; Knight's again reduced prices independently in August 1896.

Thus, throughout this period, the S.M.A. and N.S.A. were almost completely ineffective. The evidence of their minutes, like that of Crosfield's records, shows that Professor Wilson's picture of limited local markets or zones, of a 'comfortable world, gentlemanly and harmonious', represents an ideal rather than reality. No doubt raw competition was glossed over to some extent by social conviviality, but beneath the fraternal speeches and toasts lay the hard facts of unscrupulous trade rivalry. Time and again one comes across complaints of northern makers undercutting in the South, of southern makers doing likewise in the North, and of Northerners and Southerners undercutting each other. It was utterly impossible to get prolonged agreement on any matter restricting trade competition. Professor Wilson is undoubtedly right, however, in emphasizing how Lever's rise intensified this competition. Although Lever Brothers were admitted to the S.M.A. in 1889, they were still excluded from the Northern Association, in which feeling against them was obviously very strong. Their exclusion, however, rendered the Association almost powerless and constantly threatened its disruption, since members could hardly be expected to stand by its rules and watch their trade being thereby reduced.

In view of the S.M.A.'s failure to regulate the soap trade, it is not surprising that it was unable to control that in the glycerine by-product. During the 'eighties many other firms besides Crosfield's installed recovery plant; most of the glycerine was sold for making dynamite. In October 1889 the S.M.A. tried to get agreement on minimum prices, but by June 1890 the attempt had broken down, owing to lack of unanimity. It was then decided to negotiate with Nobels for the sale to them of all the soapmakers' glycerine, but the ramshackle Association was ill-fitted for combat with such a powerful adversary and had no success. Members were therefore left 'free to consult their own interests in the matter'. Crosfield's did not participate in these negotiations; they appear to have found glycerine recovery very profitable.

CHAPTER X

PATERNALISM AND POLITICS

THE surviving records of Joseph Crosfield & Sons have revealed a good deal about the buildings, processes, and products of the Bank Quay soapworks in the nineteenth century, but hardly anything about the men who worked there or about their relations with their employers. From a few scrappy extraneous pieces of evidence, however, in local newspapers, etc., it appears that the firm's employees were more happily situated than workers generally. The soap industry, as we have seen, was not very seriously affected by recurrent trade depressions, and employment in Crosfield's expanding works was much more secure than in most other industrial concerns. John Crosfield declared in November 1878: 'There has never since our concern started been one single day lost by the works being closed.' His obituary states that he 'earned for himself the reputation of a kind and considerate employer of labour. To him, his workpeople were not so many "hands": he knew most of them by name, he freely conversed with them, and those who had grown grey in his service retired on a pension.' There is a mention in 1868 of a sick club for Crosfield's employees, managed by the firm's cashier, but to what extent the partners contributed to its funds is not clear. Occasionally one comes across references to annual railway outings or excursions for employees and their families: from 200 to 250 went to Llangollen in 1869, and 1,000 to Blackpool in 1883. A prize bowling competition, 'social gathering', and tea was organized 'for the recreation of the men' in September 1892, when an illuminated address was presented to Arthur Crosfield 'as a token of the respect and esteem in which he was held by his workmen'. It referred to his 'kindness and consideration', his sense of fairness, his warm interest in the welfare of the workmen, and his efforts to promote 'harmonious feeling'. This was said to have been the first such social gathering of workmen and employers in Warrington and neighbourhood. It was intended in future to hold regular 'social evenings' in rooms built by John Crosfield at Bank Quay.

These few scattered examples of the firm's benevolence suggest that several of the features of the comprehensive welfare scheme established in 1903[1] were evolving in earlier years. Unfortunately, there are no surviving records of wages and hours of work at Crosfield's during this period. Nor is there any evidence relating to trade-union activity; the local press does not appear to have reported a single strike at the works during the second half of the century. That John Crosfield favoured peaceful settlement of trade disputes is evidenced by his agreeing to act on a local Arbitration Board established in 1872. He often emphasized in public speeches the mutual interests of employers and employed, and his respect for 'good, honest, Lancashire working men'. Thus he told a deputation from Warrington Trades Council in June 1886, when he was a Liberal parliamentary candidate (see below, pp. 131-2), 'that capital and labour were dependent upon each other, and labour was no use without capital, nor capital without labour'. He had often, he said, expressed similar sentiments to his own workmen, telling them 'that their interest in the place [the works] was as great as [that of] their employers, and the prosperity of the one meant the prosperity of the other'. Arthur Crosfield admitted in 1892 that 'we have had differences on one or two occasions', but these had left no rancour behind them; he believed that labour troubles could be settled 'by common-sense and by the spirit of fairness'. 'As for trades unions, whereas 25 years ago they were thought most terrible things, and denounced on nearly every hand, now, on the contrary, it is becoming the exception to find people who do not recognize the justice and the value of trades unions.'

The Crosfields' benevolence was not confined to their own workpeople. They were proud of being Warringtonians and contributed very generously to innumerable charitable, social, and educational schemes in the town. This generosity was inspired by deep humanitarian and religious feelings: on many occasions they expressed their concern for raising the material and moral conditions of the working classes in Warrington. There was usually, however, a strongly paternalist, 'improving'

[1] See below, pp. 150-6.

tone to their speeches, a strong sense of class superiority. The Crosfields, like other manufacturing and commercial dynasties in Warrington and other towns during this period, felt that they had an almost divine right—justified by their economic success, by their contributions to rates and taxes, and by the employment that their enterprise provided—to lead and rule their local communities according to their strongly individualist and self-righteous standards. They constantly expressed warm regard for sober, steady, and 'respectable' workmen, while they denounced improvidence, intemperance, and vice, which they generally attributed to lack of moral fibre or of religious education, and rarely to other economic or social causes.

All this is rather distasteful to modern palates, but one must remember that Victorian standards were different from those of today, and that in some ways they compare not unfavourably with the present amoral (even immoral) materialism. Most of the 'good works' of the nineteenth century were undoubtedly products of sincere religious feeling, and the Crosfields were profoundly influenced by their Quaker lineage. But the latitudinarianism of the Quakers, combined oddly with their expulsion of those who married outside the Society, led frequently to loss of members. It is also a commonplace of nineteenth-century history that rising wealth and social status were often accompanied by a shift from Nonconformity to the Anglican Establishment. These factors resulted in a breakaway by the Warrington Crosfields from the Society of Friends. George, the eldest of Joseph's sons, married a Quaker and remained in the Society throughout his life, but his two brothers, Morland and John, married nonmembers and became practising Anglicans. Nevertheless, their speeches and actions clearly reveal the profound influence of their Quaker upbringing; and their children, though brought up as Anglicans, were also imbued with, and often referred to, 'good old Quaker principles'. John Crosfield regularly attended St. Thomas's Church, Stockton Heath, but he constantly expressed a Quaker philosophy, urged religious freedom and equality, supported disestablishment of the Church of England, denounced Anglican bigotry and injustice (e.g. Church tithes, rates, and burials), and always proclaimed his belief in nonsectarian religion, based simply on the Bible, without dogma or ritual. At heart, without doubt, he remained a Quaker.

It was not at all unusual to find Joseph Crosfield attending Nonconformist as well as Anglican social functions, and to find him declaring, as he did at the annual tea party of the Golborne Street Baptist Chapel in 1881, that 'he did not profess to belong to any particular sect, except a sect called Christians . . . He wanted to see Church people and Dissenters more united.' It was for this reason that he long and earnestly supported the activities of the non-denominational Warrington Auxiliary of the British and Foreign Bible Society, as his father had done. For many years he was its treasurer, and then a vice-president (his brother George also became a vice-president), and repeatedly expressed his desire to see the Bible distributed freely among the poorer classes of the town, not merely to bring them knowledge of Christian truths, but to uplift them morally and socially, to combat drunkenness and vice. For the same reasons he became treasurer of the 'Town Mission' established in 1862, with the object of spreading God's word among the poor by means of lay 'missionaries', house-to-house visits, scripture readings, prayer meetings, and distribution of tracts. He often expressed the view that parts of Warrington were more benighted than the dark continent of Africa.

Despite liberal donations from John Crosfield and a few others, the Town Mission expired in 1869, but he continued to support one of the 'missionaries' in the Bank Quay area, and eventually, in 1871, built at his sole expense a 'Workingmen's Mission', for use as a chapel and Sunday school, to the west of the soapworks, on Liverpool Road; its cost was 'upwards of £500', according to the *Warrington Guardian*. Both the chapel and school were to be non-sectarian and open to all denominations; teaching was to be based simply on the Bible. Adjoining the Mission, he also erected a house for a 'missionary', whose salary he paid. Three years later he remarked on 'what a dissolute and neglected part of Warrington Bank Quay was' before the Mission was established; now many men were going to the chapel instead of the alehouse, and several hundred children attended the Sunday school. In 1874, therefore, he added a new school building to the chapel.

In later years he gave constant support to the Mission, for long paying practically all its working expenses. In 1885 he gave £100 towards reseating the chapel. In 1882 and 1890 he

120

provided additional school buildings; by the latter date there were over 600 scholars on the books. In 1897–9 he leased land in Thewlis Street, upon which he erected a new infants' school. In 1904, a few years after his death, when the site of the old chapel was required for extensions to Crosfield's works, his widow paid half the cost of a new one, next to the Thewlis Street school, to which the firm also made a substantial contribution. Long after the Crosfields left Warrington, they continued to contribute generously to the funds of the Mission, which still survives.

The Crosfields regarded education as the most potent means of moral and social improvement. Not merely would it enable people to read the Scriptures, but it would lead them away from drunkenness and vice to a knowledge of higher things, and would make them better workmen and citizens. George Crosfield declared in January 1868 that for a great number of years he had taken 'more interest in schools and education than anything else'. Many workmen, especially those with large families, were unable to educate their children; he therefore held it to be 'the duty of the master to pay for the education of their [workmen's] children', by providing schools, etc. In fact he was in favour of compulsory State education, for 'if they were to have the whole of the people of this country educated, they must not rely solely upon the voluntary principle'.

John Crosfield, a month later, also deplored the fact that millions of children in the country were receiving little or no education, but emphasized that even if Parliament dealt with the matter there would still be need for voluntary schools, such as those established by Anglicans and Nonconformists. Both he and his brother, however, were strongly opposed to narrowly sectarian education, believing that schools should be open to children of all denominations. They therefore joined in the Nonconformist agitation against Forster's Education Bill in 1870, because of its threatened Anglican domination of School Boards. Ten years later John Crosfield opposed the establishment of a School Board in Warrington, because Board elections would arouse religious animosity; instead he preferred that the town council should seek powers to erect school buildings.

Both George and John Crosfield continued their father's interest in the Warrington British School, or People's College as

it was renamed in 1858, which was predominantly Nonconformist in origin, though it provided non-sectarian education.
George was elected to the committee in 1844, John in 1859, and
both served for many years; in 1874 the former was elected
president. They had a hand in the building of a new school in
Slutchers Lane (off Sankey Street) in the late 'sixties, which was
extended in 1882, thanks to a donation of £700 by John Crosfield. Infant schools were also established in Cairo Street and at
Bank Quay, the latter being housed in the Mission Sunday
School built by John Crosfield. In 1886 John Crosfield's second
son, J. J., was elected a committee member and was also secretary for a time, thus completing three generations of family
service to these schools.

John Crosfield was also listed in the 1860s among the 'subscribers and friends' of the St. Paul's and Trinity Schools,
Heathside—the Heathside Schools, as they were usually called,
established in the early 1850s—and was said to have taken a
warm interest in them 'for many years'. He acted as secretary in
1868. His brother George spoke at the opening of St. Paul's
Sunday and Infant School at Bank Quay that same year; this
school was to be for all religious denominations, otherwise 'he
would not have had anything to do with it'. In the early 'sixties
John Crosfield was also a subscriber and committee member of
the Warrington 'Ragged School', established for 'destitute and
neglected children', and providing a daily meal as well as elementary education.

The Crosfield brothers followed their father's example in supporting the Warrington Mechanics' Institution, of which John
Crosfield was treasurer in the early 'sixties. But despite their
donations, it gradually fizzled out, finally collapsing in 1869.
The old Warrington Circulating Library, on the other hand, of
which Joseph Crosfield had been such a keen member, became
the first municipal rate-aided library in the country in 1848.
Joseph Crosfield & Sons contributed £100 towards a new
building for this and for a museum in 1854. An offshoot of the
Mechanics' Institution, the Warrington School of Art, established in 1853, came to be housed in the museum. George Crosfield was among the original subscribers. John Crosfield was
elected to the committee in 1872, and was regularly re-elected
every year, though he hardly ever attended the meetings. In

1879 he was elected a vice-president, and in 1882 donated £1,000 towards building a new school. In 1888 his son Arthur was elected a committee member.

Technical education was strongly supported by the Crosfields, because of its industrial usefulness. John Crosfield joined a committee set up by 'a meeting of gentlemen interested in the diffusion of technical education', held in the People's College in September 1873. Classes were to be started in connection with the Science and Art Department of the Privy Council Committee on Education. John Crosfield also attended a meeting later that same year 'for the promotion of a popular scientific movement in Warrington', to organize a series of 'Science lectures for the people', towards which he subscribed £10.

The 1873 scheme for technical classes appears to have failed, but in 1878 a Warrington 'School of Science' was successfully established, mainly due to the initiative of George Crosfield. He was elected president, and John a vice-president; they subscribed £100 and £50 respectively, and the former obtained rooms for it over Arpley Station. He 'found great benefit in his own business from a study of chemistry' and thought 'it would be an excellent thing if the youths of Warrington . . . could have a scientific training carried on as it were with their daily toil', i.e. in evening classes. John Crosfield pointed out at the School's annual meeting in September 1881 that 'Warrington is eminently a manufacturing town, and if we are to hold our own against other nations we must . . . advance the cause of science'. Crosfield's and other manufacturers continued to subscribe to the school, but unfortunately the number of students gradually declined and it had to be wound up in 1884.

In 1888 a Warrington branch of the National Association for the Promotion of Technical Instruction was founded, with the idea of establishing a technical school, or school of science and art (absorbing the existing School of Art), under Warrington Corporation. John Crosfield, of course, was on the committee. In the following year a Warrington Recreative Evening Schools Association was also established, but it was wound up in 1892, when the local Corporation began to organize classes in technical and secondary education. No one in Warrington had done more than the Crosfields to extend education by private generosity before it became a public responsibility.

One of the greatest social evils of the time, against which the Crosfields constantly campaigned, was that of drunkenness. They found it all the more objectionable because it was associated with the Tory political predominance of Greenalls, the brewers: 'Warrington is ruled by the beer barrel', John Crosfield repeatedly declared, for free beer was lavishly distributed at elections. But the social consequences, as they often pointed out, were worse than the political: wages were wasted in alehouses and gin-palaces, families were inadequately clothed and fed, children were uneducated, immorality flourished, and the poorer quarters of the towns became sinks of poverty, degradation, heathenism, and crime. Drunkenness 'filled our workhouses, our gaols, and lunatic asylums', and so increased the rates; it also led to idleness and unfitted men for steady hard work. Over and over again, in speeches throughout the second half of the century, the Crosfields deplored these evils of intemperance. They were not extremist teetotallers, but they did support the work of the Temperance Society and the United Kingdom Alliance, and frequently spoke at meetings in favour of Sunday closing and stricter licensing: they were in full sympathy with the Nonconformist, Gladstonian Liberal policy regarding 'this great curse', as John Crosfield usually called it. What they wished to see was 'a steady, earnest, hard-working, sober and religious people'.

Religion and education, of course, were the two most potent forces against intemperance, as the Crosfields often observed when assisting in the establishment of chapels and schools. But these they supplemented with other agencies: tea and coffee rooms, reading rooms, workmen's clubs and institutes, social evenings and concerts, horticultural societies, etc. To all these 'rational', useful, uplifting, or harmlessly enjoyable leisure activities the Crosfields gave very generous financial aid and personal assistance. John Crosfield was particularly active in helping such institutions. In November 1862, for example, we find him contributing £10 to a Workmen's Club in Newton Street, and in the following February supporting Saturday evening concerts organized by the Church Institute. In December 1863 he referred to 'the coffee and reading room which he opened some time since for the benefit of the working people about Bank Quay'. In the summer of 1864 he organized a Bank

Quay Flower Show, run by a new horticultural society of which he was a patron and secretary. His remarks on this occasion illustrate his attitude towards such schemes: 'there was much good . . . to be got from the cultivation of flowers: the pursuit had a moral tendency, and was a great inducement to a man to spend his time at home with his family, instead of at the public-house, where many temptations beset him'.

At Lymm, where he lived for ten years prior to 1875, he presided at 'Pleasant Evenings for the People', with readings, recitations, and songs, and was a patron and president of a Working Men's Club or Institute, which provided smoking, reading, and games rooms, winter concerts, and also some elementary education. In Warrington, similarly, in 1875, he became a shareholder in the 'British Workman Public-House Company, Ltd.', which—contrary to the suggestion of its name—provided temperance 'coffee and cocoa rooms', together with reading, recreation, and club rooms, in various parts of the town during the following years, and enabled workmen to spend social evenings 'in a rational and sober manner'. For the same reason, as well as for political reasons, he and his brother George warmly supported the Liberal Club, opened in 1875, as 'one of the very best means to draw men away from public houses, and [as] a place where they could enjoy themselves rationally and soberly'. At the same time, by raising the moral and social standards of the people, they hoped to defeat the Tories, who thrived on besotted ignorance. The Crosfields were also patrons of various middle-class societies and clubs for cultural and physical recreation, such as dramatic and operatic societies, and Warrington cricket and bowling club.

Although, however, they gave generous aid to such institutions, they were firm believers in the virtues of working-class thrift and self-help. For many years they served as 'managers' and trustees of the Warrington Savings Bank, and they were also shareholders and trustees of local building societies, such as the Warrington Provident and Permanent Benefit Building Societies, established in the 'sixties, with the main object of erecting workingmen's cottages. John Crosfield's speech at the first annual meeting of the latter society in February 1868 illustrates his combination of benevolence with sound business: he was anxious to see more cottages built 'because he believed that civilization depended a great deal upon the sort of houses the workpeople lived in . . . "Cleanliness is next to Godliness" . . . and they who had taken shares in that society had been doing a philanthropic work, whilst at the same time they had been getting a good rate of interest [6 per cent that year] for their money.' He regularly presided at the annual meetings of this society in the 'seventies and 'eighties.

Savings banks and building societies were for the thrifty and better-paid workmen. The majority of Warrington inhabitants lived on low wages in rented houses and had little surplus for savings.[1] In times of trade depression they often suffered great hardship. On such occasions we find the Crosfields serving on relief committees and rendering financial assistance. In the 'Cotton Famine' during the American Civil War, for example, John Crosfield was treasurer of the local relief committee, and his brothers also gave aid. He served on similar committees during the serious slump of 1878–9, helping to provide money, soup kitchens, etc., while he also provided personal aid to the poor of Bank Quay through the Workingmen's Mission. At this time he also presided at a protest meeting against the local Poor Law Guardians' unjust treatment of men who were unemployed through no fault of their own.

John Crosfield's strong belief in voluntary action and free enterprise is evidenced by his opposition to proposals for municipalizing the local gas and waterworks concerns. Thus in October 1866 he played a prominent part in securing the rejection of an Improvement Bill, which included a proposal for municipal take-over of the Waterworks Company. He considered this scheme would be very costly and would increase the rates, and that such concerns were more efficiently managed by private companies. Ten years later, for exactly the same reasons, he opposed a proposal for municipal ownership of the gasworks, though his brother George apparently approved it. In neither company, it should be mentioned, did he hold any shares.

He did, however, help to provide money for public amenities. He contributed generously to the Dispensary and Infirmary; he took shares in a company which built a large Public Hall in the early 'sixties; and he was a shareholder and director of another

[1] Joseph Crosfield & Sons, incidentally, never owned more than about fifteen houses, in the Bank Quay area.

company which provided public baths in 1865–6. The aim of the latter company, he observed, was 'to induce people to practice habits of cleanliness': they wished 'to make the baths as cheap and convenient as possible to the public, and at the same time endeavour to secure a respectable dividend to the shareholders'.

In later years, after long experience on the Council, his views on public enterprise changed somewhat. In October 1886, for example, at a banquet celebrating the opening of new municipal sewage works at Longford, with the building of which he had been closely concerned, he spoke in favour of expenditure on such public works for the health of the town. We have also previously noticed his support of municipal education.

The most outstanding example of the Crosfields' benevolence to the town was the gift of £9,500 by George Crosfield in 1872, which, together with £3,000 from Colonel Wilson Patten, enabled the Corporation to purchase Bank Hall and its grounds, the former residence of the Patten family, for conversion into a Town Hall, park, and gardens. (These still remain as a monument to his generosity.) He had often deplored, he said, Warrington's lack of parks and open spaces, like those of Preston, and he hoped that his gift would benefit public health and recreation.

George and John Crosfield also performed conscientious public service as local councillors and magistrates. George Crosfield was among the most active promoters of the town's incorporation in 1847, and was almost immediately elected to the new Council, but remained on it for only a few years. Business affairs made great demands on his time, and he was reluctant to engage in 'borough squabbles'. In 1869 he was appointed both a county and a borough J.P. His brother John took a much more prominent part in local affairs. He was elected to the Town Council in 1866 and re-elected till he resigned for private reasons in 1874. In 1877 he was again returned to the Council; in 1882 he was elected Mayor, and in 1885 Alderman. He resigned in 1890 and in the following year was made a Freeman of the Borough. In 1896, however, he made another come-back to the Council, on which he remained till 1900, the year before his death. He also served as a magistrate, being appointed a J.P. for the borough in 1874, and ten years later for the county;

he is said to have tempered justice with mercy, for he was by nature a fair and kind-hearted man.

The greatest of all the Crosfields' interests, however, outside soapmaking, was party politics. At times, indeed, politics appear almost to have taken priority over soap. This was because of deeply felt class antagonism against the continued landowning aristocratic predominance in British society. Neither the Reform Act of 1832 nor the repeal of the Corn Laws in 1846 had broken that predominance. In the Conservative Party created by Peel and Disraeli the traditional Tory landowning families still preserved tremendous political influence, and the House of Lords was still capable of hamstringing Liberal measures. Even in the Liberal party, the old Whig aristocratic element was still very strong. Hence the intense political chagrin and the growing Radicalism among the manufacturing and commercial middle classes, who despite their increasing economic strength, were still baulked in their efforts to achieve predominant political power. Economically, too, they were continuously irritated by the landowners' exactions of rent and royalties, while socially they resented the patronizing superiority of the ruling aristocratic families. Hence they turned again, as in 1832, to the working classes, to a combination of capital and labour—a union of the useful and industrious classes against the idle drones—by means of which they hoped finally to overwhelm the bastions of Tory privilege and influence.

Over and over again these sentiments were expressed in the political speeches of the Crosfields in the second half of the nineteenth century. Their hatred of Toryism was increased by the fact that the Tory party was the party of Anglican intolerance, of brewers and drunken ignorance, of warmongering Imperialism and increased taxation. 'Peace, retrenchment and reform' were ever on their lips, and Bright and Gladstone were their heroes.

George Crosfield joined with Joseph, his father, in the campaign of the Anti-Corn Law League. The Crosfield brothers are said to have contributed £500 to the Cobden testimonial after the repeal of the Corn Laws in 1846, and throughout their lives they remained staunch free-traders. But in Warrington—still controlled by the landowning influence of the Powys family, the Leghs, the Blackburnes, and the Pattens, combined with the financial and commercial interests of the Parrs, Lyons, and Greenalls—Toryism was dominant. The Liberals had won the first Parliamentary election in Warrington after the 1832 Reform Act, but thereafter Tory control was restored. George Crosfield became a district secretary in a Liberal party reorganization in the early 'forties, but the Tory stranglehold could not be broken, and from 1847 to 1868 'Greenallism' reigned supreme, Gilbert Greenall being repeatedly re-elected without opposition.

During this period, therefore, the Crosfields became strong advocates of further Parliamentary reform, urging extension of the franchise to the working classes, redistribution of seats, and vote by ballot, in the hope of breaking Tory predominance. George Crosfield, who was on terms of personal friendship with John Bright, agreed to stand as Liberal candidate in Warrington in the general election of 1859, provided that a requisition was signed by a fair proportion of the electors. He pointed out that 'the progress and prosperity of the country . . . was not dependant upon Lords, Dukes, and Marquises', but solely 'upon the constant hardworking industry of the masses of the people, assisted by the capitalists of the country'. Warrington, he said, should have a representative 'who would not go to increase the power of the aristocracy', but of 'the industrious classes, who were really the most valuable portion of society'. He called himself a Radical, but denied that further reform would be revolutionary. He was too Radical, however, for the electors and therefore had to stand down.

All three Crosfield brothers were very active in a local 'Reform Association'—George was a vice-president, John the secretary, and Morland a committee member—and also in the 'Lancashire Reformers' Union'. They made some very Radical speeches during the 'sixties in favour of popular rights and against aristocratic influence and corruption. They also actively supported the Liverpool Financial Reform Association, urging the substitution of direct for indirect taxation, which pressed most heavily on the masses of the people; they strongly opposed waste of public money on the armed forces, sinecures, etc. George Crosfield declared in October 1866 that he saw 'no reason whatever why universal suffrage should not be granted', and denounced the Tories' 'cunningly-devised schemes ["fancy franchises"] for keeping the governing power in the hands of the upper classes'.

He and his brother John now threw themselves whole-heartedly into the work of the Warrington branch of the National Reform Union; he and Morland were vice-presidents and John was joint secretary. (Morland, however, did not take a prominent part in politics.) They spoke at numerous meetings in the agitation leading up to the Second Reform Act of 1867. As they often pointed out afterwards, no credit was due to the Tories for this concession; popular clamour had carried the day.

This achievement was followed by the defeat of 'Greenallism' in Warrington, when Peter Rylands was returned as Liberal M.P. in the general election of 1868. The Crosfields contributed greatly to this victory, with money and personal support; several political meetings were held in the large soapery warehouse. John Crosfield was particularly active as honorary secretary of the Liberal committee: he pointed out to the new working-class voters that Liberalism stood for political and religious freedom, in Ireland as well as England, free trade, a free press, etc.—the opposite of Toryism, which was clearly antagonistic to their class interests. He accused the Tories of exploiting 'the public house system' to win votes, and the Tories retaliated by accusing Crosfield's and other large manufacturers of soliciting and even intimidating their workmen for their votes; after the election, Crosfield's were said to have dismissed workmen, or turned them out of their cottages, for voting Tory. Such accusations, however, were probably 'smears', for the Crosfields had declared over and over again that they would never attempt to intimidate their workpeople, and they were strongly in favour of the ballot to secure electoral freedom.

In 1869 the *Warrington Examiner* was started as a Liberal party newspaper, and John Crosfield was one of the directors of the publishing company. During the following years he and his brother George often spoke at Liberal meetings in support of the measures introduced by Gladstone's government, such as disestablishment of the Irish Church, vote by ballot, abolition of the purchase of army commissions, and stricter licensing, which they saw as blows against the Tory system of religious inequality, political corruption, aristocratic patronage, and drunkenness. They also applauded, on Quaker principles, international arbitration, as in the *Alabama* case, for the peaceful settlement of international disputes. But when the Government introduced its Public Health Bill in 1872, John Crosfield joined with other Warrington industrialists in a deputation opposing it, as it would interfere with their manufacturing freedom.

The Crosfields shared in the bitter Liberal disappointment at the general election of 1874, when Greenall was once again returned for Warrington. John Crosfield viewed the new Parliament as 'representing drink', and Disraeli as unscrupulous and dishonest. Peter Rylands being elected for Burnley in a by-election in 1876, George Crosfield agreed to be the Liberal candidate for Warrington at the next election, but in 1878 he withdrew owing to failing health. He was now living in London, but still lent support to the Liberal cause in Warrington, while his brother John was as politically active as ever, especially in denouncing the twin Tory curses of war and drink; Disraeli's jingoistic Imperialism he found particularly distasteful. He was very active in helping to build up Liberal party organization in the town, being treasurer for many years of the Liberal Club, established in 1875, and also of the Liberal Association, set up in 1878, with ward committees and a party 'caucus' on the Birmingham model.

These efforts led to the election of J. G. McMinnies as Liberal M.P. for Warrington in 1880. During the following years the Irish problem dominated the political scene, and provided John Crosfield with a constant theme for strong speeches against oppressive landlordism and the hereditary House of Lords, which blocked a just settlement in Ireland and tried 'to stop the business of the country when the Tories were not in power'. He waxed indignant against the Lords' efforts to stop further Parliamentary reform in 1884–5.

When McMinnies announced his intention of retirement in 1884, efforts were made to persuade either George or John Crosfield to accept the Liberal candidature. When they declined, their relative William Crosfield, of Liverpool, was brought in, but was defeated by the aged Sir Gilbert Greenall in the general election of November 1885. John Crosfield thereupon reluctantly agreed to become the next Liberal candidate. He declared that he would 'support Mr. Gladstone through thick and thin', especially on the Irish Home Rule Bill, which would give 'freedom and justice' to Ireland, instead of Tory coercion. His election address also affirmed his other well-known Liberal principles. He denounced the Whig landowning aristocratic renegades from the Liberal party and appealed to the people. He secured the support of the Warrington Trades Council, but the defection of Liberal Unionists led to his defeat by Greenall in July 1886.

He still continued, however, as Liberal candidate, denouncing Tory oppression in Ireland, Imperialism, waste of public money on armaments, and the neo-protectionist 'Fair Trade' movement. In 1889, however, he resigned as Liberal candidate. A presentation in appreciation of his services referred to his long-continued support of the local Liberal party, to whose funds he had been 'a most generous contributor'. He was still treasurer of the Liberal Club, a vice-president and later president of the Liberal Association, and still vocal at public meetings, especially in denunciation of Tory landowners. His speeches, according to his obituary in the *Warrington Examiner* of 28th December 1901, were 'characteristic of the man. Blunt, straightforward, transparently honest in his convictions, he dealt sledgehammer blows at his opponents. There was no *finesse* about his speeches; they were couched in homely and vigorous language and sometimes his expressions were a trifle strong.' The Conservative *Warrington Guardian* also bore witness to his sincerity, honest outspokenness, and 'unfailing devotion to Liberalism'.

His sons, particularly Arthur, the eldest, followed the family Liberal tradition in local politics. But they were brought up in greater wealth, as Anglicans not Quakers, went to public schools, developed upper-class sporting interests, holidayed extensively abroad, and, in general, therefore, were much less passionately Radical than their father. Moreover, the rise of Socialism tended to create concern among Liberal manufacturers like the Crosfields, whose property was threatened along with that of the landowners. Thus we find Arthur Crosfield telling the firm's employees in 1892 that 'I do not think the interests of the working-classes will be served by Socialism ... which necessarily strikes at the root of individualism'. Socialism would be 'public plunder': it would deprive of their property those men who, by their enterprise, thrift, and risk-taking, had built Britain's industrial greatness, provided employment for the workers, and were 'the backbone of our commercial system'. Moreover, it was utterly impractical, being contrary to man's individualist and competitive nature. At the same time, Arthur Crosfield was not blind to the faults of the present system, especially 'the enormous inequality . . . between the extreme rich and the extreme poor', and favoured the provision of more social amenities, to be paid for by taxing landlords' ground rents and unearned increments and by a fair system of graduated income-tax.

His remarks on the growth of a typical family business—from humble beginnings to riches—may well have had reference to his own family's rise. His grandfather, Joseph, had started in a small way and was not very wealthy, though comfortably established, by the time he died. After his death, his family continued to live for some years in the house near the works at White Cross; Slater's directory shows them still there in 1855, but the records of the local Quaker meeting show that his wife and younger children (i.e. all save George and Morland) moved into Cheshire in 1854. They went to live at Bowdon, where his wife remained until her death in 1877. George, meanwhile, had married in 1851 Isabella, daughter of Henry Ashworth, of Turton, near Bolton, also a Quaker and a very wealthy cotton manufacturer (said to have been the Oswald Millbank of Disraeli's novel, *Coningsby*). He went to live first of all at Fir Grove, Latchford; in 1860 he was living at Lymm; then, in 1863–4, he built himself a large country mansion in spacious grounds at Walton Lea, near Warrington.

His brother Morland was the first of the Crosfields to marry a non-Quaker, Margaret Davies, daughter of a Warrington solicitor. The marriage took place in 1854 in Lymm parish church, Morland having resigned from the Society of Friends. Until the early 'seventies he lived at Bank House (now the Borough Treasurer's office) in Sankey Street, but then had a large house built, 'Baycliffe' (now a private school), at Lymm, just before he died in 1875. As we have seen, he left nearly £90,000. He did not take a prominent part in public life, though he is said to have been very open-handed. He was a keen gardener and naturalist, and his two sons, Ernest and Sydney, appear to have spent their lives as sporting gentlemen, after having shown their incapacity in the soap business.

John, the youngest of the three partners, also married a non-Quaker, Eliza Dickson, eldest daughter of Henry Dickson, who came of an Ulster Protestant family in the cotton trade. The wedding took place in the parish church, Belfast, in 1864; he had resigned from the Friends' Society six years previously. The first year of his married life was spent at Bowdon; he then moved to Brookfield, Lymm, where he resided for ten years; and finally, when his brother George moved to 118 Lancaster Gate, London, in 1875, John bought his mansion at Walton Lea for £15,000, where he lived for the rest of his life. His wife bore him five sons (only three of whom survived to manhood) and four daughters.[1] She died in 1882, and six years later he married her sister Gertrude (at St. Helier, Jersey), but had no more children.

He was evidently very proud of his large house and gardens at Walton Lea, which he threw open to the public on special occasions. His wealth and social prestige grew substantially as the years passed. He took to holidaying and travelling abroad, in the South of France, Italy, and other parts of Europe, then in the West Indies, and eventually, in 1895, he toured round the world; two years later he visited India again. He died on 26th December 1901 and was buried in St. Thomas's Churchyard, Stockton Heath.

He left personal and real property valued at £155,490 gross. His industrial holdings were concentrated mainly in Joseph Crosfield & Sons, Ltd., and Brunner, Mond & Co., Ltd. In the former he held 4,255 £10 Preference shares, market value £9 per share, totalling £38,295.[2] His shares in Brunner, Mond & Co. were valued at well over twice that figure: 17,500 £1 Ordinary shares (of which, however, 1,750 were only half paid up), worth £83,125 at £5 per fully paid share, and 337 £10 Preference shares worth £5,981 15s. at £17 15s. per share. He also held 200 £10 Ordinary shares in the Salt Union Ltd., the amalgamation of Cheshire salt-producing firms established in

[1] Arthur Henry, b. 1865; Joseph John, b. 1866; George, b. 1872, died soon after birth; Horace Goad, b. 1874, d. 1880; George Rowlandson, b. 1877; Constance Eleanor, b. 1868; Aileen Gertrude, b. 1870; Gertrude Hudson, b. 1879; Hilda Elizabeth, b. 1881.

[2] He had transferred his Ordinary shares to his sons. See below, pp. 139–40, for the conversion of the firm into a limited company.

1888, but these were now worth only £325. His other share-holdings were of negligible importance. His house at Walton Lea was valued at £14,500, his furniture, etc. at £2,682. The net value of his estate, on settlement of debts and death duty, was £127,682. After payment of a few small personal bequests and £1,000 to Warrington Infirmary and Dispensary, the estate was to go to his wife and children.

PART III

THE THIRD GENERATION: COMPETITION AND TECHNOLOGICAL ADVANCE, 1896–1915

CHAPTER XI

CROSFIELD'S A LIMITED COMPANY

THE vast majority of nineteenth-century firms were, like Crosfield's, owned by a family or partnership, but after the passing of legislation between 1855 and 1862 facilitating the formation of limited companies, businessmen gradually began to appreciate the advantages of this type of organization. In addition to acquiring the legal benefits of incorporation, they were thereby enabled to expand their businesses more easily and with lessened risk, by obtaining additional capital from the investing public and by having their liabilities limited to the extent of their shareholdings. As partners or sole proprietors grew old, moreover, they found the limited company a convenient means of giving some corporate permanence to their businesses.

All these advantages were apparent to John Crosfield in the middle 1890s. He was then in his sixties. His elder sons, Arthur Henry and Joseph John, had already been made partners and had been taking over management responsibility; his third son, George Rowlandson, entered the works in 1895. Under K. E. Markel's scientific direction, they were rapidly expanding production of both soap and chemicals, but their schemes for further expansion were restricted by capital requirements. It was, therefore, decided to transform the business into a limited company, registered as 'Joseph Crosfield & Sons, Limited', on 11th July 1896. No doubt the examples of Gossage & Sons, Ltd., and Lever Brothers, Ltd., both incorporated in 1894, influenced this decision.

Incorporation did not involve any surrender of ownership or control by the Crosfields. The only outside shareholder was Dr. Markel, whose scientific and technological ability made him indispensable. The Ordinary shares of £10 each were allotted to the four Directors of the Company as follows: John Crosfield 1,597, Arthur Henry Crosfield 5,799, Joseph John Crosfield 5,798, Karl Emil Markel 1,799, altogether 14,993; seven more shares held by other members of the Crosfield family brought the total to 15,000. In addition there were 15,000 Cumulative Preference shares, also of £10 each and yielding £5 per cent per annum, entirely owned by members of the Crosfield family: John Crosfield 5,640, Arthur Henry Crosfield 3,200, Joseph John Crosfield 3,200, George Rowland-son Crosfield 1,000, Miss Constance Eleanor Crosfield 980, Miss Aileen Harriet Crosfield 980. Thus the total Ordinary and Preference share capital (fully paid up) was £300,000.

The main purpose of the incorporation, however, was to facilitate the raising of outside loan capital, and steps were immediately taken for the issue of £150,000 of 4¼ per cent Irredeemable First Mortgage Debenture Stock. The prospectus pointed out that the demand for the Company's soaps and chemicals was 'so great, that their present plant, large as it is, is quite inadequate to meet it, and further extensive additions are now necessary. The present issue is made for the purpose of providing the capital required.' The certified profits of the business, for the two years ending 20th June 1896, without charging interest on the partners' capital, had been 'more per annum than four times the amount required to pay the annual interest [£6,375] on the present issue of £150,000 Debenture Stock', i.e. the profits had been over £25,500 per annum. The Company's freehold and leasehold property, buildings, plant, etc., exclusive of the valuable goodwill, were independently valued at £179,792, while stock-in-trade was put at £86,694 and book debts at £50,000, so that its assets totalled £316,486.

The Debenture Stock was issued at a premium of 6 per cent, in amounts of not less than £50. Some of it was at first taken up by underwriting and assurance firms, but was soon disposed of to private investors, mostly in local or neighbouring areas, but some farther afield; shareholdings were numerous and generally small, in hundreds rather than thousands of pounds. The interests of these Debenture Stockholders were protected by a long and complicated Trust Deed, the purpose of which was to secure their stock by means of fifteen Debentures of £10,000 each, issued to two Trustees, to whom the Company's assets were mortgaged and who were to be allowed access to the Company's accounts and premises, to see that the business was being properly and efficiently conducted. Here, it might seem, was a possibility of outside interference, but the two

10 (*a*) John Crosfield

10 (*b*) Arthur H. Crosfield

10 (*c*) Joseph John Crosfield

10 (*d*) George R. Crosfield

Trustees were John Crosfield himself and a business associate, Charles Maxwell Holland, formerly a civil engineer of Manchester, who, after providing Brunner & Mond with a good deal of their early capital, became a director of Brunner, Mond & Co., and who was described in the Trust Deed as a colliery proprietor of Bryn-y-Grog, near Wrexham. After their deaths, in 1901 and 1906 respectively, Dr. Markel and T. J. Ridgway, Crosfield's local solicitor, were appointed Trustees. Provided that the half-yearly interest was regularly paid and the business showed no sign of running at a loss, there was little likelihood that the stockholders would wish to intervene in the Company's affairs; indeed, when stockholders' meetings were held, the Directors and Trustees were usually the only ones attending and were empowered to represent the other stockholders by proxy.

Within another year more capital was required, when Crosfield's decided to purchase several Liverpool soap businesses, with the main intention of strengthening their position in the export trade. The biggest acquisition was that of D. C. Keeling & Co., who had succeeded in 1874 to the old-established export firm of M. Steele & Son and the home-trade firm of James Blake. Their works, the Queen's Soap Works, in Kitchen Street and Blundell Street, Liverpool, together with the freehold land, goodwill, and trade marks, were bought for £95,000 in March 1897. Coupled with this purchase was that of the Liverpool Patent Soap Company, or Titan Soap Company, of 11 Dale Street and 13A Lydia Ann Street, Liverpool. Both Keeling's and the Titan Company had just been acquired by Commerce Ltd., from whom Crosfield's immediately bought them. The price for the Titan Company was £30,000, but by a subsequent arrangement half the business was sold back to Commerce Ltd. The total purchase money for the two businesses was therefore £110,000.

At the same time Crosfield's paid £14,000 for another smaller soapmaking firm, Medley & Sons, of Naylor Street, Liverpool, established in 1841. Keeling's and Medley's soaps were said to have 'a large sale for export, and are well known in the following markets: Egypt, China, Java, Dutch Indies, Australia, South Africa, West Coast of Africa, India, Brazil, South America, Central America, West Indies, &c.' It was expected 'that the profits resulting from this amalgamation will be substantially increased by the removal of the element of competition'.

Crosfield's acquired capital for these purchases by further public borrowing. In April 1897 arrangements were made for the issue of £140,000 of 4½ per cent 'A' Debenture Stock at 106 per cent. It was secured by a second charge on the whole of the Company's assets, John Crosfield and Charles M. Holland again acting as trustees for the stockholders. The issue was over-subscribed, but Medley's and the Titan Company were not, in fact, very worthwhile acquisitions and were soon disposed of. Both were sold in 1899 to a German chemist, Dr. F. O. Kloninger—Medley's (except for the goodwill and trade marks, valued at £9,300, which Crosfield's retained) for £5,500 and the half share in the Titan Company for £9,000. Keeling's, much the biggest purchase, proved to be a profitable concern, but, as we shall see, the operation of two separate soapworks soon began to cause serious doubts.

Another major reorganization was carried through in the late 'nineties, when Crosfield's trade in milled toilet soaps, shaving sticks, perfumes, etc., was transferred to a newly formed Erasmic Company. (The parent company still retained the trade in cheap unmilled soaps, as well as the household trade.) This company, incorporated on 31st August 1898, had a nominal capital of £100,000, divided into 5,000 Ordinary and 5,000 Preference shares of £10 each; 4,576 of the former were issued, but none of the latter. Joseph Crosfield & Sons Ltd. held all the issued capital and the two Boards were identical. This new company was, in fact, purely a selling subsidiary. All the Erasmic goods continued to be manufactured in Crosfield's milling and perfumery department, which was credited with a percentage on the Erasmic Company's turnover. The main purpose of the new creation was to concentrate effort on the sale of Erasmic goods, by advertising, etc., with the idea of creating a national and international market. A London office and showroom were immediately acquired at 117 Oxford Street, with the aim of breaking into the high-class metropolitan toilet trade.

Incorporation and expansion involved no immediate change in the top-level direction of the Crosfield business. John Crosfield, senior partner in the old firm, became the new Company

Chairman, while his two eldest sons, Arthur H. and J. J., together with Dr. K. E. Markel, were the other Directors. But recruitment of additional Directors was soon necessary and this enabled some of the most able of the managerial staff to be rewarded with higher responsibility. Towards the end of 1899 Charles Frederick Huffam was appointed a Director; he had started as a traveller with the firm in 1877, eventually rising to the position of home soap sales manager. At the beginning of 1900 Robert Fenemore Jones, previously manager of D. C. Keeling's works in Liverpool and retained in that position by Crosfield's, was also raised to the Board, with responsibility for the export trade. Six months later another Director was appointed, Henry Roberts, a solicitor by training, who had been associated for many years with John Crosfield as the local Liberal party agent, and had done legal business for the firm.

After John Crosfield's death at the end of 1901, his eldest son, Arthur, became Chairman, with J. J. as Vice-Chairman, but his third son, George R., though a substantial shareholder, was not appointed a Director till the beginning of 1906. He had had a long training in the business, since 1895, and had been for several years supervising the soapmaking side under Dr. Markel. Control of the business appears to have been mainly in the hands of J. J. Crosfield and Markel. Arthur, though Chairman, became more interested in political and social affairs than in soapmaking and in January 1906 he was elected Liberal M.P. for Warrington. From then on he rarely attended Board meetings and ceased to play any important part in the business, though he remained Chairman until January 1909, when he was replaced by J. J., and George became Vice-Chairman. Eventually, in March 1911, he was deprived of his Directorship.[1]

Two or three months earlier Cyril Haslam, previously manager of the chemical sales department, had been appointed to the Board. He and the other Directors selected from outside the Crosfield family, were products of the 'managerial revolution'—professional Directors, with little capital stake in the business, as distinct from the Crosfields, who combined ownership and management much like the former partners. At the time of their appointment Huffam and Jones held only the £100 minimum shareholding qualification; Roberts gradually

[1] See below, pp. 241–2.

143

acquired a more substantial holding, but still far smaller than that of the Crosfields. An indication of the increasingly professional element came at the beginning of 1902, with the appointment of the Directors as Managers of the Company, i.e. they became Managing Directors, with the following salaries: A. H. Crosfield £1,000, J. J. Crosfield £1,800, K. E. Markel £1,800, C. F. Huffam £300 plus commissions, R. F. Jones £700, H. Roberts £800. These salaries were in addition to Directors' fees, which had been at first £600 each, but were soon reduced to £300 and now to £200.

In March 1908 Dr. Markel resigned his position as Technical Director 'owing to the unsatisfactory condition of his health'. But there was more to it than that. According to George Crosfield's later reminiscences, not merely was his health worsening, but 'his judgment was deteriorating likewise. In the opinion of the Board, he was spreading himself much too much.' As we shall see, J. J. Crosfield had been strongly advocating reduced capital expenditure and more dividends, which would curtail Markel's schemes for further expansion. At the same time George Crosfield was waiting to step into the position of Technical Director. So Markel was pensioned off as Consulting Technical Director at £1,200 a year and went to live in London. But it was not entirely a sinecure, for he did continue to provide expert advice, especially in connection with the hydrogenation process; several years later he was still patenting processes for the Company. He finally resigned in November 1916. His scientific and technological innovations left an indelible imprint upon the firm: he, more than anyone else, was responsible for shaping its modern chemical development.[1]

The rapid growth in the scale and diversity of Crosfield's enterprises during this period necessitated increasing specialization and departmentalization. At the highest level, though the Board of Directors continued to be generally responsible for all matters, a division of duties was arranged. Thus in February 1901 the following arrangement was agreed on, 'with a view to avoid overlapping': the household and toilet soap trade to be the responsibility of A. H. Crosfield, with commercial matters,

[1] In the 1914–18 war he was chiefly interested in looking after German prisoners. About 1920 he developed a paralytic disease, from which he eventually died in 1932.

travelling and selling relative thereto in the hands of C. F. Huffam, and the buying of raw materials, export business and control of the Liverpool works in those of R. F. Jones; Dr. Markel was to be technical and general works managing director, but was to share responsibility for chemicals and glycerine with J. J. Crosfield; the latter was also to be responsible for costs and finance (manufacturing and commercial), together with H. Roberts, who was to exercise control over legal and clerical matters. Eventually, in April 1911, it was decided to establish special committees of the Board for Buying, Home Sales, and Export of soaps—a formal and permanent arrangement in place of earlier informal or *ad hoc* committees.

Below the Directors was a growing hierarchy of managers or heads of departments. These were divided into two broad groups, secretarial and commercial, and works or manufacturing. The former group included in 1907–8 the general office and the following departments: cashier's, ledger, forwarding, home sales, export sales, chemical sales, buying, traffic, lighterage, Erasmic, and advertising. The works was made up of many departments, which had grown in number as new products and processes were added. First of all there was the raw materials or melting department, then the vegetable butter, stearine, oil-milling, and benzine (solvent extraction) departments, producing and refining oils and fats. Next came the soap boiling, cutting, and tableting departments, making household soap, followed by the milling and perfumery and toilet departments, the soap warehouse, and the printing and box-making departments. There were also the various laboratories. On the chemical side there were the glycerine, caustic, and silicate departments, to which the new Carbosil, cement and paint departments had been added, together with the ancillary cooperage, tin-making, and packing departments. In addition there were the departments concerned with providing water, steam, gas, and electricity, and the engineers' department and stores. Altogether there were at that time thirty-three managers, some departments being grouped under a single head.

It is extremely doubtful if John Crosfield's sons were able, like their father, to know most of their employees' names, and they could no longer run the works on the same informal and personal lines. To help keep everything and everyone in order a stream of typed regulations was issued. At the same time the volume of clerical and accounting work multiplied, and it is significant that a new cost and stocktaking department was established at the end of 1906, followed in 1911 by a special audit department, formalizing arrangements that had been gradually evolving in previous years. The whole business, in fact, was put on a statistical basis: monthly, quarterly, half-yearly, and annual figures were laid before the Board; manufacturing and commercial costs were continually analysed; a watchful eye was kept on sales, prices, and profits; estimates of capital expenditure were carefully calculated; and trading prospects were frequently reviewed.

To house the expanding secretarial and commercial staff, new offices were required; those built in the middle 'eighties soon proved inadequate. The present-day office buildings (then including dining rooms, etc.) were therefore erected on Liverpool Road in 1905–6, at a total cost, inclusive of fittings and furniture, of about £17,000. The old offices were converted into the main laboratory, and have only recently been changed back to offices after the building of the new Technical Centre.

To run this rapidly expanding business efficiently, it was essential that capable managers should be selected or trained. The problem was most acute in regard to recruitment of scientifically-trained technologists. For years, as we have seen, George and John Crosfield had tried to develop technical education in Warrington, but there was at the end of the nineteenth century a serious shortage of such men. Dr. Markel—himself brought from Germany by Brunner, Mond & Co.—therefore introduced a team of foreign (mostly German) chemists, to carry out research and to develop new processes. R. Ockel, for example, a German chemist, became manager of the new oil refinery, stearine plant, and oil-mill. Another German, E. C. Kayser, was responsible for the early development of the hydrogenation process. S. J. Studer, a Swiss chemist, formerly employed by Brunner, Mond & Co., became head of the main laboratory and of the glycerine department. Another German, Machenhauer, had control over the quality of essential oils and perfumes, and later did work on hydrogenation. Two French perfumiers, Henrique and Vivadou, were also recruited, and

146

a number of other foreign scientists worked at Crosfield's during these years.

In 1907, however, as we shall see, most of the Germans were dismissed—even Markel was retained only in an advisory capacity—and replaced by British personnel. A number of the latter were university graduates, some with doctorates, especially those engaged in research and development. Dr. D. Prentice, for example, already in charge of the new cement works, also took over the glycerine department from Studer, who was replaced as chief chemist by J. Allan, a specialist in oils and fats, who had studied in the universities of Glasgow, London, and Heidelberg, and had been at Bank Quay about ten years. Allan, who also took over the buying of perfumes from Machenhauer, was ultimately to become a Director of the Company in 1925. Kayser was replaced in hydrogenation development by Dr. T. P. Hilditch. Dr. C. W. Moore came to the firm from Burroughs Wellcome & Co. in 1911 and, together with Dr. C. H. Clarke (who joined Crosfield's in 1913), carried out fundamental research on the constitution of oils and fats. He was later to become works manager and then, in 1930, Technical Director, while Dr. Clarke rose to become ultimately Technical Director of Unilever. Dr. Hilditch became the chief research chemist, but left the firm in 1925-6 to become Professor of Oils and Fats at Liverpool University. His successor was R. Furness, M.Sc., who had assisted in hydrogenation research and became manager of acetone production during the first World War; although blinded in a works explosion, this remarkable man ultimately became head of the research department. F. G. Reynolds, B.Sc., was in charge of the soap laboratory; later he was to become manager of the soapery and then of the Erasmic plant. G. A. Duff, an engineering graduate, was responsible for the engineering side of the hydrogenation plant and was eventually to become chief works engineer. Another scientist who carried out research at Crosfield's during the first decade of this century was Dr. C. W. Ormandy, who developed the production of paints and ochres, and also did work on water softening and boiler treatment.

Crosfield's thus recruited during these years a brilliant team of scientists, who came in at a fairly high level and soon rose to become heads of departments. But most managerial appointments were made from men who had been 'brought up' in the firm, after entry from school and training in the laboratories and works departments; many had continued their education, with the Directors' strong encouragement, in the evening classes of local technical schools and the Manchester College of Technology. F. Smith, manager of the soap-boiling and cutting department at this time, originally from Medley's, was a practical soap-boiler, with little academic knowledge. So was E. G. Medley, who, after Crosfield's take-over, was put in charge of the milling, perfumery and toilet department and eventually succeeded Smith as soapery manager. F. Fox also came up 'the hard way', beginning as an assistant in the works laboratory and rising to become manager first of the Liverpool soapworks and then of the new hydrogenation plant; in the early 1920s he was to become soapery manager, and later left Crosfield's on appointment as Technical Director (and ultimately Chairman) of John Knight's. His assistant in the hydrogenation plant, W. R. Jackson, who was eventually to become manager, also began as a youth in the laboratory. So did E. Ball, manager of the raw materials department, oil-mill and refinery, who in the late 1920s transferred to management of the continuous causticizing plant and then in the early 'thirties was appointed works manager, before transferring to Joseph Watson's, of Leeds, as Technical Director and later Chairman. His assistant manager in the oil-mill and refinery, C. Billington, came up the same way, via the laboratory and local technical school, and was later to become manager of this and other departments such as the silica gel and base-exchange plants, etc.

Other managers had a similar training in the laboratories, drawing office, and works departments, with education at local night schools. F. J. Burlton, the chief engineer, had started as a draughtsman. G. Dale, who became manager of the fuel, gas, and water department in the years before the first World War, began as a boilerman. Some managers were recruited from outside. J. Rose came from Brunner, Mond & Co., to be manager of the caustic soda and silicate plants; he eventually became Technical Director of Gossage's in the 1920s. J. Newall, who succeeded F. J. Burlton as chief engineer when the latter was elected to the Board in 1915, had been a marine engineer before becoming assistant engineer at Crosfield's.

Most of the managers on the administrative and commercial side were brought up in the business, beginning as clerks, or were brought in as young travellers, etc. Examples are W. H. Robinson, the Company's first secretary; J. R. Wardle, his successor in 1902; C. F. Huffam, for many years a traveller, becoming home soap sales manager, then a Director in 1899 and finally Chairman in 1923; C. Haslam, beginning as a traveller for the Erasmic Company in 1899, becoming chemical sales manager, appointed a Director in 1911 and Chairman in 1917; C. H. Hamilton, export sales manager, appointed a Director in 1916, and later Chairman of Gossage's; G. H. K. Kingdon, M.A., who began in the laboratory in 1896, but quickly transferred to the commercial side and became manager of the buying department, appointed a Director in 1913 and Chairman in 1926.

These examples illustrate how successful Crosfield's were in recruiting their managerial staff. On the one hand, they were more enlightened than most firms of that period in bringing in university graduates, especially on the research side, while, on the other hand, they were also remarkably successful in selecting and training local talent for positions of responsibility in both manufacturing and commercial departments. Moreover, there was clearly 'room at the top' for some of the most able, who rose to become Directors and even (in later years) Chairmen not only of Crosfield's but of other companies in the Lever and Unilever combine.

These men were responsible for controlling a rapidly growing labour force. The total number of employees in the Warrington works increased from around 800 in July 1896 to nearly 2,500 in July 1913, of whom 500 were women and girls. These embraced an immense variety of trades. In addition to those engaged in the production of soap, glycerine, caustic soda, silicate, etc., including the chemists in the laboratories, there were workers in the oil-mill, refineries, and fat-hardening plant; wrappers, packers, printers, boxmakers and others who prepared the products for dispatch to customers; carters, bargemen, engine-drivers, and other transport workers; draughtsmen, fitters, turners, boilermen, electricians and others in the engineering and fuel and power departments; smiths, bricksetters, joiners, plumbers, painters, and labourers concerned with building and maintenance; cashiers, clerks, and typists on the secretarial and commercial side.

All these had to be organized into a coherent whole, disciplined and regulated, yet infused with some *esprit de corps* and loyalty to the firm. The Directors sought to achieve these ends by a policy of autocratic paternalism, the details of which were laid down in a pamphlet of 1903, of which further editions were published in 1904, 1905, and 1906. There was a marked military tone about these regulations, deriving perhaps from strong links with the local Volunteers and the National Service League. The Directors' aim was to bring about 'improvement in the Physical, Mental, and Moral Conditions of the Workpeople'. They disclaimed, however, 'any specially philanthropic motive'. They simply considered 'that the interests of employers and employees are indissolubly bound together' and 'that their [the firm's] outlay is amply returned in services more cheerfully and more efficiently performed'. The preface to the later pamphlets, however, contained some idealistic sentiments. The Directors had been impressed by recent statistics showing 'a marked and serious decline' in the fitness of the working classes. 'Out of every three men presenting themselves for enlistment [in the Armed Forces], two are rejected on the ground of physical unfitness . . . The conditions of much modern employment are against healthy bodily development. Manufacturing life concentrating large numbers in small areas gives but little opportunity for outdoor exercise. This and the general lack of cleanliness make for physical deterioration.' Large firms, however, had it in their power to remedy this state of affairs 'by providing the necessary means for promoting the health of the workpeople and by generally improving the conditions of employment'. They could thereby alter the whole aspect of 'the Labour Question'. 'The workmen, instead of being bound to a task which is repugnant and which necessity compels, will find the daily routine of work a part of his educational development and his daily task will become a pleasurable duty.'

How were these high-minded aims to be achieved? Firstly, every person who had been in the continuous employ of the firm for fifteen months on 1st April was allowed a week's holiday with full pay during the summer, an unusual concession in industry at that time. But it was based on stringent conditions as to punctuality, a very small number of 'lates' being allowed. Nevertheless, the number qualifying increased from 57 per cent in 1900, to over 94 per cent in 1912, and there was said to be a noticeable correlation between improved regularity and departmental efficiency.

It had 'always been the Firm's desire to reduce the hours of labour as far as possible, without diminishing the earnings of its workpeople'. In many departments 'the men's time had been reduced [fairly recently, it seems] from 10 hours a day to 9, while giving the men the same wages as they had before. The working hours per week in these Departments are now 49½ (in some cases 46½) against the 55½ formerly. The girls' working hours have also been reduced from 55½ to 46½, while retaining the 55½ hours' wage.' A later booklet, issued by the firm in July 1913, stated that 'some few years ago, the eight-hour [shift] system was introduced into all Departments working by day and night'. Previously a twelve-hour shift had been worked. The new system was apparently introduced in 1906–7. There was, at the same time, some reduction of wages, but the Board minutes of 22nd October 1907 reveal that the Directors offered shift workers in the caustic, silicate, glycerine, and fuel departments a half-day's holiday a fortnight, or a day a month, without loss of wages.

New regulations for day workers in all departments except engineering were issued in September 1911. From the beginning of October the working week was to be 47 hours instead of 49½, without any reduction of wages. The hours from Monday to Friday would be 7.30 a.m. to 12 noon and 1 p.m. to 5 p.m.; Saturdays 7.30 a.m. to 12 noon. Overtime rates were also laid down. The pamphlet of July 1913, however, indicates an extension of the 'week' to 48 hours, work commencing daily at 7.20 a.m.

The Office or Staff hours were reduced in June 1904, to be from 8.30 a.m. to 5 p.m. on five days and to 12.30 on Saturdays, and alternate Thurday afternoons were given as a holiday to all clerks who had been punctual and had their work up to date. Clerks also had longer annual holidays than works employees: one week after one year's service, ten days after two, and a fortnight after three.

Little information has been discovered on wages paid at Crosfield's during these years. None of the wages books has survived. The pamphlets of 1903–6 declared that 'it is the policy of the Firm to arrive at cheap labour by combining high wages with a high standard of efficiency'. The minimum weekly wage for men was fixed in September 1911 at 21*s*., though this did 'not apply to old men for whom soft jobs have been found'. In some departments bonus or piece-work systems existed and up to 40*s*. or more per week could be earned. The former system was probably that referred to as 'profit-sharing' in the 1903–6 pamphlets. Quality as well as quantity of output was considered. Increments of 14 to 25 per cent on weekly wages had been earned. An annual bonus of 5 per cent was also paid on managerial salaries.

Discipline was strict and some of the works' rules were extremely autocratic. For example, anyone breaking the rules, neglecting or disobeying a foreman's orders, or guilty of 'improper conduct (including irregularity of attendance and wilful waste of time and material)', could be dismissed without notice and without wages. Order and cleanliness were insisted upon throughout the works, enforced by men specially appointed. Spitting, for example, was prohibited on pain of instant dismissal. Prizes were given for cleanliness, measures were taken to prevent injurious dust and fumes, protective clothing was provided, and an engineering inspector checked all machinery. After having been fined repeatedly for emission of smoke, the firm had given great attention to smokeless combustion, saving greatly on coal consumption and contributing to improved health. Crosfield's strongly supported the 'Beautiful Warrington Society', and even experimented with climbing plants, window-boxes, etc., in the works, and tried to make a roof garden on the new Carbosil block!

Great prominence was given in the 1903–6 pamphlets to the Works Company of the 1st Volunteer Battalion (later Territorials), South Lancashire Regiment, to the National Service League, and to the Works' Fire Brigade. Managers were encouraged to become Volunteer Officers. Every volunteer was allowed to go to camp each year for a fortnight, the firm paying full wages for the first week (in lieu of the week's holiday) and making the regimental pay up to full wages for the second. They were allowed to put in an hour's drill each week during working hours at the firm's expense.

Most of the Directors, Managers, and Foremen are members of the National Service League and advocates of Universal [and compulsory] Military Training. Along with a large number of the men they believe that such a training is desirable in the interest of our industries [especially to compete with Germany], would improve the nation physically and mentally, and develop in all classes a desire to serve the community. The interest taken by the Firm in this great question has materially helped forward the Warrington Branch of the League.

Crosfield's had even sent a circular on the subject to their customers. Captain George Crosfield, having served in the Boer War, was especially keen on these activities.

Great importance was also attached to the Fire Brigade, which was claimed to be 'the best equipped and most efficient works fire service in the Kingdom'. (It won the Northern Challenge Shield in 1912.) It was run on military lines, with an active list, reserve, and auxiliaries, and with stress on physical training, 'smartness, appearance and deportment'. The emphasis on an efficient fire brigade and fire prevention was, of course, essential in a works containing so much inflammable material. A new fire station was built in 1905–6, adjoining the new offices, at a cost of £3,000, and an electric alarm system was installed throughout the works. For similar reasons, there was a strong Ambulance Brigade in the works, and continuous attention was given to accident prevention. Great pride was also taken in the Brass Band, which won many prizes, including the Thousand Guineas Challenge Shield at the Crystal Palace Contest in September 1911. The firm provided uniforms and instruments, contributing from £250 to £500 per annum, mostly charged to advertising.

Crosfield's continued to take great interest in educational matters, with a view partly to mental and moral improvement and partly to increased technical efficiency. An inquiry in November 1901 revealed that of 123 youths employed by the firm, only twenty-seven, mostly in the offices, attended local night classes. To encourage better attendance, the Directors decided to pay the sessional fees of 5s. per head and to offer a bonus of 5s. to each of those passing. Attendance greatly improved in the next two or three years and was then made compulsory for all (both lads and girls) under seventeen years of age; in September 1908 it was agreed to allow them to leave work half an hour earlier on four days a week. Boys took technical or commercial subjects, while girls learnt needlework, dressmaking, cooking, and domestic economy. They must have passed the sixth standard at school before being employed by the firm; those who had passed the seventh standard were paid an extra shilling a week, which encouraged parents to keep their children at school for an extra year.

At the other end of the age scale, veteran employees received recognition. From 1904 onwards the firm paid £5 to those completing twenty-five years' service and £20 for fifty years' service, the presentations being made public occasions. Such long periods of service were by no means uncommon, and there were strong family connections with the firm, sons often following fathers into Crosfield's employment.

A 'Workmen's Council' was established, but its functions were very limited. It was to collect from the workmen suggestions for improvement of their working conditions and to put proposals before the Directors, but such suggestions were 'not to be in any way connected with the terms of labour', i.e. wages, hours, etc. Moreover, the Technical Director was Chairman of the Council, and a representative manager was also nominated by the firm; the workmen's representatives were elected by the various departments. The Council was also charged with control of the funds of the Recreation Club.

The latter was established in accordance with the Directors' principle of 'helping those who help themselves'. The firm did not, in other words, provide large sums for social activities, but encouraged the employees to provide these for themselves, by means of their own subscriptions, which the Directors would supplement. Thus a Recreation Fund was established, with a contribution of a penny per week, which, at the workpeople's suggestion, was made compulsory, with a view to providing a recreation ground for cricket, football, athletics, tennis, and bowls. Existing clubs for these sports were brought under one committee in March 1902, when, in response to a request for financial aid, the Directors made a grant of a mere £20 and agreed to make personal subscriptions of two guineas each. In May 1905 between nine and ten acres of land on Hood Lane, Great Sankey, were leased from Lord Lilford, at an annual rent of £50, and laid out as a recreation ground. For this purpose the Directors made a loan of £500 to the Recreation Club, at 4 per cent interest, to be repaid within five years. In future years an expenditure on 'Social Improvement account' of £500 per annum was sanctioned, out of which £100 to £150 went towards the Brass Band.

Many other social activities were developed in the works. Every fifteen-year-old lad was taught to swim, going weekly to the Corporation baths during working hours at the firm's expense, and an annual swimming competition was held. Annual athletic sports and bowling competitions were also organized. Angling, draughts, chess and other leisure activities were similarly catered for. A new gymnasium was provided by the firm and equipped by the Recreation Club. The new offices, etc., built in 1905–6, included a large dining hall, together with baths, lavatories, and dressing-rooms. On the cultural side, there were choirs and musical socials; the girls, taught by a singing master, were encouraged to sing whilst at work, whereby output was increased. A dramatic society, 'self-supporting' like the others, was started in 1904, and a works orchestra in 1905. The firm also provided regular lectures, both scientific and popular. A library of technical books and journals was provided. Many social and cultural functions were held in the Assembly Hall. Concerts, dramatic performances, social evenings, dances, etc., were very popular in the winter-time.

Self-supporting sick clubs for both men and girls were also established, providing sick pay and funeral allowances. The firm paid the fees of a consulting doctor and dentist and subscribed to local infirmaries and hospitals for the benefit of the workpeople. At the request of the men's sick club, no employee was engaged without passing a medical examination.

In these ways a strong corporate sense was built up within the firm, so that in spite of its rapid growth the employees could feel that they were part of a large team, that the new limited company was not a conscienceless corporation, concerned merely with profit-making, but had a genuine regard for their social welfare. Comparatively small amounts were expended on such schemes, however, the Directors insisting upon 'self-help': 'it is to this rule that no small part of the success on the social side is believed to be due'. The Directors and Managers, however, clearly put in a great deal of personal effort to create good labour relations, and in 1913 it was stated that 'the most friendly feelings' existed between them and their workpeople. 'Trade disputes are unknown.'

CHAPTER XII

TECHNOLOGICAL ENTERPRISE IN OILS

IT is commonly stated that in the late nineteenth and early twentieth centuries Britain was stagnating economically, that she was resting on her earlier industrial achievements, that she had lost her pioneering drive and was falling behind in the technological race with other nations. Whatever truth there may be in this view so far as other firms and industries were concerned, it was certainly not true of Crosfield's. These years (1896–1911) witnessed the most rapid growth and some of the most outstanding technological achievements in their whole history. The figures of capital, production, and employment show that the business roughly trebled in size during this short period.

The main cause of this remarkable growth was undoubtedly applied science. It is true that Crosfield's owed a great deal to German chemists. Dr. Markel, who had laid the groundwork for industrial advance in the preceding decade, remained the inspiring genius behind Crosfield's expansion during this period. And, as we have seen, he introduced a number of German and other foreign scientists, who made important contributions towards new technological developments. Moreover, a great deal of German machinery and equipment was bought, ranging from soap-cooling machines to plant for the cement works and oil-mill. These links with Germany also enabled Crosfield's to obtain exclusive licences for the use of a number of important German patents, of which the most notable were the Normann patent for hydrogenation and the Henkel patent for 'Persil'. But from about 1906 onwards a brilliant team of young British scientists was recruited, who, in several instances, made considerable improvements upon the work of their German predecessors.

Crosfield's thus acquired pre-eminence among British soap-making firms for their expertise in chemical research and technology. As J. J. Crosfield pointed out to Sir William Lever in April 1914, 'You are at the top of the tree as advertisers . . . our strength lies in our supremacy on the technical side, where-by . . . we calculate that our "Perfection" is made from £3 to £4 per ton cheaper than "Sunlight" . . . and of as good a quality.' This pre-eminence was based upon research work in their several laboratories. In addition to the main laboratory, at first located in some converted cottages near Quay Fold and from 1906 in the former offices, there were several smaller ones for research into soapmaking processes, perfumery, fats and oils, and hydrogenation. A few of their records have survived, showing, for example, the meticulous way in which raw materials were chemically analysed, perfumes were compounded, and new processes were painstakingly developed, from small-scale experimental plants to large-scale production. Another indication of technological innovation is the increasing number of patents taken out by the firm, or by directors, in addition to their quick-witted adoption of licences to use processes newly patented by others.

The most intensive scientific research was directed towards producing cheaper raw materials. Increasing competition for fats and oils, not only from other soapmakers but also from margarine producers, together with the generally rising trend of prices from 1896 to the first World War, caused Crosfield's to search keenly for ways of reducing costs. Thus from 1901 onwards they established new plant for the extraction and re-fining of oils, not merely for soapmaking but also for production of 'vegetable butter'. From 1905 they began research on fat-hardening (hydrogenation), based on the Normann patent, and were the first firm in the world to operate it industrially. They also developed several 'fat-splitting' processes, for producing fatty acids and glycerine prior to soap-boiling. Processes for by-product recovery were also exploited: lime (previously waste) from the caustic soda plant was used in a new cement works; waste pitch from the stearine plant was used, together with oils, etc., in paint manufacture; exhaust steam from engines or from evaporators was condensed to produce pure water needed for their chemical manufactures or to save boiler-cleaning costs, and their experience in this field led them into providing plant for water-softening and fuel economy. At the same time the firm continued to expand remarkably its production of caustic soda and silicate of soda, and to utilize these in new products such as 'Carbosil', an improved washing and bleaching powder. Thus applied chemistry not merely strengthened Crosfield's position as soapmakers, but also widened their industrial base by leading them increasingly to become chemical manufacturers.

Throughout these years, however, Crosfield's continued to be primarily a soapmaking firm, though the manufacture of chemicals proved more profitable and grew more rapidly. The most important developments affecting soap manufacture were in the production of raw materials.[1] The firm continued, of course, to import most of its fats and oils in barrels and casks, which merely required melting out, filtering, and bleaching before being piped to the soap pans; and more boilers, melting pans, and bleaching plant were installed on the old quayside site, next to the soapery. But during these years raw material costs were rising: average annual prices of tallow, for example, rose from £28 to £34 per ton between 1900 and 1911; palm oil from £27 to £34; copra from £15 to £24. Crosfield's therefore began to develop new manufacturing processes in an effort to reduce these costs, and at the same time they entered the field of oil refining and vegetable butter manufacture.

The first suggestion along these lines appears in the Directors' minutes for 25th March 1901, when 'Dr. Markel brought forward proposals for the erection of two purification plants including stills, agitators, filter presses, &c. The first plant is for supplying the soap works with cheaper fats & the second for making edible fats & also fats more suitable for toilet soaps.' The proposals were accepted and £3,000 was voted for each of these distillation plants or refineries. In fact during the next few years the original plans were considerably extended and much more capital was invested. The first to be built was the oil-refining (vegetable butter) plant, followed by a stearine (fatty acid distillation) plant, and then, in 1904, it was decided to erect an oil-mill, with crushing and extracting plant. The capital valuation of all these (buildings and plant) was over £21,000 at the end of 1907, after allowing for depreciation.

Crosfield's were pioneers in this country in the large-scale refining of vegetable oils, instead of animal fats, for margarine

---

[1] See below, p. 178, for the predominance of fats and oils in soapmaking costs.

and other edible purposes. The refinery, or (as it became known) the Vegetable Butter (V.B.) department, was built immediately south of the wharf warehouse, on land leased from Pochin & Co., and was placed under the management of the German chemist, R. Ockel. It handled a variety of oils—coconut, mowra seed, cottonseed, Illipe nut, palm kernel, etc. These oils were at first purchased, but were soon to be produced by the firm's own stearine and extraction plants. After settling and filtering, the crude oils were neutralized, i.e. free fatty acids were removed, by adding caustic soda and then drawing off the resultant soap solutions by repeated washings; deodorizing and decolorizing (or bleaching) followed, when necessary, and then the oils were vacuum-distilled with superheated steam and finally condensed.

The first product of this department was 'Veberine', Crosfield's trade name (first registered in 1903) for 'a pure neutral sterilized Vegetable Butter', made mainly from copra (coconut) oil. It was 'prepared in two forms, viz. hard and soft. It is largely used for household purposes to replace butter, by cake and biscuit manufacturers and confectioners . . . and also extensively in the manufacture of margarine.' Deliveries rose quickly from 125 tons in 1902 to 2,033 tons in 1903, but then fell off almost as rapidly to only forty-eight tons in 1906. Some was exported, 'Veberine' being registered in several European countries. But its manufacture proved unsuccessful and was stopped in 1907.

Another product was 'Palm Butter', a cocoa-butter substitute made from Illipe-nut oil. It was used mainly by the chocolate trade. Terry's of York and other manufacturers were customers in 1908 and probably earlier. Sales grew from sixteen tons in 1903 to 1,009 tons in 1910, but fell off somewhat in the next few years. The earlier brand-name 'Veberine' was eventually substituted for 'Palm Butter', some time after production of vegetable butter from coconut oil was dropped. Other raw materials were also used. Production of 'Par-la' from refined Chinese vegetable tallow was started towards the end of 1908, rising quickly to 2,127 tons in 1910, but then apparently ceasing, when other products, such as 'Kaynut' and 'Teenut', began to be manufactured from hydrogenated oils.

These new products put the V.B. department on a profit-making basis. Until 1908 it had been run almost continuously at a loss, partly due to Ockel's mismanagement. Sales which had shot up from £5,012 in 1902 to £74,514 in 1903, then fell gradually to only £10,754 in 1906, and losses averaged around £1,000 per year. From 1908 onwards, however, under new management, sales rose to a peak of £171,559 in 1910, and although they fell off in the next few years substantial profits were now being made.

Crosfield's marketed their vegetable butters through T. E. Oldfield & Co., commission agents and merchants of Liverpool, who in April 1908 were appointed the Company's sole agents for the sale of 'Palm Butter' in the United Kingdom, on a commission of 5 per cent. By a further agreement in 1913, Oldfield's became sole U.K. agents for all Crosfield's vegetable butters, with a commission of 2 per cent (reduced in 1915 to 1 per cent) on 'Veberine', formerly 'Palm Butter', and 1 per cent on the rest, including 'Kaynut', 'Monut', and 'Teenut'. In France, similarly, in 1907 the firm of William A. Young, of Lambersant-Lille, was given the sole agency for the sale of 'Palm Butter' on a 5 per cent commission.

The other distillation plant proposed by Dr. Markel in 1901, in addition to the edible oil refinery, became known as the Stearine plant. It was built on the western side of the tallow yard, adjoining Robinson & Co.'s glassworks—it is now the control laboratory for the Synthetic Fluid Catalyst plant—and was occupied in producing what was called commercially 'cotton stearine', or refined fatty acid (stearic acid), from cottonseed oil 'soapstock'. Crude cottonseed oil is of a dark reddish brown colour, unsuitable in its crude form for soapmaking. By neutralizing with caustic soda, much of the colour and other impurities are precipitated. The neutral oil, known as refined cottonseed oil, was used extensively in soapmaking, but the dark residue or 'soapstock' was difficult to dispose of and could be imported cheaply from the U.S.A. for 'splitting' or decomposing and distillation. The soapstock was steamed from the barrels, decomposed by boiling with sulphuric acid in wooden vats, and the fatty acids were then vacuum-distilled, to be used for making both soap and vegetable butter.

Crosfield's output of these fatty acids rose to about five tons per day. A by-product of this process was residual pitch, run off from the stills into barrels and sold as a roadmaking material. Soon it was utilized, however, to produce black paint and enamel, particularly good for protecting metal structures; they were so used throughout Crosfield's works and were also sold. This led on to the manufacture of waterproofing compositions for use on felt roofs, etc., and of electric insulating material. The paint department, established in 1904, on the eastern side of Factory Yard, adjoining the main L.M.S. railway,[1] also produced ochres and turkey reds (hydrates of iron) from the spent acid cleaning liquors of local wireworks; other products were gums and pastes. But it was never very large, it ran at a continuous loss of several hundred pounds a year, and so was closed down in 1910.

Another waste-saving economy was the erection, in the same area as the stearine building, of a small solvent-extraction plant for treatment of fatty residues from the raw materials department of the soapery and from the refinery. It was known as the Benzine plant, since this was the solvent used in extraction; the benzine was driven off from the extracted fats in steam-heated stills and recovered by condensing. The maximum throughput was about fifteen tons of residues per week; the recovered fats were used in soapmaking. This plant was eventually destroyed by a disastrous explosion in 1920, and was not rebuilt.

From the refining of vegetable oils it was but a short step to the production of the raw oils themselves. In 1904, therefore, it was decided to build an oil-mill, next to the stearine plant. This was generally known as the Coprah plant, because it was originally installed for extraction of coconut oil from that raw material, though other nuts and seeds were also used eventually. It consisted of a seed-crusher—flaking rolls were later added to grind the seeds or nuts to meal—and two solvent extractors working on the same principle as those in the benzine plant, with two cylindrical presses, from which the oil was filtered. (Both extractors and presses, incidentally, were of German make.) The mill contained no meal-drying equipment, but the accounts reveal small sales of 'nut residues', to be converted into

---

[1] Land east of Factory Lane, adjoining Railway Square and Factory Yard, was acquired in 1902 and 1912, the first part on a 999 years lease at a yearly rent of £42, and the second part freehold for £2,200. The Bank Quay Mission Room, several cottages and warehouses stood on this land.

dried meal and press cake for cattle food. The throughput of nuts and seeds in this plant varied from about seventy to one hundred tons per week. The oils were used in both the soapery and the V.B. department; a small amount was also sold. All these new departments—V.B., stearine, benzine, and oil-mill— were under Ockel's management, until he was dismissed in 1907.

In June 1908 it was decided to erect a larger and more efficient oil-extraction plant on the 'tongue land' across the river. This was not the firm's first development on the Cheshire side, a cement works having been built there a few years previously.[1] The land, comprising nearly sixteen acres of hitherto undeveloped marshy land, was acquired from Sir Gilbert Greenall in 1904, on a 999 years lease, at a yearly rent of £158 18s. 8d., but the freehold was bought four years later for £3,726. There was no other land then available for expansion on the Warrington side, so the firm was obliged to make this leap across the river, despite the inconveniences of having to move goods by transporter bridge (built for the cement works) and ferry, and the considerable expense of draining, pile-driving, and building jetties.

Crosfield's paid £1,250 to the Premier Oil Extracting Mills Ltd., of Hull, for a licence to work their patent process in the new oil plant, which was erected by Rose, Downs & Thompson, engineers, also of Hull. It was completed in September 1909 at a total cost in buildings and plant of over £14,600. It operated on similar principles to the old plant, with crushing and flaking rolls, solvent extractors, stills, condensers, and oil storage tanks, but was of considerably greater capacity, and also included a rotary meal drier. It proved so successful that in November 1909 it was decided to double the plant, involving additional capital expenditure of about £11,200. To this was added a further sum of nearly £19,000 for huge storage silos (not completed till the end of 1913) for nuts and seeds, which were mechanically elevated and conveyed from barges alongside the wharf. All types of oil seeds were used—Illipe nuts, mowra seed, palm kernels, copra, soya beans, etc.—and the weekly throughput could be as much as 600 tons on some kinds. In addition to the oils extracted for the soapery and refinery, substantial quantities of cattle meal were now produced: an average of over

[1] See below, p. 205.

163

6,000 tons per annum in 1910–11. James Simpson & Co., of Liverpool, were appointed the Company's sole agents for the sale of 'feeding stuffs and manure meals', on a 1 to 1½ per cent commission, by an agreement of November 1911.

The extraction plant on the Lancashire side was now gradually closed down. The stearine plant had meanwhile dwindled into insignificance. In the middle of 1911 it was decided to extend the oil refinery (V.B. department), but this scheme was cancelled a year later, after the foundations only had been laid, and instead the Directors decided to proceed with the erection of a large new refinery on the Cheshire side, alongside the new oil-mill and fat-hardening plant.

This latter plant, for hydrogenating liquid oils, was the biggest single project undertaken at Crosfield's during this period, and strikingly illustrates the application of scientific and technical skills to the solution of the problem of rising costs of raw materials. It was also of central importance in the most dramatic series of events in Crosfield's whole history. Oils and fats, as we have previously noticed, are glycerides of various fatty acids, i.e. they are formed by union of the latter with glycerine. These fatty acids and their glycerides are combinations of carbon, hydrogen, and oxygen, and variations in their physical properties are due to variations in these chemical combinations. The main physical difference is between those which are solid and those which are liquid at ordinary temperatures. The chemical difference is that in the former all the carbon atoms are 'saturated' with hydrogen atoms whereas in the latter one or more pairs of carbon atoms are 'unsaturated'. Thus stearic acid, $C_{18}H_{36}O_2$, is 'saturated', whilst oleic acid, $C_{18}H_{34}O_2$, is 'unsaturated', in that the molecule contains a pair of carbon atoms capable of combining with two more hydrogen atoms—it has, as it were, a deficiency of hydrogen. If, therefore, oleic acid or its glyceride, olein, could be 'hydrogenated', they would be converted to stearic acid and stearin respectively, and thus 'hardened'. Liquid oils, especially whale and fish oils, which were abundant and cheap, could then be made available for use in soap and margarine manufacture, in place of naturally hard fats such as tallow, the cost of which was rising sharply.

At the end of the nineteenth century, scientific research was on the point of achieving this break-through. Two French chemists, Sabatier and Senderens, were the first to carry out catalytic hydrogenation, between 1897 and 1901. They showed how various unsaturated hydrocarbons, such as ethylene, acetylene, and benzene vapours, could be saturated by being passed, together with hydrogen, over finely powdered and heated nickel, the latter acting as a catalyst. But they believed that this could only be achieved with vapours, and they also found that the reaction was uncertain.

From the very beginning, Crosfield's became interested in the possibilities of hydrogenation. George R. Crosfield has related how Dr. Markel and himself met Sabatier at a meeting of the Society of Chemical Industry in Rome, 'and I remember Sabatier saying then that he had not had any success with the hydrogenation of liquids, and even with bodies in the gaseous state the nickel did not always react. His actual words were: "c'est comme une femme, elle a ses caprices".'

In February 1901, however, Dr. Wilhelm Normann, of the Herforder Maschinenfett und Oel Fabrik, owned by Leprince and Siveke, at Herford, in the province of Westphalia, Germany, succeeded in hydrogenizing liquid oleic acid, converting it to solid stearic acid, by a catalytic nickel reaction. Leprince and Siveke (the latter was Normann's uncle) took out a German patent in August 1902 (D.R.P. 141,029), but they had insufficient resources for industrial development of the process, which presented serious difficulties. In January of the following year Normann applied for a British patent, which was granted on 26th November 1903 (No. 1,515). This soon came to the knowledge of Dr. Markel, who entered into negotiations with Normann and with Leprince and Siveke, as a result of which Crosfield's acquired a licence to work the patent process. Unfortunately it has not been possible to discover a copy of this agreement, dated 23rd June 1905, and we do not know how much Crosfield's paid Normann. Kayser, one of their German scientists, was sent over to Herford and was subsequently put in charge of the hydrogenation project at Warrington.

Normann's patent specification was brief, vague, and even misleading. He had, he said, found hydrogenation 'easy', but even in a laboratory this was not so, while on a large industrial scale it was to prove far more difficult. Normann said very little about how large quantities of hydrogen were to be produced, except that it was not necessary to employ pure hydrogen and that 'commercial gas mixtures containing hydrogen, such as water gas', could be used. Nor did he say anything about pre-treatment of the oils. Yet he declared that 'the same nickel may be used repeatedly'. In fact, however, catalytic 'poisons', such as sulphur or arsenic, in either the hydrogen or the oils could quickly stop the process, and even the most careful precautions could not prevent the necessity of 'revivifying' the catalyst. Normann was even vague about how the catalyst should be prepared: he stated that it was 'preferably distributed over a suitable support such as pumice stone', but this, too, was to prove a serious problem. The temperature of the reaction, which Normann said was 'immaterial', in fact had to be carefully controlled.

It took several years of intensive research before Crosfield's completely overcame these difficulties. Normann himself frequently came over to Warrington, to assist Kayser. By the end of 1905 twenty-pound batches of cottonseed oil could be hardened with some regularity, and in the following year an experimental plant was built in some old property in Factory Yard. It consisted of a single hydrogenator to treat one-ton charges of cottonseed oil, and a roaster for reducing the nickel catalyst. In 1907 a total of 100 tons, including whale oil, were hardened. But a letter from George Crosfield to Markel (from whom he was about to take over as Technical Director) in January 1908 referred to 'the immense amount of research work which is [still] requisite in connection with the hardening process'.

Unfortunately, they had been experiencing serious difficulties with their German chemists. Kayser was an eccentric and rather unpractical character, who refused to conform to regulations and came in very late every morning, evidently thinking he was indispensable. He therefore had to be dismissed, whereupon he left for the United States, sold his knowledge to Procter and Gamble, and eventually took out fat-hardening patents of his own. At the same time, Ockel, manager of the V.B. department, oil-mill, etc., was dismissed, because he was too stubbornly conceited, too autocratic towards the workpeople in his department, and incompetent in his accounting. Studer, head of the main laboratory, was also dispensed with, for similar reasons. It seems probable, however, that these dismissals were also motivated by growing anti-German feeling.

Kayser was replaced by F. Fox (previously managing the Liverpool works), Ockel by E. Ball, and Studer by J. Allan. These changes, according to George Crosfield, had very satisfactory results. Ball, for example, soon succeeded in doubling the output of Palm Butter. Fox quickly got a grasp of the hydrogenation process, and George Crosfield was able to report in January 1908 that 'we are making steady reliable progress both in the laboratory and on the large scale'. Normann continued to give expert help and another German, Machenhauer, did research work on revivifying the catalyst. Dr. T. P. Hilditch and others finally solved the chemical problems, while G. A. Duff was responsible for the engineering.

In June 1908 it was decided to build a large-scale fat-hardening plant, together with the new oil-mill, on the Cheshire side of the river, to be capable of treating 120 tons of cottonseed oil or 150 tons of whale oil per week. It was nearly completed by the autumn of 1909. Its eventual cost was well over £20,000. But this was only a beginning: large extensions were added, so that by the end of 1911 further capital expenditure totalling about £38,000 had been approved and mostly carried out, and, as we shall see, even bigger sums were to be spent in the following years.

In this plant the chemical-technological problems that had been ignored in Normann's original patent were finally solved. Some of them, however, took a long time. On 1st March 1910, for example, we find George Crosfield writing to Normann: 'I regret to say that we are . . . faced with very serious difficulties in connection with the hardening process, especially with the production of hydrogen. I must confess that we have altogether underestimated the difficulties that we should be faced with so soon as we got working with this process on the large scale.' Nevertheless, such difficulties were eventually overcome.[1]

The oils had to be carefully pre-treated by filtering, neutralization and earth bleaching to remove mucilaginous matter,

[1] The following account is based on a description in a private process book, dated 3rd June 1910. A somewhat different procedure is described in a Crosfield–Markel patent of 30th December 1910 (No. 30,282). According to Mr. C. Billington's recollections, however, the former was the process actually practised.

catalyst 'poisons', such as sulphur, and other impurities. Preparation of the catalyst required similar care. Nickel carbonate was precipitated upon a supporting base of finely powdered kieselguhr, a highly absorbent material, by mixing soda ash (sodium carbonate) with nickel sulphate. The precipitate was filtered, thoroughly washed to remove all trace of sulphate, dried, and then reduced to nickel by roasting in an atmosphere of hydrogen. This catalytic metal, being pyrophoric, was at once dropped into the oil.

The oil to be treated was fed into an autoclave, or closed cylindrical vessel, fitted with an agitator and heating/cooling coils. After the catalyst was added, the mixture was stirred vigorously and hydrogen was blown through it. The reaction being exothermic, it was necessary to cool the charge so as not to degrade the oil; above 180° C. free fatty acids were generated.[1] The reaction could be stopped at any point, according to the degree of hardness required. The catalyst was recovered by means of filter-presses and dropped into the following oil charge. It could be used as many as twenty times, providing the oil and hydrogen were free from catalyst poisons. When it became too inactive, it was treated with sulphuric acid to get nickel sulphate.

It was necessary, of course, to produce large quantities of hydrogen, as free as possible from sulphurous and arsenic poisons. This was done in two stages. Water gas, a mixture of hydrogen and carbon monoxide, was obtained by the well-known method of blowing steam through incandescent coke. The gas was purified by passing it through iron oxide, to remove sulphur, and then stored in a gas-holder. In the next stage, Spanish iron ore was heated and reduced by passing water gas through it. Steam was then blown through the incandescent iron, being thereby split: the oxygen was absorbed into the iron, and the hydrogen passed into a gas-holder. These methods of large-scale hydrogen production have since been widely used in industry.

Crosfield's endeavoured to maintain the closest secrecy in

[1] Another Markel–Crosfield patent, of 6th June 1911 (No. 13,519), emphasized the importance of keeping the temperature 'as low as possible, preferably just above the melting point of the desired product', when converting certain oils, such as whale oil and castor oil, in order to prevent the splitting off of the hydroxyl groups.

regard to the hydrogenation process. All chemists, including Normann, who worked on the plant eventually had to sign agreements not to divulge information, and efforts were made to prevent workers from acquiring any confidential knowledge. To disguise the materials used, it was ordered in February 1909 that the plant should be called 'the Oil Treatment Plant', that hydrogen should be referred to as 'Retort Gas', the nickel catalyst as 'Metal', whale oil and fish oils as 'White Oil' Nos. 1 and 2 respectively, and the various hardened oils as 'Treated' oils, with their respective numbers. Moreover, the isolated site on the 'tongue land' or 'island' across the river also helped to maintain secrecy.

The hardened oils were successfully used both in soaps and edible fats. Crosfield's had been producing small quantities of hardened cottonseed and whale oils for soapmaking since 1906–7. They had obtained a patent in 1907 (No. 13,042) for the manufacture of a specially hard industrial soap made from hydrogenated oils. The building of the large-scale plant on the Cheshire side of the river made available far greater supplies. This triumph, George Crosfield has written, 'enabled us to meet with equanimity both Lever's competition and the rising cost of raw materials'. In actual fact, however, hardened fats did not prove as successful in soapmaking as had been hoped, for the soaps produced had poor lathering properties. Hundreds of experimental boils were carried out in the soap laboratory to determine the optimum amounts of hydrogenated oils that could be incorporated in soap charges.

Fat-hardening eventually proved to be of greater importance for production of edible fats. Normann, working on a small scale at Herford, produced hardened cottonseed oil for two German margarine factories in 1909—the first use of hardened fat for edible purposes. In the following year Crosfield's converted whale oil into edible fat for the first time; hydrogenation, it was discovered, removed the fishy smell. They also used other hardened fats to produce a variety of 'vegetable butters', in addition to the earlier 'Veberine' and 'Palm Butter'. In 1910, for example, they began to make 'Kaynut' from hydrogenated palm-kernel oil, which was refined as a cheap cocoa-butter substitute and toffee butter; around 200 tons per annum were produced in 1911–13. 'Teenut', hydrogenated cottonseed oil,

169

was refined as a lard substitute for the bakery and confectionery trades; production began in 1913 and reached nearly 1,400 tons that year. 'Monut' was a similar product. Most of Crosfield's hardened oils were thus used in their own products. As yet, only small quantities were sold, totalling about £16,000 in 1911.

The hydrogenation plant started operation in the autumn of 1909. Output rose rapidly: 243 tons in 1908; 595 tons in 1909; 2,941 tons in 1910; 6,069 tons in 1911, and increasing amounts in the following years. The enormous expenditure on this plant, however, added to that on oil-refining, not to mention numerous improvements and extensions to other parts of the works, put a very great strain on Crosfield's resources. They were, George Crosfield recalls, 'sadly in need of additional capital'. We shall see later how more share capital was raised, but this was nowhere near enough fully to exploit the hydrogenation process both at home and abroad, for which Crosfield's had generally secured exclusive rights. Further agreements with Normann and Leprince and Siveke were negotiated in 1908–10, but cannot now be located. Other evidence, however, indicates that Crosfield's acquired the English patent on 20th September 1908, on a royalty-paying basis, and less than a year later, according to a brief statement in the Directors' minutes of 21st June 1909, these royalties were commuted for a lump sum of £4,000. On 5th July 1910 Leprince and Siveke agreed to assign the German patent to Crosfield's, and by agreements of 24th November 1909 and 30th November 1910 Crosfield's also acquired rights to exploit the process in all other countries, except Russia. Rights in the latter country were purchased from Normann in April 1913 for £1,000.

Thus Crosfield's had acquired a world-wide monopoly of the Normann process. But the building of their Warrington plant alone had strained their capital resources. Anton Jurgens, of the famous Dutch margarine-manufacturing firm, has expressed the view that Crosfield's were mistaken in not taking out patents in countries other than England and Germany and in not exploiting the process internationally. 'In one way and another Crosfield's had been too careful regarding financial expenditure, thereby losing the hold on a movement which later proved to be worldwide.' This, however, looks rather like hindsight. It is very improbable that Crosfield's could have raised the necessary capital to have exploited the process on such a vast scale. Moreover, as we shall see, their patent was by no means unchallengeable and they had some very powerful opponents. Crosfield's did not, in fact, endeavour to maintain a worldwide monopoly of their hydrogenation process, but sought to sell it at the highest possible price to certain leading soap and margarine manufacturers in other countries. In this way they hoped to replenish their capital resources. Thus they entered into negotiations with Procter & Gamble, the biggest soapmakers in the U.S.A., but were unable to clinch the deal. J. J. Crosfield, the Company's Chairman, therefore told his brother George (as the latter has recalled)

to take a bag of samples to the United States and to offer the process for £100,000 to the first firm who would take it up. This I proceeded to do, and while in the States, visited Cincinnati and, without calling on Procter & Gamble, took the opportunity of looking over the fence surrounding their grounds. I was interested to spot Kayser [recently dismissed from Crosfield's] going into one of the outbuildings. I then realized why Procter & Gamble were not coming to terms. However, the action taken with the other soap firms had its effect, Proctor & Gamble very speedily buying the process from us.

They paid £40,000 for the North American rights. Crosfield's would not export any hardened fats to, nor Procter & Gamble from, North America.

On the European continent Crosfield's first of all sold the rights in Austria-Hungary for £6,000 to the large soapmaking and oil-refining firm of George Schicht A.G., of Aussig, Bohemia. The latter agreed, in addition, to let Crosfield's inspect their plants for manufacturing edible oil and distilling fatty acids, and also their autoclave process.[1] Schicht's would not export any hardened fats, except candles, nor would Crosfield's export them to Austria-Hungary.

Negotiations were also begun for sale of the German patent. In a letter of 22nd October 1910 Crosfield's offered to sell it to Schicht's for £20,000, but reserved the rights of manufacturing edible products for sale to Jurgens. This offer was not accepted, however, and the whole German patent rights were eventually sold to the latter. Anton Jurgens, recalling these events, states

[1] For Crosfield's interest in the two latter processes, see below, pp. 174–5. They also obtained soap-cooling machines from Schicht's.

171

that Crosfield's were 'great friends of ours', with whom they had earlier agreed to exchange information on oil-refining. He had discussed the hydrogenation process with George Crosfield during a visit by the latter to their Hamburg refinery in 1909. Anton and Gerard Jurgens met George Crosfield and Cyril Haslam in London in November of that year, to negotiate terms for sale of the process, but an agreement was not reached and negotiations dragged on through 1910. Jurgens considered Crosfield's price too high, and they were also made cautious by claims then being made for a rival German process.

Patents of such fundamental importance as fat-hardening are inevitably subject to an immense amount of piracy and evasion, and Normann's, unfortunately, was so inadequate as to invite attack. In July 1908 Normann had made an agreement with a German, Persitz, for the sale of the Russian rights and for the erection of a hydrogenation plant at Nijni-Novgorod. A chemist named Mose Wilbuschewitsch had been sent to Herford to acquire full knowledge of the process, and the Russian plant had been erected. But the agreement with Normann was then repudiated and Wilbuschewitsch proceeded to seek patents in many European countries for a process differing only in minor points from Normann's. He worked in alliance with E. Higgins—formerly in charge of Crosfield's soap laboratory —who became his patent agent.[1] By the end of 1910, he had acquired patents in Germany and elsewhere, but his applications in the U.K. and various other countries were opposed by Crosfield's.

This was not the only threat to Crosfield's. Dr. Erdmann, of Halle, had applied for a fat-hardening patent in Germany in 1907, and had gone into partnership with F. Bedford and C. E. Williams to patent and develop it in England in 1907–8. They formed a company, Hydroil Ltd., which disposed of their rights in various countries. The U.K. rights were eventually acquired in 1912–13 by Ardol Ltd., whose shares were held by Hydroil, Price's Patent Candle Co., and Joseph Watson & Sons of Leeds. Another process, provisionally patented in Britain by a Swedish chemist, Nils Testrup, in March 1910, was acquired by the Techno-Chemical Laboratories Ltd., specially promoted

[1] Wimmer and Higgins later (in 1913) took out a fat-hardening patent in the U.S.A. Kayser, as we have previously noted, did likewise.

for that purpose by Testrup and others. Yet another inventor, Professor Carl Paal, who applied for a German patent in 1910, sold his rights to the Vereinigte Chemische Werke, A.G., of Charlottenburg.

Crosfield's anxiety to maintain their exclusive patents is evidenced by the fact that, by an agreement of 31st May 1911, they bought the Paal patents from this German company for £15,850. According to the defendants' brief in the Testrup case of 1913, Crosfield's also offered in February 1911 to pay Wilbuschewitsch £11,000 for his patent rights, but the latter declined and later sold them instead to Richard Curtius G.m.b.H., of Bremen, who subsequently transferred them to the Bremen Besigheimer Oelfabriken, an associated company. Crosfield's were similarly unsuccessful in negotiations with Bedford & Williams. They now, therefore, began to prepare for legal action against all those who had, as they considered, infringed their patent rights.[1]

They convinced Jurgens of the strength of their legal position and of the success of their process, including secret parts not patented, with the result that an agreement was reached, dated 3rd March 1911, for sale of the Normann patent in Germany. Jurgens were to pay £20,000 and 5s. per ton on all hardened fats till these royalties totalled £15,000. They would export no hardened products for inedible purposes (soap or candles), but they could export margarine, even to the United Kingdom (but not to Russia, North America, and Austria-Hungary). Crosfield's, on the other hand, would not export hardened products to Germany, nor would they use them for making any edible products in the U.K., except for use in biscuits, chocolates, caramels, or sweets, i.e. Crosfield's would not use them to make margarine, but only in 'vegetable butters' for the confectionery trades. A few months later the German Paal patents were also transferred to Jurgens. Crosfield's agreed to give full information about their hydrogenation plant to Jurgens, who sent over their technical manager, together with Dr. Normann, whose services Crosfield's now relinquished, and who, together with one of Crosfield's employees, W. R. Jackson, helped to erect Jurgens' hydrogenation plant, the Oelwerke Germania, at Emmerich.

[1] See below, pp. 249–51.

The two firms agreed to collaborate technically and also against infringers of their patent rights. It was hardly likely that Lever's, Van den Bergh's, and others, who had not been favoured with licences from Crosfield's, would acquiesce in a position of such economic disadvantage. The hydrogenation process was soon to become the crucial factor in an immense international struggle. But whatever the outcome, one thing is clear, as Horatio Ballantyne, Lever's chemical consultant in this battle, later admitted: 'To Crosfields' chemists must be given the credit of having succeeded, by dint of prolonged investigation, in getting the thing to work.' On their achievements was based a revolution in the modern edible fats and soap trades. Moreover, the development of the hydrogenation process had a wider significance. It not only gave a great impetus to the study of the complex chemistry of oils and fats, but as the first large-scale industrial exploitation of a catalytic reaction, it pointed the way to innumerable similar applications.

In other ways, too, during these years Crosfield's chemists were experimenting with fats and oils in order to reduce manufacturing costs. Several catalytic 'fat-splitting' processes were developed for the decomposition of fats and oils into fatty acids and glycerine prior to soap-boiling. The fatty acids could be saponified more easily and sodium carbonate could be used instead of the dearer hydrate, thus saving the costs of causticizing. The glycerine could also be recovered at strengths up to 16 per cent, instead of the usual 4 per cent by the batch soap-boiling process, and so evaporating costs would be reduced. These, at any rate, were the hopes. In actual fact, none of these processes proved successful, but they are worth mentioning as further evidence of chemical ingenuity at Crosfield's during this period. They were carried out in the raw materials department, adjoining the soapery.

All of them involved mixing, agitating, and in some cases boiling fats and oils, together with water and a catalytic agent, so as to produce the desired split. In the first, the Twitchell process, the catalyst was a sulpho-fatty-aromatic acid, made by sulphonating a mixture of fatty acid and benzene or naphthalene. Unfortunately, the fatty acids produced were too dark in colour. Another similar process, the zinc oxide autoclave process, suffered from the defect that impurities such as zinc soaps were difficult to remove. A third process was the castor enzyme fermentation process; the enzyme was prepared from castor seed in the former stearine plant during the years 1910–12. This was a German process, patented in 1902, for the use of which Crosfield's obtained a licence from the Vereinigte Chemische Werke, A.G., of Charlottenburg, on condition of paying a royalty of £1 5s. per ton of glycerine manufactured thereby. But the process was discontinued, as the refined glycerine produced had an objectionable odour. Altogether several thousand pounds were spent in vain on these fat-splitting processes.

CHAPTER XIII

SOAPMAKING AND SELLING IN 'FRENZIED COMPETITION'

DURING the dynamic developments in the manufacture of oils and fats, there was comparatively little change in soap-boiling operations, but a considerable increase in the scale of production. Booklets published by the firm during this period, and many years later, proudly proclaimed that the 'Waterloo' soap pan was still in use. The soapery buildings were entirely reconstructed, however, in the late 'nineties and manufacturing capacity was extended by erecting more new soap pans—eight, for example, in 1898, each with a capacity of 100 tons—though these were basically similar to the old ones. Increased output meant that more and more frames had to be installed, and the problem of cooling tended to become acute until cooling machines, with water-cooled cylinders, were introduced. Dr. Markel patented such a machine in 1904–5, 'for producing soap bars by a nearly continuous process with rapid cooling', but it does not appear to have been very successful and the firm soon bought a number of Schicht and Jacobi coolers, although soap frames remained in use for many more years. Soap-drying machines (e.g. Cressonnier machines) were also installed, together with improved milling, plodding, stamping, and wrapping machines (often American) for increased production of toilet soaps, while the growing manufacture of soap powders and flakes required installation of grinding and flaking mills and packing machines. The extension of the 'Erasmic' and other buildings was made possible by purchases in 1906 of the leasehold land and houses in Glasshouse Row and the westerly arm of Factory Lane, for a total of £6,000.

Constant experimentation with soap 'boils' was going on in the soap laboratory, using various proportions of different fats, oils, and alkali, with the aims of improving quality and reducing costs. A small experimental laundry was also put up. Research was conducted in the perfume laboratory, with a wide

11 (*a*) New soap pans, *c.* 1900

11 (*b*) Soap milling and plodding, *c.* 1900

variety of essential oils and other perfume bases, brought from all parts of the world; in addition to the natural scents obtained from flowers, etc., a growing number of synthetic products were being chemically manufactured. These were used not merely in toilet-soap manufacture, but also in other, increasingly varied, 'Erasmic' products, including shaving soaps, bottled perfumes, smelling salts, face creams, etc.

All these developments necessitated heavy capital expenditure. The value of the soapery buildings and plant at Warrington (exclusive of land) in 1896 was put at nearly £42,000. By the end of 1910 the figure was over £108,000, after allowing for depreciation. Most of this expansion occurred within four years after incorporation in 1896, when the soapery was rebuilt. To this must be added the increase in the buildings and plant for milling, perfumery, and tabletting: these were valued at only £3,700 at the end of 1898, but twelve years later were worth over £19,000.

Meanwhile, the Liverpool soapworks, formerly Keeling's, had also been extended and improved, especially in the years immediately after their purchase in 1897. The land, buildings, and plant in Blundell Street were valued at £35,000 at the end of 1896. By the end of 1902 they had increased to over £50,000, new soap pans, melting and glycerine plant, etc. having been installed. By 1904, however, the question of moving the Liverpool works to Warrington was being discussed, as it would be more economic to concentrate production in one plant. (It had already been decided, at the end of the previous year, to transfer the office staff to Warrington.) It was not, however, until the middle of 1909 that a final decision was reached. The removal took about three years to complete, at a cost of about £17,000. A large new 'Export building' was erected at the Warrington works, immediately to the south of that for 'Erasmic' milling, tabletting, etc., on the site of the old Glasshouse Row and other houses.

During these years, scientific and technological skills were intensively applied to Crosfield's soapmaking operations. The most impressive results were achieved, as we have seen, in oil-refining and hydrogenation, but applied chemistry was also important in other processes, especially in control of the quality of raw materials. On 28th March 1904, when the Directors

177

considered 'the work which has been accomplished during the
last few years by the Technical Department with regard to Raw
Materials for Soapmaking', they agreed that not only should the
Technical and Buying departments be in close touch, but that
'the Technical Department must now exercise sole control as
far as quality of Raw Materials is concerned'. A note-book
recording hundreds of chemical analyses shows how carefully
this control was exercised.

The great emphasis on reducing costs of fats and oils is understandable when one sees what a large proportion these formed
of total soapmaking costs. The trading accounts for these years
show that this proportion was nearly 80 per cent for household
soaps; other raw materials, such as oil-bleaching chemicals,
silicate, perfumes, etc., accounted for about 6 per cent; wrappers, labels, and card boxes for about 7 per cent; while wages
and salaries formed only 3 or 4 per cent, and steam and fuel a
mere 1 or 2 per cent.

Unfortunately, there are no surviving statistics of the prices
per ton paid by Crosfield's for raw materials during these
years.[1] There are, however, some figures of the total costs of the
different fats and oils at the beginning and end of this period.
These show that in the later 'nineties tallow was still the most
important material used in the soapery. It accounted, in fact,
for more than half the total purchases of fats and oils, though
considerable quantities of vegetable oils (cottonseed, coconut,
palm kernel, and palm oil) and rosin were purchased, to produce the better-lathering 'washer' soaps. Then, as the stearine
and extraction plants came into operation, they began to provide oils for soapmaking, though they could cater for only a
small proportion—less than 6 per cent in 1905–6—of the total
requirements. The building of the new extraction and hydrogenation plants on the Cheshire side of the river, however,
enabled much larger quantities to be produced and by 1911
there had clearly been a very marked swing away from tallow
towards cheaper vegetable and hardened oils. In that year
tallow accounted for less than 11 per cent of the total purchases; vegetable oils (mainly coconut and palm oils) nearly
45 per cent; extracted oils (mainly soya bean oil) 7 per cent;

---

[1] See, however, Wilson, *op. cit.*, Vol. ii, appendix 9, for movements in
the prices of raw materials.

hardened oils 26·5 per cent; and rosin just over 7 per cent, with V.B. plant 'returns' and sundries making up the total.

Hydrogenation had clearly eased Crosfield's position in regard to raw materials, but they still obtained the major part of their requirements from natural fats and oils. Almost all of these, and the whale oil, etc. treated in the hardening plant, were imported from various parts of the world. It is not therefore surprising to find the Directors standing firmly in support of Free Trade during this period, when a tariff protectionist campaign was developing. Joseph Crosfield would have applauded their reaffirmation of Liberal economic faith in January 1906:

that . . . the prosperity of the British Soap trade and its further expansion can only be secured by the continuance of the present Free Trade Policy of this Country, which enables Soap Manufacturers to purchase their materials in the best and cheapest markets, and also gives them a practical monopoly of the Export Soap trade of the world. Any departure from the policy of Free Trade, whether by Colonial Preference or Protected Duties of any kind or degree, would inflict serious and lasting injury upon this great industry.

Fats and oils continued to be drawn from much the same markets as in the past. The growing demand for vegetable oils caused the Directors to send John Allan out to the East at the end of 1904, 'to inquire into supplies of various raw materials'. And early in the following year we read of 'an arrangement come to with E. B. Muspratt in Fiji . . . to place £1,000 at his disposal for buying Coprah'. Competition for raw materials was impelling the Company to establish direct links with foreign markets, instead of merely purchasing through merchants or brokers in Liverpool, London, or Hull, but no information about contracts has survived for this period.

In the spring of 1911 a new company, Apol Ltd., was incorporated to acquire certain patented inventions relating to the production of palm oil and kernels; supplies of palm nuts were to be secured from West Africa. Crosfield's paid £3,000 for the patent rights and acquired the whole of the issued capital of £25,000; by the end of 1912 they had paid up about £15,000.

The efforts to secure cheaper fats and oils were of crucial importance in this period, but other soapmaking costs were also tackled. Expansion and improvement of the caustic soda and

179

silicate plants cut the costs of these raw materials. Increased efficiency in the fuel and power department brought further economies. Improved wrapping and packing machines were also introduced. Despite rising prices of raw materials and increasing competition, therefore, Crosfield's soap production expanded considerably during these years, while most other soapmaking firms were experiencing stagnation or decline, or were being absorbed by Lever's.

Total hard soap deliveries from the Warrington and Liverpool works rose from 22,455 tons in 1898 to 36,611 in 1913. Warrington's contribution usually averaged about three-quarters of the annual total. Crosfield's share of the total U.K. soap production rose from 7·2 to 9·3 per cent between 1900 and 1912. They overtook and surpassed Gossage's, their old rivals, whose yearly sales declined from an average of 27,301 tons in 1899–1905 to 21,343 tons in 1906–13. They also surpassed Watson's, whose yearly sales fell to 31,900 in 1914, and they were even overhauling Lever's. Port Sunlight's total sales, which had risen from 53,325 tons in 1900 to 63,024 tons in 1905, dropped to 49,227 in 1907 and were still only 55,686 in 1914, whereas Crosfield's continued to expand their deliveries, with only slight setbacks in 1907 and 1912. Thus Crosfield's became the second largest soapmaking firm in the country. Lever's, however, had begun the policy of absorbing rival firms, so that the sales of the whole Lever group totalled 119,476 tons in 1912, between three and four times as large as Crosfield's.

Crosfield's, as we shall see, continued to produce a wide variety of soaps. Their main 'line', however, was still 'Perfection', sales of which rose from 3,167 tons in 1898 to 10,030 tons in 1911, i.e. from about one-seventh to nearly one-third of their total output of soap (including that of the Liverpool works). In a trade-mark action of 1909 (see below, p. 190), it was stated to be 'the third largest brand of Soap on the market', though it came a long way behind Lever's 'Sunlight' and Watson's 'Matchless Cleanser', each of whose sales were then about 40,000 tons per annum; the two latter each accounted for some 16 per cent of the total home consumption of household hard soaps, compared with the 4 per cent of 'Perfection'. Another line produced by Crosfield's, Pink Carbolic (later 'Pinkobolic'), also proved fairly popular, rising from 529 tons in 1900 to 2,135 tons in 1911.

Throughout this period Crosfield's sold about two-thirds of their soaps in the home market and one-third overseas. Home sales grew fairly steadily from 15,832 tons in 1898 to 21,848 tons in 1911. The great majority of their customers were wholesale and retail grocers and, to a lesser extent, chemists. In 1909 they were stated to be supplying 'Perfection' to 'no fewer than 6,400 customers', of whom one-quarter were wholesalers, and the soap was said to be retailed in about 40,000 shops. Most of it was still sold in the North and Midlands, though it was claimed to be sold 'in every County except Cornwall, and in almost every town and village in England'. It was admitted, however, that 'as the distance from Warrington increases, the percentages [sold] likewise decrease. Thus, London takes only 2% of the output of "Perfection", South West England takes only $\frac{1}{4}$%, Southern Scotland only $1\frac{1}{4}$%, and the sales in Ireland are practically negligible.' Home sales of their other household soaps must have been a good deal more localized. Of their toilet soaps, however, principally 'Erasmic', a larger proportion—between one-quarter and one-fifth in 1899, and over one-third by the years 1907–11—was sold in London. Chemists, especially Boots, were their best customers for toilet soaps, but grocers also sold a good deal.

Export sales nearly doubled during this period, from 6,623 tons in 1898 to 12,394 tons in 1911. The great bulk of these were still bar soaps, though relatively small quantities of 'Perfection' and 'Erasmic' were also exported. Mottled soaps sold in the greatest quantities abroad, together with the cheaper household pale and brown soaps and lower quality toilets such as Old Brown Windsor. Special brand names and emblems for export soaps were registered in a great many countries: 'Comet', 'Umbrella', 'Handprint', 'Fan', 'Flag', 'Crescent', 'Camel', 'Elephant', and many others; the 'Pyramid' mark also became a distinguishing feature of many of Crosfield's products.

During this period Crosfield's contributed 15 to 20 per cent of all United Kingdom soap exports, and as exporters they were second only to Gossage's, who sent out nearly half the total. Lever's were not serious competitors in the export of bar soaps until after their purchase of Hodgson & Simpson's in 1907.

Crosfield's had been greatly strengthened in this field by their acquisition of Keeling's business in 1897. On average only one-fifth of their annual exports during the years 1898–1911 were listed as 'Warrington export deliveries', the other four-fifths going from the Liverpool works, which concentrated mainly on production for export.

The detailed records of the Export Department have not survived, but the general trading accounts provide some evidence about the main overseas markets. Keeling's (as they were still called) developed a particularly good trade with South Africa, which took nearly £28,000 out of their total sales of £113,000 in 1903. Their South African sales declined in the following years, but exports to other markets grew. In 1908, for example, out of export sales totalling about £108,000, those to South Africa were worth less than £7,000, Hong Kong nearly £5,000, India £14,500, Gibraltar £18,500, and the West Coast of Africa over £19,000. But these were by no means the only overseas markets. A list of 'the various Markets with which the Firm do business', in 1913, included countries all over the world, and this evidence is supported by innumerable foreign trade-mark registrations.

The minutes of the Export Soap Committee, set up in April 1911, reveal Crosfield's concern at the decline of their trade in South Africa, which had 'fallen during the past few years from 50 tons weekly to 20 tons, and Messrs. Lever having now control of all South African soap companies, this Company must face either losing all its business [there] or putting down a works in South Africa'. Negotiations were started with De Beers regarding the formation of a joint company, but these fell through; Crosfield's then considered establishing a soapworks of their own in South Africa, but the project was dropped. The eventual outcome, however, was acquisition of shares in the Natal Soap Works Ltd.[1]

Growing competition also forced Crosfield's, as we shall see, to strengthen their commercial organization in other parts of the world. But they still held a substantial share of the trade in various export markets and were making fair profits. In India, for example, it was stated in the spring of 1911, their sales were 'some 1,500 tons annually and the estimated profit will be

[1] See below, p. 255.

about £2 per ton'. In addition, 'Erasmic' goods worth about £3,000 were sold there. In the West Indies, 'our trade is 1,800 to 2,000 tons per annum and we have 30 to 35 per cent of the total trade. We sell at the same prices as Gossages. From May onwards if prices of soap are not reduced our profit including glycerine should be £2 per ton.' On the West Coast of Africa, 'we at present have about one-third of the total exports, our proportion amounting last year to 2,500 tons. At present market prices there is a profit including glycerine of £2. 10/- per ton.' In Egypt 'our sales for 1910 were 183 tons; for first four months 1911, 183 tons. In Alexandria we have 43 per cent of total imports.' In other markets too, such as China, Crosfield's were trying to expand their trade. At this time, indeed, exports were lagging behind orders. But the struggle for markets remained very keen. Later in 1911, for example, there was reference to 'a serious loss due to Levers' competition' in mottled exports, which Crosfield's decided to meet with a cheaper quality.

Crosfield's scientific and technical pre-eminence among soap-making firms was not enough to ensure economic success. It had to be supported by strong sales pressure, owing to the severe competition, particularly from Lever's, but also from Watson's, Gossage's and other rival firms. In consequence, cost-reducing developments on the production side were more than out-weighed by increased selling costs, especially on advertising.

During these years Crosfield's extended the new marketing techniques which they had been driven to adopt in the ten years before 1896. At the same time, however, they continued to place great reliance on traditional selling methods. Among their selling expenses, the salaries, commissions, and expenses of travellers, the discounts and bonuses allowed to customers, and costs of carriage continued to figure very prominently. At the end of May 1911 the firm employed twenty-seven travellers in the home soap trade, most of whom had an assistant. The travellers' salaries varied between £156 and £572 (though in some cases only a nominal amount), in addition to which they were paid commissions of 10s. to 15s. per ton or about 2½ per cent for household soaps, and between 5 and 7½ per cent on toilet soaps, plus expenses. The assistant travellers were gener-ally paid between £100 and £150. These travellers appear generally to have sold other Crosfield products, such as 'Carbosil' and glycerine, as well as soap.

During this period sales depots were established in many of the large towns. A London office was opened at 225 Shoreditch, but was closed in 1900; it is not clear whether or not other London premises were then leased, but a new office was opened in Lloyd's Avenue in 1905. The Erasmic Company also had an office and showroom at 117 Oxford Street, acquired in 1899. Between 1897 and 1901 depots or shops were leased in Liverpool, Sheffield, Belfast, Crewe, Brighton, Cardiff, and Newcastle, and later on in other towns.

Sales were also encouraged by discounts and bonuses to customers. The usual rate of discount was 5 per cent on payment within fourteen days, dropping to $3\frac{3}{4}$ per cent within one month and $2\frac{1}{2}$ per cent in two months. At the same time, while small orders (below 3 cwt. or 3 cases) were usually charged 6d. per cwt. extra, an allowance of 3d. per cwt. was generally given on ton orders; for 'Perfection' and 'Pink Carbolic', this was given on 5 cwt. orders, and 6d. per cwt. on half-tons. From December 1903 onwards, bonuses were also given on customers' total yearly purchases, varying from $\frac{1}{2}$ to $2\frac{1}{2}$ per cent on turnovers ranging from £60 to £1,000 and over. Discounts and bonuses together rose from about 20s. to 26s. per ton on average during this period. Moreover, carriage to customers was always paid, averaging about 15s. per ton.

In the export trade, Crosfield's continued to rely either on export merchants or on agents in overseas markets, the business being controlled by the Export Department, under the direction mainly of R. F. Jones, with C. H. Hamilton as manager. (He also managed the Erasmic Company's exports.) In the late 'nineties, for example, 'Erasmic' soap was exported to India by Okell & Owen, general merchants, of Liverpool and Bombay, by Forbes, Forbes & Co., India merchants, of London, and by J. F. Kendrew & Co., of London, who described themselves as 'an Agency House', exporting to India and other places, while the Erasmic Company also had agents, Messrs. Rustomjees, in Karachi, and perhaps others elsewhere. Okell & Owen stated that their trade in 'Erasmic' soap was by 'orders given direct to Liverpool by Lotia Brothers direct from Karachi. There were no consignments to Lotia's; it was entirely orders.' There is plenty of evidence in Crosfield's trading accounts, however, that a good deal, probably most, of their export trade was done by consignments, i.e. by sending out batches of goods to an agent or factor for sale, rather than in response to specific orders.

Crosfield's had agreements with scores of agents in different parts of the world. For example, their South African agents were Price & Son, of Cape Town, who, according to an agreement of October 1907, were to 'visit each and every port and all the principal centres of trade' in Cape Colony, Natal, Transvaal, and the Orange River Colony at least three times a year, and who might also be asked to make special journeys, and were to keep Crosfield's regularly posted about their activities. They were to 'attend to the delivery to customers of goods from the stocks which the Company shall from time to time send out', and they were to collect and remit payments. They were to be paid a salary and commission on sales: $2\frac{1}{2}$ per cent on toilet soaps, $\frac{3}{4}$ per cent on bar soaps, and $2\frac{1}{2}$ per cent on Carbosil. They also acted as agents for the Erasmic Company, getting $2\frac{1}{2}$ to 5 per cent commission, and for the sale of Crosfield's chemicals (glycerine, caustic soda, silicate of soda, etc.) on commissions from 1 to $2\frac{1}{2}$ per cent.

Swift & Co. were the agents in Australia, Marcus & Co. (later Padova & Co.) in Egypt, Balensi & Co. in Gibraltar and Morocco, Alston & Co. in Trinidad, and there were many more in other parts of the world. By the end of this period, however, Crosfield's were becoming dissatisfied with this system and began to change to 'direct representation', i.e. to establish their own salaried travellers or representatives in foreign markets. In 1911–12 such representatives were appointed in China, India, the West Indies, the Middle East, and the West Coast of Africa, at salaries ranging from £250 to £500 per year, plus expenses, the total annual cost of each being about £800 to £1,000.

In Europe, they had adopted such a policy some years earlier. In 1897 they appointed one of their employees, Adolphe Secretan, to be a traveller, based in Switzerland, at a nominal salary of £25 with commission of $2\frac{1}{2}$ to 5 per cent on orders. (Secretan, who later became their London representative in the chemical trade, carried out many important commercial negotiations on the Continent.) In the following year a similar agreement was made with Max Leusch, of Berlin, who was to travel in Germany and 'devote the whole of his time to the service of the Company', for a salary of £225 per annum plus expenses. It is not clear whether Secretan and Leusch were to sell soap or chemicals or both; nor is there any surviving evidence of how many other such agents were employed in Europe.

Total 'selling expenses' in the Warrington soap department, comprising travellers' salaries, expenses and commissions, customers' discounts and bonuses, cost of freight and carriage, etc., but not including advertising, rose from about £43,000 per annum in the years 1900–3 to £67,000 in 1911. But this was mainly due to the growth of trade. Expressed as costs per ton, they rose very little, from about £2 10s. to £2 13s. per ton. Moreover, despite their absolute growth, they tended to decline slightly as a proportion of total soap department costs. Between 1900–2 and 1907–8, their proportion fell from 11·6 to 10·2 per cent, since they did not rise to the same extent as the costs of raw materials.

Travellers and trade discounts, however, were not enough to keep up and expand sales during these years of increasing competition. Crosfield's were forced to extend their advertising and other marketing devices. In 1896–7 they introduced a novel type of prize scheme by offering a life assurance policy paid up for one year in return for 112 'Perfection' wrappers. This was stated to have been advertised in about 500 evening and weekly papers, but it does not appear to have proved very successful and was soon dropped. The increasing importance attached to publicity was signified by the firm's appointment in 1897 of its own full-time advertising agent, E. H. Bernhard (formerly assistant manager; E. E. Bernhard was general manager), instead of relying on outside agencies. It was his job to devise new advertising schemes and to arrange for their publicizing by posters, handbills, circulars, show-cards, and shop-window displays, the printing of which was now mostly done in their own works.

At the end of 1897, Lever played into the hands of Crosfield's and other competitors by stopping the wrapper gift scheme— the exchange of soap wrappers for gifts—which he had introduced about ten years previously. He was now prepared to discourage such practices, to co-operate with other makers and join the Northern Soap Makers' Association. Crosfield's and other firms, however, seized their opportunity to fill the void. In 1897 a scheme for a new 'Rainbow' (2d. tablet) soap was inaugurated, cheap jewellery and other presents being exchanged for the wrappers. Soon 'Erasmic' toilet soaps and perfumes were added to the presents, as a means of publicizing both soaps: 3 wrappers for a 1d. tablet, 6 for the 2d., and 9 for the 3d. 'Erasmic' soap had for some years been exchanged for 'Perfection' and 'Pink Carbolic' wrappers, and later on 'Erasmic' shaving-sticks and perfumes were included in the presents. As Arthur Crosfield pointed out many years later (in a letter of 30th April 1923 to Lord Leverhulme), the cheap jewellery, toilet soaps, and perfumes 'were just the kind of extra luxuries on which the ordinary thrifty working-man would consider that he could not afford to let his wife spend money, but which at the same time would be dear to the heart of working-women everywhere'.

The 'Rainbow' scheme was publicized by show-cards, window-dressing, etc., and by advertisements in local newspapers. It proved very costly: inclusive of selling expenses, its cost was estimated in August 1898 to be £7 5s. per ton, producing a loss on sales of over £2 per ton. The Directors—to Arthur Crosfield's chagrin—got cold feet and decided to reduce the weight of the 2d. tablet from $10\frac{3}{4}$ oz. to $10\frac{1}{2}$ oz. ($10\frac{1}{4}$ oz. for some areas), and later introduced a new $2\frac{1}{2}d$. tablet, to weigh $12\frac{1}{2}$ to 13 oz. at first, but eventually to be reduced to 12 oz.

Further additions to the scheme are evident from references in the accounts of 1899–1900 to 'Lotteries and Watch Competitions' and to 'Vans and Motors'. The earliest mention of the latter occurs in the Directors' minutes of November 1896, when they considered 'the purchase of a number of Motor Cars to take the place of the Advertisement Carts and Delivery Vans at present used by the Company'. Machenhauer was dispatched to the Continent—British motor-car manufacture having hardly begun—but it seems doubtful whether Crosfield's bought any at this time; horse-drawn vans were still preferred. By May 1900 the Company was employing ten such advertising vans, touring the country, at a cost of £3 each per week. In April 1901 forty canvassers were put on to work with these ten vans, advertising 'Perfection', at a total cost for vans and canvassers of £85 to £90 weekly. In addition, twenty men were then canvassing for 'Rainbow' in the Liverpool district, but were stopped shortly afterwards as results were disappointing. Nevertheless, this method of advertising by vans and 'canvassing teams' was extensively used in the following years. Lever described in September 1903 how Crosfield's operated 'a highly painted elaborate horse van in Manchester delivering their prizes from door to door':

When this elaborate van drives up into a side street, a smartly dressed attendant jumps out, goes to the door of the cottage and knocks, the whole street is aroused and every neighbour looks out to see what the van is going to Mrs. Jones's door for. The man I understand hands to Mrs. Jones the prizes she is to have for her wrappers, with the compliments of the firm, and the pleasure it gives them to hand the prizes to a user of their soaps. The van then rattles away to a neighbouring street. The neighbours put their heads together, go and look at the prizes Mrs. Jones has had, and presumably, encouraged by her example, consider it good business to use the same soaps that got Mrs. Jones these prizes.

Lever was therefore obliged to resume the wrapper schemes and, as he foresaw, 'a regular deluge of advertising and schemes to sell soap' then began, as competition became more frenzied.

Between 1898 and 1902 Crosfield's total expenditure on soap advertising averaged about £34,000 per annum, mainly on the 'Rainbow' scheme. The latter was wound up, however, in 1903, and advertising was concentrated on 'Perfection' and 'Pink Carbolic'. Total expenditure was reduced to a yearly average of less than £25,000 in 1903–4, but shot up to over £39,000 in 1906. There was a sharp fall in 1907; the number of canvassing teams was reduced to twenty, in an effort at economy. But the increasingly bitter competition, which, as we shall see, followed the failure of the 'Soap Trust' in 1906 (see below, pp. 225–7), soon caused an increase in advertising again.

In November 1907 the Directors decided to adopt 'a large scheme of Press advertising', on which they had previously spent little. The settlement in the following month of the Company's libel action against Associated Newspapers Ltd., arising out of the *Daily Mail* attacks on the 'Soap Trust', facilitated such a campaign: Crosfield's got £10,000 in cash and a rebate of 30 per cent on an advertising contract to be placed with Associated Newspapers Ltd. for £10,000 spread over two years. This accounts in part for the great leap in their total expenditure on advertising, etc. to nearly £47,000 in 1908. In November of that year they decided to spend £20,000 on press advertising over the next six months, together with £5,000 on a new 'cash prizes competition', which was combined with the existing wrapper schemes and renewed activity by their vans and canvassers. At the same time, show-cards, posters, leaflets, and shopwindow displays were still utilized. In July 1911 there were seventy-two canvassing teams operating, at a weekly cost of £594. In that year advertising expenditure totalled about £41,000 (including that on 'Carbosil' and 'Persil', as well as on 'Perfection' and 'Pink Carbolic').

Crosfield's total expenditure on soap advertising between 1898 and 1911 was not far short of half a million pounds, or an average of £33,000 per annum. This was concentrated on a few major lines, notably 'Rainbow' and 'Perfection'. The amount spent on general advertising was negligible. During the 'Perfection' trade-mark case of 1908–9 (see below, p. 190), Crosfield's claimed that between 1886 and 1908 they had spent considerably over £270,000 on advertising this soap, or nearly £12,000 per annum, the amounts increasing in later years. Their trading accounts bear out this claim. In the years 1899–1906 the total spent on advertising 'Perfection' and 'Pink Carbolic' together—mainly the former—was about £146,000, an average of well over £18,000 annually; it increased to about £29,000 in 1906, and must have been a good deal higher in 1908, but there are no further detailed figures until 1911, when it was just over £27,000. Expenditure per ton on 'Perfection' was probably around £1 10s. in 1899, rising to around £3 in 1902–3, and perhaps as high as £3 10s. in 1906 and 1908— about 15 per cent of the wholesale price—but was reduced to £1 10s. by the second half of 1911. (It was still, however, £3 per ton on 'Pink Carbolic'.)

The great bulk of this expenditure was in the home trade. On a number of occasions sums were voted for export advertising, but they did not amount to much. The two largest items were £600 spent in 1904 on canvassing 'Perfection' and 'Pink Carbolic' in South Africa, and £1,000 in 1909 on developing the export trade to China. (C. A. Hamilton, the export manager, made a special Eastern journey in 1910.) But the total expenditure was comparatively small, less than £2,000 per annum in 1905–6 and a mere £100 in 1911.

Advertising, of course, went hand-in-hand with trade marks (names and brands). Considerable sums were spent by Crosfield's during these years both on new marks and on extending the registration of old ones in countries throughout the world. A constant look-out was also kept for infringements, and in 1900 Crosfield's joined in the formation of a 'Northern Soapmakers' Trade Marks Protection Association'. But although hundreds of new marks were registered, their established ones remained the most important, with the addition of a few newcomers such as 'Carbosil' and 'Pinkobolic'. 'Perfection' continued to be their main line, though they had failed in 1887 to get the single word registered, due to Lever's opposition. They tried again after the new Trade Marks Act of 1905, but once more Lever opposed them. A legal action was fought in 1907–9, but Crosfield's were beaten, to their bitter chagrin, mainly on the grounds that 'Perfection' was not distinctive but a commendatory or descriptive word in common usage. The case cost them nearly £13,000, of which they got nearly £3,000 from the Trade Marks Protection Association, which had to be wound up (to Lever's annoyance, as it was largely his creation). Lever's action appears to have been motivated by spite against Crosfield's, arising from the 'Soap Trust' affair. It served to add personal acrimony to the competitive struggle of these and later years.

Another form of publicity was display at international exhibitions, such as that at St. Louis in 1904, the Anglo-French exhibition of 1908 in London, and that at Turin in 1911, at each of which Crosfield's won a Grand Prix. Even greater importance was attached to the acquisition of a royal warrant in August 1905 appointing the firm 'Soapmakers to His Majesty the King'. The royal coat-of-arms was from then on given great prominence on their letterheads, etc. Likewise, for the benefit of their export trade, they succeeded in getting themselves appointed in 1909 as 'Manufacturers of Soap and Perfumes to His Imperial Majesty the Sultan of Turkey', and similarly to the Khedive of Egypt, and later, in 1916, they became 'Soapmakers to H.M. the King of Spain'. Donations to charitable and patriotic funds were sometimes arranged with an eye to publicity. Thus their contribution to the West India Fund in November 1899 was 'governed by the contributions given by our Trade competitors', and during the South African War it was decided that 'something [should] be arranged to benefit the Company in the manner of giving to the [War] Fund', so a gift of soap was sent to the hospital train and the 'Perfection' advertising scheme was linked to the War Fund.

Having surveyed the costs of raw materials, manufacturing, selling, and advertising, let us now attempt to trace the variations in total costs, compare these with the prices obtained, and thus discover how Crosfield's profit margins and aggregate profits on soapmaking varied during this period. Such an analysis is made extremely difficult by the almost bewildering complexity of the firm's manufacturing processes, products, and accounts. For each soap, new 'boils'—varying the kinds and proportions of different fats, rosin, alkali, etc. in the 'charges'— were constantly being tried, and Crosfield's sold dozens of different kinds of soaps, of varying qualities, weights, and prices, and in differing amounts. An average cost or price per ton of soap is therefore somewhat unrealistic, and also very difficult to calculate from the surviving records. Although separate accounts were kept for the soap department (mostly household soaps) and for the milling and perfumery department (toilet soaps), and although the Erasmic Company was legally separate from the parent company and had its own accounts, in actual fact the affairs of all these were almost inextricably connected and separate accounting was to a large extent artificial. For example, the basic soap for all their products came from the soapery; toilet soaps were produced for Crosfield's as well as for the Erasmic Company, and toilet requisites, as well as soaps, were manufactured in the milling and perfumery department; Crosfield's manufactured all the products of the Erasmic Company, and each company acted as selling agent for the other's products as well as its own; complicated inter-company and inter-departmental accounting transfers were therefore necessary, which also involved other than the soapmaking departments. Moreover, the complications were increased by relations with the Liverpool (Keeling's) works, soaps being exchanged between there and Warrington.

The variations in the qualities, costs and prices of the many different soaps is revealed by a surviving book of monthly sales during 1897–9 and a price-list of 1900. The latter shows a distinction first of all between the toilet and household or laundry soaps. All the former were branded specialities, sold in tablets, while the household soaps were divided into similarly branded and tabletted products and traditional non-branded bars. The main toilet specialities were, of course, the 'Erasmic' soaps, including 'La Belle' (6*d*. tablet), 'Peerless' (4*d*.), and 'Herb' (3*d*.), but there were also cheaper ones, such as the 'Dewdrop' series (all 2*d*.) and 'Old Brown Windsor', 'Eureka' Carbolic, and 'Osborne' Assorted (all 1*d*.). The leading specialities in household tablets were 'Perfection' (3*d*.) and 'Rainbow' (2½*d*.), together with 'Uncle Toby' (2½*d*.), 'Good Judge' (2*d*.), 'Miracle' (2*d*. and 1*d*.), 'What Next' (1½*d*.), 'Guardian' Pink Carbolic (3*d*.)—abbreviated in 1907 to 'Pinkobolic'—'Defiance' Carbolic (2*d*. and 1*d*.), 'Gipsy' Brown (2*d*.) and 'Defiance' Brown (2*d*. and 1*d*.). The prices quoted here were retail. Profit margins, varying from one-sixth to one-eighth on these prices, were allowed to their customers. Moreover, the invoice prices were 'subject to normal discount'.

A range of the older-fashioned, non-proprietary, but tabletted and scented soaps were also sold, including various 'Honey', 'Skin', 'Castile', 'Windsor', and 'Carbolic' soaps, with invoice prices ranging from 19*s*. 6*d*. to 24*s*. per cwt. The bar soaps also included a few new branded specialities, such as 'Sweet Clover' (22*s*. 9*d*. per cwt.), 'Busy Bee' (21*s*. 3*d*.), and 'Peep o'Day' (17*s*. 6*d*.), while the old pales (ranging from 13*s*. to 22*s*. 6*d*. per cwt.), browns (from 15*s*. 6*d*. to 18*s*. 6*d*.), mottled (from 12*s*. 6*d*. to 18*s*. 6*d*.), and white curd soaps (from 19*s*. to 24*s*.) were still being sold.

But we do not know the varying compositions of these soaps at this time, nor do we know the various weights of the tablets. In both respects, as we have seen, alterations were often made. Fortunately, however, the monthly sales book for 1897–9 provides information not only on tonnages and selling prices, but also on manufacturing costs and profits. They show, first of all, that much the most important lines were 'Rainbow' and

'Perfection'. During 1898 'Rainbow' sales totalled around 5,000 tons, those of 'Perfection' nearly 3,200 tons. Sales of these two soaps about equalled those of all the rest put together. They were followed, at a considerable distance, by other household brands, such as 'What Next', which sold over 1,100 tons, 'Miracle' about 750 tons, 'Defiance' Carbolic nearly 700, 'Guardian' Pink Carbolic nearly 400, and 'Uncle Toby' over 200. Sales of pale household soaps (Golden Pale, Tallow Crown, etc.) totalled nearly 1,900 tons, mottled soaps 500–600 tons, and a number of others below 200 tons each; about 750 tons of 'dry soap' or soap powder were also sold.

Tonnages of toilet soaps sold in 1898 were only a small fraction of the sales of household soaps. Altogether they amounted to less than 700 tons, of which 'Peerless' Erasmic accounted for over 220 tons, 'Herb' Erasmic over 100 tons, Old Brown Windsor about 230 tons, 'Osborne' just over 80 tons, and 'Eureka' below 30 tons. The rest—'Bijou', 'La Belle', 'De Luxe', and 'Lavender' Erasmic soaps, 'Dr. Stuart' and 'Dew-drop'—sold in very small quantities of only 5 to 10 tons per annum. Total sales of shaving sticks, production of which apparently began towards the end of 1897, amounted to well under one ton in 1898.

It might be thought that production of such relatively small quantities of toilet soaps was hardly worth while, but the profit margins on these soaps were far higher than on household soaps. The price received for 'Perfection' and 'Rainbow' (i.e. the 'value ex-factory') during 1898 was from £23 5s. to £23 10s. per ton, on which—after deducting costs of raw materials, manufacturing, discounts, commission, and carriage, and adding the value of glycerine recovered (averaging about £1 5s. per ton)—there was a profit margin of around £5. On cheaper household soaps, selling for £10 to £20 per ton, it was a good deal lower; some were actually sold at a loss, while the profit on others varied from a few shillings to £3 or £4 per ton. By contrast, the price obtained for 'Peerless', the best selling Erasmic soap, was £186 13s. 4d. per ton, on which the profit margin varied between about £20 and £55 per ton. 'De Luxe', the most expensive Erasmic soap, selling for £536 10s. per ton, produced a profit margin of £132 10s. 5d. The comparatively small sales of toilet soaps, therefore, yielded a substantial aggregate profit (£12,951), though it was considerably less than that accruing from the vastly greater sales of household soaps (£43,761).

No such detailed figures of the costs, prices, and profits of the different soaps have survived for the years after 1900, but from the firm's general trading accounts averages can be calculated and the broad trends revealed. In view of the accounting difficulties previously mentioned, however, this analysis must be confined to household soaps—the bulk of total output—produced at Warrington, mainly for the home trade.

Year	Delivery (tons) from W'ton	Total Costs[1]	Average Cost per Ton	Sales	Average Price received per Ton	Aggregate Profit (+) or Loss (−)
		£	£	£	£	£
1900	16,936	360,257	21·3	357,680	21·1	− 2,522
1901	16,533	347,252	21·0	360,873	21·8	+13,621
1902	17,827	403,028	22·6	402,303	22·6	− 726
1903	18,933	405,500	21·4	414,201	21·9	+ 7,386
1904	20,493	426,368	20·8	446,183	21·8	+19,857
1905	20,891	431,896	20·7	457,927	21·9	+25,953
1906	22,263	474,737	21·3	498,839	22·4	+24,102
1907	21,860	544,071	24·9	530,974	24·3	−12,939
1908	22,810	566,049	24·8	544,799	23·9	−22,319
1909	22,874	548,161	24·0	534,800	23·4	− 8,523

The most obvious conclusion to be drawn from these figures is that, although Crosfield's were selling increasing quantities of soap throughout this period, they were doing so either at a loss or with very small profit margins. The continuous losses from 1907 onwards are particularly striking. (It must be noted, however, that no credit was allowed in the accounts of the soap department for the crude glycerine recovered from the soap

[1] Including costs of raw materials, manufacturing, selling, and advertising. In the trading accounts there was a change in book-keeping procedure from 1907 onwards, whereby interest on capital, depreciation, and general expenses were charged to the various departments, instead of to the general profit and loss account. This raised the soap department's costs, as entered in the books, by £26,000 to £27,000 per annum in the years 1907–9, and also, of course, increased the losses by the same amount. (Thus the losses in the books were £39,360, £49,851, and £34,457 respectively during those years.) We have revised these figures, however, on the pre-1907 basis, for the sake of consistency.

lyes. See below, pp. 198 and 209.) This unfortunate state of affairs was due to the fact that, whilst the prices of raw materials were rising during this period, soap prices did not rise to the same extent. Two main factors were responsible for the inability to raise soap prices. The first was a fall in the general standard of living. Whereas during most of the second half of the nineteenth century real wages—and therefore consumption per head of soap, etc.—were rising, in the years between 1900 and 1914 this trend was reversed. Total U.K. soap consumption still went up, with rising population, but not so rapidly: between 1891 and 1900 it had grown from 260,000 to 320,000 tons, but thereafter it rose more slowly, to 366,000 in 1912. Moreover, 'frenzied competition' (as Lever called it) between soapmaking firms was also keeping down soap prices, and, at the same time, together with the growing demand from margarine makers, was driving up the prices of raw materials. It was also forcing soapmakers to incur increasingly heavy advertising and selling costs, which ate into profits.

Crosfield's profits and losses on soap during these years clearly reflected the fluctuations in the raw material markets. (Note also the same contra-cyclical tendency as in earlier years.) Although improved buildings and plant effected economies, these were of only marginal significance in view of the overwhelming predominance of fats and oils in total costs. The Directors' reports from 1899 to 1902, years of small profits or losses, complained of the high prices of raw materials, but these prices fell in the latter half of 1903 and a cheerful tone pervaded the reports until that for 1907, when 'the abnormally high prices of raw materials' started a long run of losses. Prices remained high in 1908-9, and rose sharply again in 1910, when 'the exceptionally high prices of raw materials' gave a sombre tone to the Directors' report. Heavy losses were sustained in 1910-12, averaging £69,500 annually according to the unrevised trading figures.

The Liverpool works experienced rather better fortunes during this period. The export trade was not as badly affected as the home market by cut-throat competition. But for most of this period sales revenue stagnated around £110,000—though rising sharply to £148,000 in 1910—and profits were very modest, averaging little more than £3,000 annually; in some years, when the prices of raw materials rose sharply, small losses were suffered.

The toilet and perfumery trade also experienced great difficulties, though the Erasmic Company did achieve some success. The Board minutes and surviving ledgers reveal vigorous efforts to expand sales by a variety of methods: shop-window dressing; distribution of show-cards, bills, and leaflets; displays at exhibitions in London and provincial towns, and also abroad; advertisements in the press, magazines, etc. (mainly through Smith's Advertising Agency); publication of booklets and illustrated catalogues; generous discounts; free samples of soaps and perfumes; redemption of wrappers; prize competitions (offering up to £500); more unusual 'gimmicks', such as a soap-bubble fountain at Harrod's stores in 1908; and, of course, the continuous activities of travellers and agents, including visits to European countries, India, and Australia. The most notable development was the increasing amount of press advertising. Altogether, these and other selling expenses rose from about £14,000 annually in 1898-9 to about £27,000 by 1911. A. V. Baxter, secretary and general manager (eventually managing director in 1914), was largely responsible for developing the Erasmic Company's trade.

All these efforts brought about a substantial increase in the Erasmic Company's total turnover, from £59,278 (including exports £5,749) in 1902 to £92,136 (exports £12,686) in 1911, but the heavy selling costs caused trading losses for some years. Unfortunately, the Erasmic profit and loss accounts for this period have disappeared, but references in the Board minutes show that the Company did not get 'out of the red' until the end of 1909. It had to face strong competition, especially from the Vinolia Company after Lever's take-over. Not until 1913 did Crosfield's get any dividend on their Ordinary shares in the Erasmic Company. The accounts of Crosfield's milling and perfumery department, which manufactured all the Erasmic products, as well as cheaper toilet soaps, also tell a rather dismal tale. Profits dwindled from just over £6,000 in 1901 almost into insignificance in later years, with small losses in 1908-9.

Throughout these years, of course, the Directors were acutely conscious of the parlous condition of the soap trade, and made constant efforts to cope with it. But the situation was largely beyond their control. The hydrogenation process seemed to offer the most promising avenue of escape, by providing cheaper raw materials, and one can understand why they put so much endeavour and capital into its development. Combination or even amalgamation also offered a solution, but during this period, as we shall see, these did little to prevent cut-throat competition. Crosfield's were therefore forced to carry on with expensive advertising, 'even though the loss on the soap trade is so serious' (January 1911), and constantly to seek out possible economies.

On 1st December 1898, for example, the Directors decided 'that it was absolutely necessary to in some way cheapen the cost of the soap ["Rainbow"]. The question as to whether this should be done by a slight reduction in the weight, in the colour, or in the "charge", was discussed.' It was decided to reduce the weight of the tablets, while maintaining their price, and to experiment with new soap 'charges' or 'boils', reducing the fatty acid content. Similar actions were taken on innumerable occasions. Lever's famous reduction of 'Sunlight' tablets from 16 oz. to 15 oz., so much publicized by the *Daily Mail* in 1906, was certainly neither the first nor the last occasion when this expedient was adopted. On other occasions, by contrast, weights were *increased* to keep up sales, as in May 1911 when an increase in the weights of 'Good Judge' and 'Good Luck' tablets was 'forced on us by Levers' competition', but when, at the same time, new soap 'charges' were adopted to keep down manufacturing costs.

Sometimes the Directors were obliged to sell soap deliberately at a loss in order to meet competition. In October 1899, for example, it was decided to push sales of certain cheaper soaps 'though they show a serious loss at present'. Similarly, in September 1907: 'In spite of the continuance of high prices in raw materials, the Board feel compelled to reduce the price of "Perfection" tablets from $3\frac{1}{2}d$. to $3d$. per tablet owing to the severe competition of [Watson's] "Matchless Cleanser". This will involve a heavy loss to the Company during the next few months.'

This malady, which became chronic in the following years, and this remedy, could not have been endured had it not been for the fact that the chemical side of Crosfield's business was producing growing profits (see below, pp. 203–9). Their chemicals, it would seem, carried their soaps during this period. But such a conclusion would be based on too departmentalized a view of the business, as portrayed in the trading accounts. The oil-milling, hardening, and refining, caustic soda, silicate, glycerine, and other departments were all integral with soap-making: oils, soda, and silicate as raw materials and glycerine as a by-product. Unfortunately, there is no evidence as to the principles on which joint costs were allocated between these interdependent departments, and as to how departmental transfers were calculated. One point, however, should be noted: no credit was allowed for glycerine in the soap department. Lord Leverhulme was later (in 1921) to criticize this accounting deficiency, pointing out that the allowance for glycerine 'is really and has been for over twenty years a big proportion of the profit on soap'. Viewed broadly, therefore, the losses on soap-making seem much less serious, since the whole business, as an integrated concern, continued to show substantial profits.

Moreover, even on the soapmaking side, there were some very significant developments during this period which pointed the way to future expansion and prosperity. One of the most outstanding features of the twentieth-century soap trade has been the rapid growth in sales of soap powders and flakes, which have replaced hard soap for many washing purposes. The beginning of this changing pattern is visible at Crosfield's during this period. Already, in the late nineteenth century, they were manufacturing some 'dry soap', or soap powder, and washing soda. Now greatly improved products were developed. Production of 'Carbosil' began in the late 1890s, though the trade mark was not registered till 1900. This, a double salt of carbonate and silicate of soda, was advertised for its water-softening and bleaching action. It was 'a far stronger washing soda than the old-fashioned lump soda', and was 'in the handiest form— it's a powder'. Dissolved in hard water, it considerably reduced soap consumption and was used both as a household and textiles detergent. It was also 'a brilliant bleacher—makes linen and calicoes snowy white'.

At first 'Carbosil' was sold 'in bulk', but from 1902 onwards mainly in bags or packets as well as in tin boxes. The plant for its manufacture, drying, and packing was erected in (or on the site of) former stores and warehouses adjoining the silicate works. Valued at a mere £357 at the end of May 1902, the 'Carbosil' buildings and plant were worth well over £18,000 by the end of 1910. Improved grinding, bag-making, tin-making, and packing machines were introduced.

Sales were pushed by vigorous advertising. Thus in May 1903 the Board decided 'to spend up to a sum not exceeding half the profits on Carbosil. At first only about £25 per week will be spent on van canvassing.' By November, however, expenditure had risen to about £70 weekly, and was to be increased to £100 if thought desirable. 'Carbosil' was generally advertised by the same canvassing teams as for 'Perfection' and 'Pink Carbolic' and was sold by the same travellers. Scores of thousands of show-cards and leaflets were also used, and free samples were distributed. Advertising expenditure on this product rose from £5,000 in 1904 to over £8,500 in 1911, varying between £1 and £1 5s. per ton.

Production, sales, and profits soared upwards. From a mere 41 tons in 1898, output rose steadily to 10,228 tons in 1911. At first 'Carbosil' was accounted for with silicate, and there are no separate figures for sales, prices, and profits until 1904. In that year sales were just over £43,000 (£7·9 per ton), rising to nearly £89,000 (£8·7 per ton) in 1911, while profits rose from about £5,000 (£0·9 per ton) to over £18,000 (£1·8 per ton).[1] The 'Carbosil' trade mark was registered in many foreign countries, but exports were almost negligible. In 1905, the only year for which figures have survived, they were 37 tons.

'Persil', destined to become the most famous of Crosfield's soap powders, came originally from Germany. The process for its manufacture was invented by Professor Hermann Giessler and Dr. Hermann Bauer, both of Stuttgart, and was patented in Great Britain on 19th October 1903 (No. 22,580). Various earlier attempts to produce soaps with a bleaching agent, e.g. by adding sodium peroxide, had proved unsuccessful, due to rapid decomposition of the peroxide and caustic effects. But Giessler and Bauer solved this problem.

By the use of stable salts of the super acids . . . we have succeeded in producing soaps of unlimited durability, which are . . . of greater

[1] The latter is a revised figure, on the pre-1907 basis (see above, p. 194, n. 1).

bleaching and purifying efficiency than has hitherto been obtained, and which are completely free from caustic effects. . . . Soap of this kind is obtained by mixing with ordinary soap 10 per cent, 20 p.c. or more of sodium perborate or ammonium perborate . . . or per-carbonate of sodium, three very stable salts rich in oxygen.

This oxygen was 'slowly and continuously liberated' when the soap was dissolved in water, producing 'a high degree of cleansing and bleaching efficiency', capable of removing most stains, yet not damaging the most delicate fabrics nor the human skin.

This patent was soon acquired by Henkel & Co., of Dusseldorf, who used it to develop a soap powder for which they first registered the name 'Persil' in 1906 (1907 in the U.K.). They formed a company to market this and also a bleaching soda in Great Britain. Crosfield's very soon opened negotiations with Henkel & Co. (already well known to them as silicate manufacturers), and eventually, by an agreement of 10th April 1909, they acquired the patent rights and trade marks for the U.K., the British Empire (excluding Canada, Australia, and New Zealand), Egypt and Sudan, the Azores, Madeira, Cape Verde Islands, Liberian Republic, Danish and Dutch West Indies, and Dutch East Indies. They were also permitted to trade with China and Korea, but without exclusive rights. Henkel's assigned to Crosfield's their contract with the Castner Kellner Alkali Co. Ltd., of Runcorn, for the supply of perborate of soda for use in manufacturing 'Persil',[1] and they agreed to provide Crosfield's with full technical information. Crosfield's were to pay Henkel's 39,000 marks, about £1,900, plus a royalty on 'Persil' sales of 2 per cent for five years and 1 per cent for the following five years. At the same time, they bought Henkel's bleaching soda business, for a further sum of nearly £2,900, and thus reduced competition against 'Carbosil'.

This deal with Henkel's was ultimately to prove the most profitable stroke of business Crosfield's ever made. But sales grew very slowly at first. 'Persil' manufacture was started in a small extension of the 'Carbosil' building; a sum of £3,500 was

[1] By a supplementary agreement of 22nd April 1909 with the Castner Kellner Alkali Co. Ltd., who controlled certain British patents for the manufacture of perborate of soda, Crosfield's agreed to purchase all their supplies of this chemical from this company, at a price of 120s. per cwt. The Castner Kellner Co. would supply it to no one else for use in washing materials within the countries covered by Crosfield's patent rights.

voted for this in April 1910. Deliveries were only 122 tons in 1909, 539 tons in 1910, and 503 tons in 1911. Hudson's (recently acquired by Lever's) dominated the trade in soap powders, and there was also competition from 'Rinso', an improved product, which Lever's at once brought out.

Advertisements for 'Persil' emphasized that it would 'wash clothes without rubbing'—simply by soaking, boiling, and rinsing—thus dispensing with dolly and washboard, and ending washday toil, backache, sore hands, etc. By its bleaching action, moreover, this 'Oxygen Washing Compound' would render clothes 'snowy white'. It was sold at first in $3\frac{1}{2}d$. half-pound packets until 1913, when smaller 1d. and 2d. packets were introduced. It was advertised by much the same methods of canvassing, etc. as 'Perfection' and 'Carbosil'. To break into Hudson's market and to compete with Lever's, however, heavy expenditure was necessary, and Crosfield's were not bold enough. In 1911 they spent little more than £5,000 on 'Persil' advertising. They do not appear to have fully appreciated the revolutionary significance of this new soap powder; perhaps also they were put off by the initial losses of £3,000 annually in 1909–10 (though there was a profit of £800 in 1911). They were also inhibited at this time by their difficulties in the soap trade and by the strain on their capital resources of their oil-milling and hydrogenation schemes. 'Persil' sales therefore remained fairly small until after the first World War. The British housewife was not easily moved out of her habits.

Two more products were added to this side of the business in 1912—'Glitto' and 'Feather Flakes'. The former was doubtless produced in imitation of Lever's 'Vim' (brought out in 1904), and Crosfield's advertising was on similar lines. This scouring powder (made from silica, soda, and soap), it was claimed, 'Cleans everything from Attic to Cellar'—in fact 'everything but clothes'. It was retailed in 8 oz. penny packets, supplied to wholesalers in April 1912 at 8s. 9d. per gross.

Another innovation at this same time was 'Feather Flakes', along the lines of Lever's 'Lux' (brought out at the turn of the century). These, publicized as 'the Ladies' Soap', were described as consisting of 'highest grade pure concentrated soap'—they were, in fact, made from a charge containing four parts of tallow to one of copra oil—which quickly dissolved in hot water and were particularly suitable for washing woollens, babies' garments, and delicate fabrics of silk and lace. They were put on the market in 2 oz. penny packets, supplied to grocers, etc. at 9*s*. 3*d*. per gross.

Both these products were heavily canvassed and brought to public notice by a 'Free Deal', whereby they were given away to both traders and consumers with orders of 'Perfection', 'Pink Carbolic', 'Persil', and 'Carbosil'. Not surprisingly, therefore, losses of about £3,300 on 'Glitto' and nearly £6,900 on 'Feather Flakes' were suffered in the first year. Combined with those on 'Persil' and the far heavier losses on hard soaps, they made the future of Crosfield's soap manufactures seem anything but rosy.

CHAPTER XIV

CHEMICAL MANUFACTURES AND BUSINESS PROSPERITY

CROSFIELD's chemical manufactures provided a brighter prospect than soap production during the period between 1896 and 1911. The buildings and plant for caustic soda, silicate of soda, and glycerine were greatly extended and improved, output soared, and substantial profits were made. Dr. Markel stated before a Select Committee on the Manchester Ship Canal Bill of 1907 that

our reputation as chemical manufacturers . . . is based on the fact that we have brought out the purest caustic soda that has yet been made, and the purest silicate of soda also. . . . We are the second largest caustic soda manufacturers in England, and it also means a very large export trade. The same applies to silicate of soda.

A considerable trade in caustic soda was developed, in addition to its use in the factory for making soap, Carbosil, etc. The processes for its manufacture remained basically the same as in the late nineteenth century. When the Society of Chemical Industry visited the works in July 1906 they found that both the older lime process and the newer ferrite process were being used. The solution thus obtained was

evaporated . . . to a strength of 90°Tw. in which state it is sold to soap manufacturers and for use in the textile industry, its high degree of purity specially fitting it for use in mercerizing, bleaching, dyeing, and the manufacture of colours. Further evaporation of this strong liquor is carried out in cast-iron pots where it is eventually heated to dull redness. This produces solid Caustic Soda which is packed in drums, or converted by further treatment into Ground, Flake, Detached, and Stick Caustic.

The caustic buildings and plant were rapidly extended in the years immediately after the firm's incorporation, nearly trebling in value from about £17,600 in July 1896 to about £49,000 at the end of 1901. Comparatively little further capital was invested in this department, however, during the next ten years. As in soapmaking, raw materials predominated in manufacturing costs. Soda ash, of course, was much the most important, accounting for nearly half total costs; hence the great value of Crosfield's preferential terms from Brunner, Mond & Co.[1] In addition, lime, iron oxide, etc. had to be purchased, and casks, drums, tins, and cases had also to be provided, by the firm's own cooperage and tin-box making departments; steam, fuel, and electric power accounted for about 12 per cent of total costs, and wages for only 6 to 7 per cent. Costs of carriage were substantial, about 14 per cent, but selling costs (discounts and commissions) were low, about 3 per cent.

Sales of caustic soda leapt up as a result of the plant extensions in the years after 1896, rising from 11,646 tons in 1898 to 19,623 in 1904.[2] More than three-quarters of these tonnages were of liquid caustic, but from then onwards there was an increased demand for the solid and powdered products. Thus in February 1905 the Board minutes refer to the installation of new caustic pots on account of 'the slackness of orders for liquid Caustic', and in September 1910 over £5,000 was voted for extending the powdered caustic plant. Sales of liquid caustic, which had doubled from about 8,000 tons in 1898 to nearly 16,000 tons in 1904, fell back to below 8,000 tons annually in 1909–11. Deliveries of solid caustic, on the other hand, rose from around 2,000 tons annually at the beginning of this period to nearly 6,000 tons by the end, and powdered caustic from below 1,000 tons to over 3,000. These products were marketed in many foreign countries, as well as at home, but there are no surviving export figures.

The decline in sales of liquid caustic brought total deliveries down to about 16,000 tons annually in 1908–11, but since the prices of solid and powdered were substantially higher than those of liquid, total sales revenue continued to rise; from an annual average of £73,000 in 1899–1901 it doubled to £147,000 in 1909–11. (Prices, as we shall see, were fixed by agreements with other manufacturers.) Profits rose even more

---

[1] See below, pp. 239-40.
[2] It is not clear on what basis these tonnages were calculated. They are probably actual tons, though in later years it was usual to calculate output as 70 per cent Na_2O.

12 (*a*) Caustic revolver, 1886

12 (*b*) Caustic pots, 1896

13 (*a*) Silicate furnace, 1913

13 (*b*) Glycerine stills, 1896

remarkably from about £7,000 to £40,000 annually over the same period.[1]

A by-product of the caustic-soda plant was lime sludge (resulting from the reaction between soda ash, or sodium carbonate, and slaked lime, which produced a solution of caustic soda and precipitated lime, or calcium carbonate), which for years Crosfield's discharged as waste into the River Mersey. By the middle 'nineties they were thus disposing of about 150 tons per week. The Ship Canal Company, the Mersey Conservancy Board, and Warrington Corporation therefore brought pressure upon the firm, which was eventually prosecuted in March 1899. Just before that date, however, Crosfield's had completed plant, costing £5,000 to £6,000, for dealing with the lime precipitate, which was removed in large filter presses and then sold, mostly to farmers. (A little was also used to make whiting and disinfectant powder.) Sales rose from over 10,000 tons in 1899 to around 20,000 tons (about £3,000) annually in 1904–6. It was generally taken from the works by horse and cart, but in 1903 the firm bought its first motor lorry, a tip wagon, 'for delivering waste lime to farmers'.

In 1905, however, it was decided to make more economic use of the waste lime by erecting a cement works on the 'tongue land' recently acquired across the river. This involved firstly the building of a suspension bridge, from the wharf warehouse, bearing a goods transporter and iron pipeline, costing altogether nearly £4,000. The buildings and plant for the cement works were erected in 1906–8, at a cost, including electrical installation, of about £22,000. The plant and machinery were obtained from G. Polysius, of Dessau, Germany. The lime precipitate from the caustic plant was first mixed with clay in a wash-mill, and this 'slurry' was pumped into a rotary kiln, where it was heated with coal dust to produce cement clinker, which was then ground to powder. Clay was obtained from the near-by Arpley Meadows, bordering the new Mersey diversion. About twenty acres of this land was leased in March 1907 for thirty years from the Wilson-Patten family, at an annual rent of £29 10s., plus a royalty of 9d. per square yard of clay. A further area of nearly three acres was leased in July 1912 from Henry

---

[1] Throughout this chapter, profits for the years after 1907 have been revised on the pre–1907 basis.

Lyon, at a rent of £2 per year and the same royalty. (These clay lands were in later years to be the site of the Thames Board Mills.)

Production of Portland cement began at the end of 1907 and grew from over 9,000 tons in 1908 to nearly 15,000 tons in 1913. It proved an unprofitable manufacture for the first three years, due to a slump in the building trade, but from 1911 onwards, as cement prices rose, production increased, and profits began to be made, reaching nearly £4,000 in 1913. The cement was sold through agents, such as the Warrington Slate Co. Ltd.

Silicate of soda continued to be one of Crosfield's chief chemical products during this period. The buildings and plant were considerably extended and improved, by the installation of new, larger, and more efficient furnaces, dissolvers, and evaporators. Their capital value rose from less than £8,000 in July 1896 to over £21,000 at the end of 1911. The process of manufacture was described thus in 1906:

Soda Ash and Sand are fused at a white heat in a regenerative gas-fired furnace. The molten product is run into iron trays and allowed to solidify, producing the so-called Lump Silicate. This product varies in composition, being alkaline or neutral according to the nature of the furnace charge. Although soluble in water, Silicate of Soda is not easily dissolved, and many users prefer to purchase it in the form of a solution which can be readily diluted with water to any extent required. It is dissolved under a high steam pressure giving a weak solution, which is afterwards concentrated in vacuum evaporators to various strengths.

The regenerative furnaces (supplied by Siemens) were said to be 'the largest of their kind in use for this purpose', and the firm was using a 'novel gas producer'. As in the manufacture of soap and caustic soda, raw materials (soda ash and sand) were much the biggest item (about half) of total costs, followed by carriage, casks and drums, steam and fuel, while wages and salaries were relatively unimportant (about 6 per cent).

The great bulk of silicate production was sold; comparatively little was now used in the firm's own soap manufacture. In 1896 just over 800 tons, roughly 10 per cent of total output, was supplied to the soapery; by 1901 the figure had gradually fallen to about 250 tons, a mere 3 per cent of production. Crosfield's supplied silicate, however, to a number of other soapmaking firms. In 1906 we find that it was also being sold for use 'as a special detergent in the textile and straw industries, for weighting silk, in the preparation of fire-resisting paints, artificial stone and cement, also in the form of a solution, for egg preserving, etc.' It was sold through commission agents, like A. J. Luke & Co., of 33 Great Tower Street, London, who in February 1897 were appointed Crosfield's sole agents for the sale of silicate within a thirty-mile radius of Charing Cross, at £3 12s. 6d. per ton, plus carriage from Warrington; their commission was 2 per cent.

Silicate sales more than doubled during this period. In actual tonnages (both liquid and glass) they rose from below 8,000 tons in 1898 to nearly 17,000 tons in 1911; calculated as glass, they rose from about 5,000 to nearly 11,000 tons. Prices rose somewhat at the turn of the century, but then remained fairly stable, averaging between £4 and £5 per ton. (We shall later examine manufacturers' price-fixing agreements.) Profits rose from about £4,000 in 1899 to an annual average of £14,000 in 1909–11.

Glycerine production naturally increased with rising soap output. Its manufacture was described as follows in 1906:

Spent lye from soap pans, after chemical treatment, is filtered through presses and concentrated in vacuum evaporators . . . capable of evaporating 300 tons of water per diem. During concentration, salt is automatically removed, washed free of glycerine, dried in centrifugal machines, dissolved in water, and returned to the soapery in the form of brine; thus the salt completes a 'circular tour'.

Crude glycerine containing about 80 per cent of glycerine and 10 per cent of salt (remainder being chiefly water), is subjected to a process of double distillation, and converted into glycerine for manufacturing purposes (such as dynamite), and chemically pure glycerine. The distilling plant for glycerine is one of the largest of its kind now in use.

Productive capacity was greatly increased during this period. Within two to three years of incorporation the Company had built 'an entirely new Glycerine Plant, of the latest design, capable of dealing with double the output hitherto made'. Further improvements were made in the following years, with the result that the capital valuation of the buildings and plant rose from less than £12,000 in 1896 to nearly £55,000 by the end of 1906, around which figure it then remained stabilized.

Raw materials (mostly spent soap lyes) were even more predominant in the total costs of this department than in those of the other chemicals and soap. In 1904, for example, they accounted for about 87 per cent of total costs in the distilling department; steam and fuel for about 4 per cent, wages and salaries between 2 and 3 per cent, the remaining 6 to 7 per cent being costs of carriage, discounts, and commissions.

Most of the crude glycerine output went to the distilling department, though a varying amount—from about 200 to 700 tons annually—was sold. The bulk of glycerine sales, however, were of the double distilled product. Some of the latter was used in the firm's own toilet preparations, but most of it was marketed, either for dynamite manufacture or as 'chemically pure' for pharmaceutical purposes; small quantities of 'commercial' and 'half white' were also sold. It was supplied in a wide variety of containers, ranging from small bottles to large carboys, tins, and drums.

Glycerine provides an interesting example of a commodity in joint supply and composite demand. Being a by-product, its supply was determined by the output of soap, but fortunately it was in demand for both pharmaceutical and dynamite purposes. Production could be switched from one to the other according to demand: thus C.P. and dynamite deliveries generally fluctuated conversely, the level of demand for the latter appearing to have been the dominant factor.

Total distilled sales rose from less than 700 tons in 1898 to an annual average of nearly 2,000 tons in 1909–11. Prices, however, fluctuated considerably, between about £40 and £60 per ton until 1910–11, when they rose very sharply to well over £80 per ton, so that distilled sales revenue soared from about £38,000 in 1900 to over £154,000 in 1911. (Attempts at price-fixing by the Glycerine Association will be dealt with in the next chapter.)

In September 1903, total annual sales of C.P. glycerine in this country were estimated by the Glycerine Association at about 2,650 tons. Crosfield's then held about 20 per cent of the market. In the following years their sales rose considerably and by 1913 they claimed to be 'the largest producers in this country of chemically-pure glycerine'. Markets for both C.P. and dyna-mite glycerine were also found abroad, but no export figures have survived.

Total profits on glycerine (both crude and distilled) rose enormously during this period, from about £19,000 in 1899 to nearly £82,000 in 1911. But these figures are very misleading, since the soap department, which provided the spent lyes, was given no trading credit on that account, though suffering large losses, while the crude glycerine department was thereby making enormous profits. This accounting anomaly did not, of course, affect the Company's overall profits, but distorted the trading situation.

Crosfield's main manufacturing processes—the production of refined oils, soap, and chemicals—necessitated a wide range of ancillary activities, concerned with provision of water, steam, and power, engineering construction and maintenance, ware-housing, bag- and box-making, coopering, packing, printing, transport, and commercial and clerical business, which together occupied a sizeable part of the total labour force. Enormous quantities of water were consumed in the works, almost all of it pumped from the Mersey. Evidence on the Manchester Ship Canal Bill of 1907 shows that Crosfield's consumption averaged 135,000 gallons per hour, or about ten tons per minute, day and night throughout the year. This supply, of course, was free, but even if they could have afforded to purchase their water from Warrington Corporation, the latter could not have supplied such an enormous amount, twice the total non-manufacturing consumption in the town. About one-tenth of this water was used in their manufactures. Much of it was converted to steam in boilers, partly for driving engines, but mostly for heating or boiling, by injecting the steam into liquids (as in soap pans), or for evaporating by means of closed steam coils. Large quantities of water were required for cooling: condensing was necessary in various processes, and the firm also made a great deal of condensed or distilled water for use in their manufactures, to achieve greater purity. They economized by condensing exhaust steam from their engines and also from their evaporators, but more and more steam-raising boilers had to be installed. In 1907 there were twenty-four or twenty-five boilers in the works, mostly of the Lancashire type. The rapid increase in the capital valuation of steam engines, boilers, etc., from £12,500 at the end of 1898 to over £57,000 by the end of 1910, was mainly on account of boiler installations.

Crosfield's devoted careful study to the economical operation of their boilers and developed a number of improvements, some of which they patented. They devised mechanical and chemical processes for the treatment of boiler-feed water, to remove air, mud, and grit and to soften the water, thereby preventing sedimentary or scaly deposits in boilers, and thus increasing their efficiency, saving fuel, and reducing cleaning costs. At the same time they further economized on fuel by analysis of coal supplies, improved boiler settings, control of combustion (regulating air, fuel, and temperatures), mechanical stoking, improved flues, pre-heating the feed water by means of the waste gases (using fuel 'economizers'), and similarly 'superheating' the steam. Crosfield's were claiming in 1903–6 that they were thereby saving 1,000 tons of coal per week, and they were also boasting of the cleanliness of their 'works with smokeless chimneys'.

Their experiences in this field of water purification and economic boiler-firing led to the establishment of a separate department, which began to publicize 'the Crosfield System of Economizing Fuel' and to urge its adoption by other firms, Crosfield's undertaking to provide technical advice and regular supervision. The business offered such possibilities that in spring 1906 discussions were started with the Vulcan Boiler Insurance Co., with the result that a new company—the Fuel Saving and Water Treating Co. Ltd., with a nominal capital of £15,000, of which half was issued—was jointly established, to which Crosfield's sold their relevant patents, goodwill, etc., taking shares in exchange. But this creation did not last long: after suffering losses totalling over £2,000 in its first two years, it was liquidated in April 1909. This venture into industrial water-softening, however, pointed the way to the later successful development of 'Doucil', after the first World War.

Crosfield's dependence upon the Mersey for water supplies made them, as we have seen, very apprehensive about possible increase in its salinity by the Manchester Ship Canal. This danger was renewed by the Canal Company's Bills of 1904 and 1907, which provided for raising the level of the canal by pumping water from the river estuary, in order to accommodate larger vessels; more salt water would thus be sluiced into the river above Warrington. Crosfield's, therefore, together with other local manufacturers, fought successfully to secure protective clauses in these Bills. Nevertheless, increased salinity did occur, whereupon they took legal action against the Canal Company, which was settled by an agreement in February 1908, whereby Crosfield's were paid £1,250 in damages plus legal costs, and the Canal Company agreed in future to give a month's notice of the opening of Walton sluice.

Just as Crosfield's had been among the earliest firms to adopt electric lighting, so too they were quick to appreciate the possibilities of electric power. The installation was started in 1902, to drive part of their machinery, and proved so successful that it was greatly augmented in 1905–6, so as to have 'Electrical Driving adopted generally throughout the works' (Directors' report, January 1905). According to a report in 1906, electric power was produced 'at a cost which, including depreciation and interest on all the plant and mains, is only 60 per cent of that which obtained when steam was the motive power'. It also had other advantages: 'economy of space, increased cleanliness, ease of starting and stopping, and general adaptability'. The generating plant and buildings were valued at £10,150 in May 1907. Further extensions, costing £6,300, were made in 1910–11.

The rapid growth of Crosfield's production necessitated more buildings for storage of raw materials and finished goods. A large new warehouse—the Wharf Warehouse—was erected between 1896 and 1899, at a cost of nearly £19,000, on the site of the former Pottery Warehouse and Patten's Quay (where the modern Technical Centre now stands). This was primarily for raw materials, taken from ships and barges berthed alongside. In 1902–3 another large building, costing £6,000, was erected on the site of the former Bank Quay Glass Works, for use as a soap warehouse and also for printing and lithography, cardboard box-making and paper stores, for which it is still used today. This building was extended in 1904–5, and again in 1910 at a total cost of over £5,000. At the same time new buildings for saw-milling and wood box-making were established on the other side of Factory Lane, across from the timber stores, to which they were connected by a bridge. In 1903–4 the cooperage department was similarly extended by the building of a new cask-making plant for about £2,000, 'the Company not being able to procure a sufficient number of suitable casks'. The making of bags and tin boxes had meanwhile been added to the Carbosil department, and later on the introduction of 'Persil' and 'Feather Flakes' necessitated packet-making machines.

There was no end to the stream of constructional projects at Crosfield's during these years, requiring a growing force of engineers, draughtsmen, turners, fitters, boilermakers, bricklayers, plumbers, joiners, etc. In 1905–6 about 500 such men were employed, and more in later years. In 1904 a new engineers' fitting shop, costing £3,500, was erected on Liverpool Road, adjoining the *Ship* inn, where the Mission Chapel had stood. The new electric power station was built on the site of the old engineers' shop, adjoining the soapery boilers, and a new pumping station was put beside it, on the river bank. The former cottages in Quay Fold, after having been converted into laboratories, now became engineers' and builders' stores. A new boilermakers' shop was built in 1906 between them and the Garston railway.

Towards the end of 1904 Crosfield's sub-leased nearly two acres of land across Liverpool Road (including the Mission Schools and cottages), bounded by Thewlis Street and Baxter Street, on part of which they at once erected new buildings for their joiners, pattern makers, plumbers, etc., and also engineers' offices, at a cost of about £2,200. The 900-years leasehold was eventually purchased in 1914 for £2,500.

All these new buildings had to be fitted with machinery for box-making, printing, engineering, etc. The latest types of equipment were installed, making possible large-scale production. In 1906, for example, the wood box-making department was reported to be converting 'more than 5,000 tons of timber into over one million boxes' per year. 'The seasoned timber is cut to the required size in the saw mills, and made up into boxes by means of automatic nailing machines. The finished boxes are distributed to various parts of the works by means of overhead conveyors.' In 1907 machines were installed to turn out 500,000 'Perfection' and 'Pink Carbolic' card boxes per week. The firm's printing (letterpress and lithographic) department produced large quantities of advertising literature (handbills, show-cards, etc.), in addition to printing wrappers, cartons, and bags. In 1903, for example, 500,000 copies of a single handbill were printed, advertising a prize 'washing-dolly' scheme. These developments required considerable capital expenditure. Thus at the end of 1910 the buildings and plant in the engineering department were valued at nearly £18,000, in the printing and lithography department at nearly £17,000, and in the packing department at nearly £8,000.

The firm's goods continued to be moved by water and by rail. Great importance was still attached to the Mersey even after the opening of the Manchester Ship Canal, but the latter provided improved facilities, so Crosfield's further increased the size of their shipping or lighterage department. In July 1896 they had three steam vessels and a single barge. Within a few years they acquired three more steamers and three more barges, each with a carrying capacity of between 100 and 200 tons, and two more barges were bought in 1909. The capital valuation of their steamers and flats rose from nearly £8,000 in June 1896 to over £14,000 at the end of 1910, after allowing for depreciation. With these they not merely brought in most of their raw materials (fats, oils, rosin, salt, lime, sand, timber, etc.) and shipped out manufactured goods, but they also became public carriers, advertising a daily service between Warrington and Liverpool, with rates around 3s. per ton.

At high tides they continued to go by the river; on other occasions they went by the Ship Canal, entering at Walton Lock. Unfortunately, however, the Ship Canal Company failed to fulfil its river-dredging obligations under the Act of 1885 and later agreements, so that navigation became increasingly hazardous; boats were often delayed or went aground. Crosfield's and other Warrington traders therefore claimed free passage along the Ship Canal, in accordance with the agreements, but the Ship Canal Company refused. Prolonged legal proceedings ensued between 1902 and 1907, first in the Chancery Division of the High Court of Justice, then in the Court of Appeal, and finally in the House of Lords. The decision went against the Ship Canal Company, which was ordered to return the tolls previously paid under protest and also to pay damages and legal costs, totalling over £13,000.

The depth of the river, however, was controlled not only by

the amount of dredging, but also by the volume of water taken out and let in by the Ship Canal Company. Thus the petitions of Crosfield's and other Warrington traders against the Ship Canal Bills of 1904 and 1907 were motivated by concern not merely about the quality of the river water, but also about the quantity. Crosfield's pointed out that their business was 'largely dependent upon the facilities afforded by water carriage'. They therefore sought to secure that the flow of the river should not be diminished by the increased demands of the Ship Canal Company, and they managed to obtain protective sections in the 1904 and 1907 Acts.

Movement of their products to inland areas continued to be by rail. After experimenting with a motor car in the late 'nineties, the firm decided to retain horse vans for advertising, and although they bought a motor tip-wagon for removing lime in 1903, no more lorries were bought during this period, and horses and carts were still used for local transport. But the internal railway system was extended for loading goods directly into wagons within the works and for bringing in coal. The capital value of their locomotives and trucks trebled from £3,150 in June 1896 to about £9,500 at the end of 1910.

Having surveyed developments in the main departments of Crosfield's soap and chemical business during these fifteen dramatic years, let us now take an overall view of the Company's affairs. The growth of its total assets is shown by the following figures.

	Total Assets	Land, Buildings, Plant, Machinery, etc.	Stocks on Hand	Goodwill	Sundry Debtors	Cash and Invest- ments
	£	£	£	£	£	£
July 1896	373,132	179,792	86,694	56,646	50,000	—
November 1911	1,240,370	650,424	271,453	100,000	122,338	96,155

The new capital for this expansion was raised mainly from the public. As we have seen, the original capital of £300,000 (in Ordinary and Cumulative Preference shares) was owned entirely by members of the Crosfield family and Dr. Markel, but their resources were insufficient to provide for all the new developments, and £290,000 of Debenture loan capital was at once raised in 1896–7. In March 1898 share capital was increased by the creation of 25,000 5 per cent Cumulative Pre-Preference shares of £10 each, 20,000 of which were at once issued to the public, while the remaining 5,000 were held in reserve until 1910. In Spring 1904 the Ordinary share capital was also increased by £50,000, and again at the beginning of 1910 by a further £100,000. Thus by the end of 1911 the total authorized and issued share capital was £700,000—£300,000 Ordinary and £400,000 Preference—but the 10,000 Ordinary shares recently created were as yet only half paid, so that the total paid-up share capital was £650,000.

A similar expansion occurred in Crosfield's sales. At the beginning of this period, hard soap formed three-quarters of their trade, but by 1911, although sales of soap had increased considerably, they now formed only half the total sales. Those of 'Carbosil', glycerine, caustic, and silicate had grown more rapidly, while new products, such as 'Persil', oils, vegetable butters, cattle meal, and cement had also been developed.

Crosfield's Sales (£)[1]

	1899	*1911*
Total Sales	565,089	1,264,017
Soap	407,769	639,692
Glycerine	47,087	177,997
Caustic Soda	77,693	146,910
Silicate	}	76,914
Carbosil	} 32,539	88,773
Persil	—	27,739
Vegetable butters	—	38,274
Extracted oils	—	37,050
Hardened oils	—	15,981
Cement	—	14,687

The Company's trading profits fluctuated considerably, due mainly to changes in prices of raw materials, but rose substantially over the whole period (see p. 216). Gross trading profits had doubled in aggregate, but expressed as percentages on sales they had declined slightly, from 12·2 to 11·5 per cent

[1] Excluding those from the Liverpool works (for which, see above, p. 195).

Crosfield's Gross Trading Profits (£)[1]

1898	75,957	1905	110,063
1899	68,944	1906	120,300
1900	45,948	1907	90,785
1901	77,311	1908	101,149
1902	75,685	1909	141,151
1903	85,022	1910	142,726
1904	102,178	1911	145,014

between 1899 and 1911. From these gross trading profits, there had to be deducted general works and management expenses, depreciation allowances, and interest on capital. On the net profits remaining, the interest on the Debenture stock (£12,675 annually) was, of course, the first charge, followed by the dividend on the Pre-Preference and Preference Shares (£17,500 annually until 1910), and then the Ordinary shareholders would get whatever dividends were available.

Things began fairly well, with Ordinary dividends of 5 per cent and 7½ per cent respectively in 1897 and 1898. But in the following years a different financial policy was pursued: no more Ordinary dividends were paid until 1904, while Preference dividends were postponed for a time. This was partially due to the more difficult conditions in the soap trade: higher prices of raw materials reduced profits in 1899–1900. But when profits recovered in the following years, the Directors decided to strengthen the Company's financial position, instead of paying out dividends. Thus they started a General Reserve Fund, which was raised to £50,000 by January 1904; a total of about £36,000 was allowed for depreciation; and the figure for goodwill was reduced from an inflated figure of over £133,000 at the end of 1898 (after purchase of Keeling's, etc.) to £100,000, at which it remained throughout this period.

This careful policy, though it greatly strengthened the Company's finances, evidently began to cause concern to some of the Ordinary shareholders, especially since they were at the same time faced with demands for more capital to finance new manufacturing developments. At the Annual General Meeting in January 1905, therefore, it was decided that although 'Reserves and Depreciation . . . should be adequately provided for before any Dividend is paid on the Ordinary Shares', the

[1] Again excluding the Liverpool works. The profits in the trading accounts for the years 1907–11 have been revised on the pre-1907 basis.

Ordinary dividend 'should be continued as far as possible at the rate of 10% free of Income Tax' (the amount just declared for 1904).

Trade improved considerably in the following years, so that it was possible to satisfy the appetites of the Ordinary shareholders by maintaining dividends at 10 per cent in 1905 and 1906. At the same time, financial rectitude was maintained by further large allowances for depreciation and reserves—the funds for which stood at nearly £88,000 and £100,000 respectively in January 1907.

Another change in the trading climate in 1907, however, with prices of raw materials rising again, caused more heart-searching and head-scratching among the Directors. It was felt that Markel was over-extending the Company's manufacturing activities, involving excessive capital expenditure and possibly threatening the Company's trading profitability.[1] It was considered that such schemes, involving large public issues of Debentures or Pre-Preference and Preference shares, not merely placed too heavy a strain on the Company's resources, but diverted too much of the Company's profits into pockets other than those of the Ordinary shareholders.

J. J. Crosfield drew up a lengthy memorandum, which was approved by the Board in June 1907. He advocated, firstly, 'a sound financial policy', including investment of £10,000 to £15,000 annually outside the business, redemption of Debentures (which were 'a debt and should be so treated'), writing down Goodwill ('a mere book entry'), creation of more liquid assets in the shape of a bank balance or stocks, and avoidance of any further capital expenditure till these aims were achieved. At the same time, however, he favoured 'maintenance of dividends': indeed, he considered that the Ordinary shareholders had a right to expect even higher returns than in the previous three years. This policy should be coupled with 'strict economy' in the running of the business. He proposed cutting expenditure not only in the works but also in the General Office, e.g. by reducing the number of typists: 'It is a mistake for Managers to be above putting pen to paper.' Finally, he declared that there should be 'no diversion from the main business of the Company. I should at once close down the Paint, Ochre and Gum depart-

[1] See above, p. 144.

ments, etc. We have done no good in these and each month only adds more to the loss . . . The policy of the Company must be to attend to our business, and our business is Soap, Carbosil, Silicate, Caustic, and shortly Cement.'

This memorandum bore fruit in stricter attention to costing, the abandonment of some non-paying manufactures, investments in the Company's own Debentures, and also outside in railway stock, etc. Moreover, the Company did succeed during the next few years in not merely maintaining but actually increasing Ordinary dividends. There was only a temporary lull, however, in capital expenditure: even greater sums were soon to be spent on oil-milling, hydrogenation, and other projects, necessitating considerable expansion of the engineering department. But most of the additional capital was raised by the Ordinary shareholders.

In view of these new commitments, it is not surprising that the Company did not invest much money outside the business. Its chief investment was just over £45,000 in its Erasmic subsidiary. It also acquired some houses at Lower Walton (which had belonged to John Crosfield), some of which were occupied by managerial staff. Brief dabbling in the stocks of Warrington Corporation and the Mersey Docks & Harbour Board in 1904–5 was followed by several investments in railway companies— the Midland, the London & North Western, the Great Western, and the Lancashire & Yorkshire—but these totalled only about £6,000. Investments in the Fuel Saving & Water Treating Co. and in the Northern Ochre Co. (a mere £200)—both related to their own manufactures—soon proved abortive. In 1908 about £100 was invested in the British Uralite Co., and at the end of 1909 about £1,000 was put into 2½ per cent Consols. Thus the Company's investments outside its own sphere remained relatively negligible. The £15,000 placed in Apol Ltd. in 1911–12 was intended to safeguard supplies of vegetable oils for soap-making.

The policy of paying higher dividends to Ordinary shareholders was steadily maintained from 1907 onwards. Although heavy losses were suffered in the soap department, these were far outweighed by rising profits on chemicals. The Ordinary dividend was therefore maintained at 10 per cent in 1907 and 1908, raised to 14 per cent in 1909, and then kept at 12 per cent in 1910 and 1911. At the same time, the Reserve Fund was built up to £170,000 by the end of 1911, and £20,000 a year was provided for depreciation. A self-congratulatory and optimistic tone therefore pervaded the Directors' annual reports.

Ownership of the Ordinary shares, and thus control of the Company's affairs, was kept predominantly in the hands of the Crosfield family. J.J. became the largest shareholder, followed by his elder brother Arthur, and his younger brother George. The latter, however, had to bring in an associate, Joseph Benson, of London, to provide some of the capital for the purchase of shares, which were jointly held. Markel, together with his wife and daughter, still had a sizeable holding. The pattern of ownership in November 1911 was as follows:

	Fully paid Shares (£10)	Half paid Shares (£5)
J. J. Crosfield	7,731	3,900
A. H. Crosfield	5,434	2,717
G. R. Crosfield	2,320	1,160
J. Benson	1,400	700
K. E. Markel	900	500
Ada J. Markel	1,200	600
Marie V. Markel	300	150
H. Roberts	544	272
A. L. Crosfield (Mrs.)	71	1
C. Haslam	100	—
	20,000	10,000

There was a similar concentration of Crosfield ownership of the Preference shares.

The third generation of Crosfields had ample cause for pride in this great business, which they had expanded on a scale that dwarfed the achievements of Joseph, the founder, and his sons. But large though the Bank Quay works had become, it was surpassed by the creation of their erstwhile neighbour, now at Port Sunlight. Lever, tired of the Soapmakers' Association, was now rapidly acquiring one old-established soapworks after another. In this competitive struggle Crosfield's—despite their rapid growth—had eventually to seek the massive support of their old friends, Brunner, Mond & Co., whom Lever was also challenging. How would Crosfield's fare in this battle of the giants?

CHAPTER XV

COMBINATION AND AMALGAMATION

ONE of the main features of industrial organization in the late nineteenth and early twentieth centuries, not only in Great Britain but even more markedly in Germany and the United States, was the movement towards combination and amalgamation—towards cartels, trusts, pools, rings, associations, conferences, etc.—which aimed at restricting competition, controlling output and prices, and maintaining or increasing profits. In some cases these were little more than gentlemen's agreements; in others, firms ceased to be independent and were absorbed or amalgamated into large businesses. The trend towards joint-stock organization, facilitating transference of ownership through the share market, encouraged these tendencies, which were also associated with the greater capital requirements of modern industry and efforts to achieve economies of large-scale production and distribution.

All these changing aspects of industrial organization are visible in the soap, oils and fats, and chemical trades during this period.[1] In the years after 1896 Crosfield's continued to play an active part in the Northern Soap Makers' Association, of which Arthur Crosfield was still secretary, while the national body remained practically a London or Southern Association. The most important problem facing the northern makers during the years 1896–7 was the growing competition from Lever's, who were still excluded from their Association, though admitted to the national one. The 'ruinously low prices' of pale soaps from Port Sunlight threatened to bring about the Association's collapse. Watson's of Leeds broke the rules and met Lever's

---

[1] Professor C. Wilson's *History of Unilever* contains a good account of these developments in the soap trade. We shall be mainly concerned with Crosfield's part therein; on some points we shall amplify and modify Professor Wilson's account. We shall also examine combinations among manufacturers of glycerine, silicate of soda, and caustic soda, which Professor Wilson does not mention. H. R. Edwards, *Competition and Monopoly in the British Soap Industry* (1962), deals very sketchily with this period and relies heavily on the Unilever history.

competition by giving additional discounts, bonuses (or rebates), and gifts, and by lowering their prices independently, much to the disgust of other makers. On 28th April 1897 John Crosfield 'expressed a very strong feeling of indignation at such practices existing in the Soap Trade', but, as we have seen, his firm was soon forced to adopt them. The situation became so desperate that on 5th January 1898 'a determination was expressed that the Association would not be undersold by Lever, and that if he went down we would immediately follow in competing qualities'.

Such cut-throat competition, however, would obviously have very damaging effects upon the whole trade. Negotiations were therefore started to bring Lever's into the Association, and at the next meeting, on 2nd March, we find 'a cordial welcome' being extended to Robert Barrie, Lever's representative. Lever's now agreed, for the first time, to co-operate with the other northern makers in advancing the prices of bar soaps. All appeared to be in harmony.

The time seemed opportune for united action throughout the whole trade, and the London makers were therefore urged to join in the advance. But Knight's refused to do so, with the result that northern makers, finding themselves undersold by London firms on their own ground, threatened to retaliate in the metropolitan market. Largely through Arthur Crosfield's diplomacy, however, conflict was prevented and at the half-yearly meeting of the national Association in January 1899 it was decided to appoint a joint committee of northern and southern makers 'to meet once a month or as occasion may render necessary to decide on any question of change in prices'.

London representatives attended a meeting in Liverpool later that month, when an advance was agreed on. But the London-ers, unlike the Northerners, still found it impossible to secure joint action, Knight's being particularly independent, and by July 1899 it was clear that they were 'not sufficiently united to agree with the Northern makers as to fixed prices'. The northern makers, too, were having their own difficulties in regard to the old evils of 'booking forward', terms of payment (discounts), bonuses or rebates, and newer ones such as alterations in the weights or qualities of tablets, and gift schemes. But the minutes of their monthly meetings indicate a much firmer unity than in earlier years, especially on general advances or reductions in prices. The latter applied mainly to traditional bar soaps, but were gradually extended to household 'specialities', such as Gossage's 'Magical', Lever's 'Sunlight', and Crosfield's 'Perfection', though not to toilet soaps. In January 1900, moreover, Lever's proposal for a 'Northern Soap Makers' Trade Marks Protection Association' was adopted.

In the summer of 1900 yet another effort was made to secure united action in London and the South, and eventually it was agreed that prices in that region should be regulated by a committee of five leading London houses. In May 1901, moreover, it was decided to recognize reality by forming a separate London and Southern Association, primarily for fixing prices, as was already done by the northern and the western makers in their respective areas; the various regional associations could then co-operate to secure simultaneous advances or reductions, while the national body would continue to exist for 'Imperial purposes'. The Scottish makers had long had a separate association and the Irish had just formed one; makers in both countries had co-operated for some years with the Northern Association.

The division of the United Kingdom into these five districts, each with its association, represented on a central committee, was formally adopted at the annual meeting of the national body in June 1901. Each association would recognize the prices fixed in other regions, to avoid underselling. Arthur Crosfield described this meeting as 'historic', the culmination of years of effort to secure effective combination in the soap trade. He himself, as secretary of the Northern Association, had played no small part in bringing this about.

As chairman of the next general meeting in January 1902, he held forth at length on the benefits derived from the Association:

. . . it is a very pleasant feature of our trade that we can take the cut and thrust of competition in good part and meet at our monthly and annual meetings as we do on such a cordial and friendly footing.

That good fellowship in the trade does undoubtedly add to the value in solid hard cash to us Soapmakers of our Association . . . I have heard Mr. Knight, speaking for the Southern Association, put the value of that down to London makers at 10/- a ton . . . and many a time I have heard our respected Chairman of the Northern

Association [F. S. Timmis, of Gossage's] say that it is worth many thousands a year to its members.

He went on to say that the Northern Association had 'practically put a stop to underselling' of non-advertised soaps—bars and tablets alike—although differences naturally existed between these and advertised varieties. 'Quality for quality we all sell on a level and . . . the constant intercourse between us prevents inadvertent underselling.' Thus, although bar soaps formed a smaller proportion of the trade than formerly, 'the prices have been well kept up, and in spite of the [high] price of raw materials, we have maintained an excellent margin of profits for a long time past'.

He also pointed out the convenience of fixing 'the number and weight of tablets in our leading non-advertised sorts', and also 'the abolition of contracts [booking forward] and the protection of trade marks'. But household 'specialities' presented a problem. In view of the rising costs of raw materials, he favoured advancing the retail prices of these tablet soaps, rather than reducing their weights, as had been done. But all firms would have to move together and there were clearly differences of opinion. He concluded by emphasizing that 'whatever we may have to face in the battle of the soaps there is one thing . . . we should avoid, and that is "dog in the manger competition". As long as we make a good profit ourselves, we should be willing to follow the good old Quaker maxim and let the other man live'.

The northern makers did, in fact, agree a few months later to raise 'specialities'—though Lever's refused to raise 'Sunlight'—and the Association held together during this period of rising costs. The working arrangement between the regional associations worked fairly well, but there were some difficulties. Both Lever's and Watson's, for example, insisted on independence as to terms of payment and they also issued uniform price lists for the whole country, refusing to send out separate lists for the different regions, since they were catering for a national market. Lever also claimed 'a free hand in altering the price of specialities without necessarily giving notice'. Perhaps it was in order to get him to co-operate more readily that he was elected Chairman of the Northern Association for 1903.

By May of that year the northern makers had come to the

conclusion that there should be uniformity of prices throughout the country and therefore arranged a meeting with the southern makers, 'in the hope that the prices might be regulated by one Central Association'. A special meeting of the whole Association was immediately summoned, at which H. S. Timmis referred to 'the growth of the "Speciality" trade in which one price was recognized from Land's End to John O'Groats', and therefore urged that the various associations should 'form a working committee for the whole country', to 'discuss and arrange general prices'. He also urged greater stability in prices, regardless of fluctuations in the tallow market.

These ideas were adopted by the Association's annual meeting a month later, Crosfield's giving their support. It was agreed that there should be Association meetings 'on alternate months —or more frequently if necessary—to fix prices with a view to making a uniform price for the two best Yellows [pale soaps] all over the United Kingdom'. These meetings, held alternately in London and Liverpool, enabled soap prices to be maintained in the years 1903–6. They were greatly helped by steady markets for raw materials. But, as Professor Wilson has pointed out, stability in trade made for instability in the Association. Thus Watson's withdrew for some months in 1904, and Knight's and Lever's in 1905, though they continued to work amicably with the Association. On resigning the Chairmanship of the Northern Association in May 1904, Lever expressed his opinion that while the Association 'helped the bar soap maker to maintain level prices . . . it could never help the tablet trade'. That is why he left the Association a year later, because, as a manufacturer exclusively of tablet soaps, he had 'failed to find any benefit' from membership.

Crosfield's, on the other hand, were still substantial manufacturers of bar soaps, together with Gossage's and many others, with whom they had long been accustomed to co-operate. They therefore remained loyal members of the Association and very few complaints were made against them. At the same time, while they were prepared to accept regulation of the prices of speciality 'washers', like 'Perfection', they were quite free to push the sales of such products by extensive canvassing, advertising, bonuses, gift schemes, etc., for these matters remained outside the scope of the Association, though their pressure on the bar soap trade was increasingly felt. Thus competition was in many ways keener than ever.

It was for this reason, and because of rising prices of raw materials, that Lever launched his famous scheme for a combine or amalgamation—popularized as a 'Soap Trust'—in July 1906. As Professor Wilson has observed, Lever had come to recognize the inadequacy of such a 'loose-knit combination' as the Soap Makers' Association. It is doubtful, however, whether his combine scheme was motivated merely by a desire for 'genuine economies and industrial efficiency'. He had always made it perfectly plain that he was in the soap trade mainly to make profits. These, however, were becoming harder to achieve, now that the competitive advantage of his earlier commercial innovations had dwindled and other firms were engaging in what he called 'frenzied advertising' and 'frenzied competition'. (This was rich, coming from the originator of such schemes!) Crosfield's, as we have seen, were spending very large sums on selling and were more than holding their own in the competitive struggle. At the same time, the market for soap was no longer expanding so rapidly as in the later nineteenth century, since real wages were tending to fall, so that competition was becoming keener. Undoubtedly, economies could be achieved by a combine, in both marketing and manufacture, and these, as Lever pointed out, could result in cheaper soap for consumers. But were these his basic motives? Was he not, rather, aiming to extinguish competition, build up his own empire, and increase profits?

His 'working arrangement', first mooted at a meeting with Crosfield's, Gossage's and Watson's in Liverpool on 27th July 1906, concerned with the glycerine trade, was accompanied by a threat that Lever's might start selling 'Perfection' and other soaps, which, he considered, could not be protected by trademark registrations. According to his scheme, other firms would exchange their shares for holdings in Lever's, whose capital would be expanded accordingly, so that they would inevitably lose their independence. What was proposed, in fact, was a sellout to Lever's. At another meeting, on 2nd August, Lever explained that each firm would 'conduct its own affairs as at present', but that the amalgamation would be 'controlled by a central body', formed of representatives from the constituent firms 'according to the *pro rata* interest that each bears to the whole'. In such an arrangement his own influence would undoubtedly tend to preponderate; indeed, some of those who eventually agreed to participate in the scheme wished to take mostly Preference shares or cash and would cease to play any active part in management.

On 19th August, after Watson's and Gossage's had reached agreement with Lever, Crosfield's Board decided that they would 'join the amalgamation provided the terms are satisfactory and the individuality of the company is maintained'. Lever called at the works on 21st August, when Crosfield's agreed to come into the working arrangement on the basis of the exchange of their Ordinary shares for shares in Lever Brothers, no cash payment being made. Crosfield's Ordinary shares, totalling £200,000, would be exchanged for £225,000 Ordinary, £75,000 10 per cent Preferred Ordinary, and £25,000 'B' Preference shares in Lever's, i.e. for a total of £300,000. There was no provision for sale of their Preference shares or Debentures. Crosfield's existing Directors were to continue in office for at least ten years, and two of them would also sit on Lever's Board.

In the next two or three months they began to participate in arrangements for joint marketing, including formulation of a combined price list. During October, however, the *Daily Mail* and other Northcliffe newspapers started their vicious attacks upon Lever and the 'Soap Trust' (as described by Professor Wilson), with alarming effects on the trade of the associated firms. At a meeting in Liverpool on 23rd November, therefore, Crosfield's and the others decided to abandon the combine. Lever's and Watson's suffered most. Crosfield's found that 'our own orders are keeping up in a manner which has surprised us', and C. F. Huffam considered that the effects of the press agitation were confined mainly to the middle classes, but it was obviously impossible to maintain the 'working arrangement' in the prevailing state of public opinion.

The break-up of the combine, as Professor Wilson has observed, left a legacy of bitterness and disunion, but the fault was by no means all on the side of Lever's former associates. One major source of animosity was Lever's acquisition at this time of the two firms of Hodgson & Simpson (Wakefield) and the

Vinolia Company (London), which proved to be unprofitable purchases. He maintained that they had been acquired for the purposes of the combine and that his former associates should share all the consequent losses with him. In fact, however, as J. J. Crosfield pointed out—and as Lever himself admitted in evidence in the *Daily Mail* libel case—the agreement for the purchase of Hodgson & Simpson had been made before the combine was proposed. And Crosfield's had never been consulted about nor approved the purchase of Vinolia. They agreed, however, to 'subscribe *pro rata* towards the purchase price of Vinolia and also join in any final loss or profit on the sale of Hodgson & Simpson's works', since Lever declared 'that he could not continue to work them as part of Messrs. Lever Brothers, on account of public feeling'. But the situation was entirely altered when Lever decided to keep the two companies, thus entering the bar-soap trade through Hodgson & Simpson's and the toilet trade through Vinolia. Crosfield's, threatened by this powerful competition, naturally considered that 'any question of subscribing towards the two companies is entirely at an end'.

Lever, however, long continued to feel very sore on this point, alleging that he had been left to shoulder losses. He referred to it, for example, at the Annual Meeting of Lever Brothers on 11th March 1910, whereupon Crosfield's, Watson's, Thomas's and Gossage's met to draft a press statement emphatically denying his accusations. Lever's bitterness was increased by the fact that, after he had borne the costs of the lawsuit against Northcliffe's Associated Newspapers, the other firms made easy and lucrative settlements for damages. Crosfield's, as we have seen, did quite well out of it.[1]

The collapse of the amalgamation scheme was followed by very difficult years in the soap trade. The possibility of higher prices had not, as Professor Wilson says, 'disappeared with the combine', for the Soap Makers' Association agreed in February 1907 to large increases of £3 to £4 per ton on both bar-soaps and 'washers'. But during the following twelve months Lever's (including Hodgson & Simpson's) and Watson's reduced prices independently, which obliged the northern makers to follow suit, so that the recent gains were lost. Competition made it

---

[1] See above, pp. 188–9.

impossible to raise soap prices proportionately to the higher costs of raw materials. Association meetings were held less frequently in the next two or three years, but agreed advances were made by joint meetings of the Northern and Southern Associations in November 1909 and January 1910.

Throughout these years, Crosfield's remained loyal to the Association, but continued to spend large sums on advertising, canvassing, and gift schemes. This expenditure, combined with higher prices for raw materials, caused them heavy losses in the soap trade, even though their output was rising sharply from 1909 onwards. Relations with Lever were further embittered by the 'Perfection' trade-mark case. At the same time, as a result of Lever's acquisition of Hodgson & Simpson's and Vinolia, they experienced growing competition in both the bar-soap and toilet trades. Moreover, in 1908 Lever bought Hudson's famous soap-powder business, which threatened Crosfield's in another field, and in 1910 he brought out 'Rinso' as a rival to their newly established 'Persil'.

Lever still remained convinced of the necessity for rationalization in the soap trade and in 1910 he set about trying to rebuild the combine. At the end of August he wrote to J. J. Crosfield, William Gossage, and Joseph Watson suggesting a meeting, 'in view of the present high prices for raw materials and the low prices of soaps—today showing a very serious loss'.[1] This meeting took place in London on 7th September. According to J. J. Crosfield's notes, Lever suggested that 'we might all come together again now', but that, although there would be no danger of another attack from the 'yellow press', they must carefully avoid publicity: 'Let it ooze out, not splash out.' The basis of his proposed arrangement was an exchange of shares much the same as in 1906. Ordinary shareholders would be given 'such number of 15 per cent cumulative preferred ordinary shares in Lever Brothers as would bring in a like income' to that obtained from the last few years' trading of their respective companies. J. J. Crosfield, however, gave Lever's plan a very cool reception:

I said that when the last combine ended we considered the matter

---

[1] Professor Wilson says nothing about these negotiations, merely mentioning 'an offer to both Gossage's and Crosfield's', but Lever's plans—though not publicized—were clearly as far-reaching as in 1906.

finished with once and for all. That I had no idea we should discuss it now and that all I could do was to put the matter fully before my co-shareholders, but I added that in our case there would be considerable difficulty in the way on account of business we were engaged in apart from soap.

Further negotiations failed to alter his views. He was, like Gossage and Watson, suspicious of Lever's accounting and the value of the Preferred Ordinary shares. Moreover, he shared Gossage's dislike of their firm becoming 'only a Department of Port Sunlight' and being 'gradually merged into Lever Bros.' Lever was prepared to consider cash purchase, but the three firms wanted too much. It was difficult, moreover, to separate the soap from the chemical side of Crosfield's business. Eventually, therefore, on 17th October, after further meetings, Lever was informed that Crosfield's considered it 'impossible to divide up our business. This precludes all negotiations for the sale of it'. At the same time, however, it was hoped that 'our two firms though destined to be competitors may continue on the present friendly terms'.

It appears, however, that Arthur Crosfield did not agree with his brothers, J.J. and George, in regard to Lever's proposed take-over. Unfortunately, there is very little surviving evidence, but it seems that Arthur was prepared to sell out. He was more interested in political and social activities than in business. He was the leading figure in local Liberal politics and, after standing unsuccessfully as Liberal candidate for Warrington in 1900, was elected M.P. in 1906 and held the seat till December 1910. He was very popular socially, a talented pianist, and an outstanding sportsman, playing cricket, tennis, and, above all, golf. His home, significantly, was at Hoylake, and in 1901 he was said to be 'known on most of the golf links throughout the United Kingdom and the Continent, where he has obtained valuable prizes, while quite recently he won golden opinions on the other side of the Atlantic'. He frequently holidayed on the Continent, won the French amateur golf championship in 1905, and became captain of the Cannes golf club. In Paris in December 1907 he married Miss Domini Elliadi, daughter of a wealthy naturalized Greek merchant, of Southport and Smyrna; she, too, was very accomplished at music, tennis, and golf, and also a great socialite. They travelled to many parts of the world and entertained largely, both at home and abroad; the Grand Duke Michael and his retinue were invited to Hoylake.

These social and political activities precluded any sustained interest in soap and chemicals. After being elected to Parliament in 1906, he ceased to take any active part in the business. Indeed, according to a letter that he wrote to Lever many years later, on 5th May 1921, there had long been a rift between himself and his brother J.J.

Once my father's health began seriously, and worse of all for me, suddenly—before I had time to take . . . precautionary measures— to fail, J.J.C. and Markel, having together the preponderance of shares, used their position to carry things with a high hand, whether in personal questions or in matters of policy, without the slightest regard for myself or for any protests I could make, and *did* make, against the way in which they played fast and loose with, and even deliberately destroyed, far the most valuable parts of our soap trade.

Arthur Crosfield had been strongly opposed, for example, to the reduction of the quality and weight of 'Rainbow' tablets in 1898, but his views on this and other matters were outweighed by those of J.J. and Markel. The above letter and others indicate that for years there was much ill-feeling between him and the other Directors. J.J., on the other hand, may have resented his elder brother—so taken up with social and political affairs— being head of the business. Undoubtedly, J.J. did gradually acquire control. He eventually secured more shares than Arthur, who was finally deprived of the Chairmanship in January 1909 and then, in March 1911, of his Directorship.

This last event clearly caused a family and business crisis, as evidenced by the Board minutes, but these divulge nothing of its causes and there is no surviving correspondence to throw light upon it. It seems probable, however, that Arthur Crosfield had quarrelled with his brothers over Lever's recent take-over proposal and had been intriguing with Lever behind their backs. Unlike them, he had always been on friendly terms with Lever, for whose business ability and character he had often expressed admiration. He had now little interest in the firm, save as a source of income, and was attracted by the prospect of its profitable sale. From a letter which he wrote to Lever ten years later, recalling these events, it is clear that he had been negotiating with Lever with this object. His brothers, J.J. and George, however, and other Crosfield directors had developed a strong feeling against Lever and regarded Arthur's conduct as treachery.

They had every reason for alarm in 1910–11, when Lever, balked again in his scheme for a combine, began a policy of piecemeal conquest, absorbing one old-established soap firm after another (as Professor Wilson has described). Before considering the next moves in this commercial battle, however, let us trace Crosfield's participation in other associations concerned with the marketing of chemical products, since soap and chemicals were closely related not merely in their manufacturing and trading operations, but also in the increasingly complex manœuvres against Lever in which Crosfield's were soon to be involved.

Attempts at controlling the glycerine market in the late 1880s had broken down, but on 29th July 1898 representatives of Lever's, Crosfield's, and Thom's met in Liverpool and decided 'that inasmuch as competition between manufacturers of Chemically Pure Glycerine had reduced the market price for this article to a figure which was anything but remunerative [prices of raw materials were rising sharply], it was highly desirable that some arrangements should be arrived at amongst the makers to, if possible, prevent any unnecessary cutting of prices'. They agreed to form a 'Glycerine Association', which other makers should be invited to join. Draft rules were drawn up, whereby members would 'bind themselves to agree to the prices fixed by the Association', with a penalty for underselling of £100 payable to charity. A provisional price-list was drawn up, but this was modified slightly at a further meeting of the three firms in Liverpool on 10th August. Prices were to be on a sliding scale, varying from £51 per ton (naked) for ¼-ton lots to £48 10s. per ton for ten tons and upwards. Extras were also fixed for packing in drums, carboys, tins, and cases, but carriage was free. Discount 'terms' were to be 2½ per cent for payment in fourteen days. One per cent was allowed for brokerage. It was decided not to have a penalty clause, but to rely on members' pledges. Meetings of the Association were to be held monthly.

The difficulties facing this Association were revealed at the next meeting, on 14th September, when it was stated that there was 'sufficient plant in the United Kingdom to refine very much more glycerine than there was any demand for', while fears of German competition were also voiced. At another meeting, therefore, a week later, prices were reduced by £1. On 23rd November it was agreed 'that export prices are controlled equally with home ones', and on 7th December that the Association's scope should be extended to include commercial (or industrial) glycerine, prices of which were fixed at £2 per ton below those for chemically pure. The question of German competition was also discussed and 'indignation . . . was expressed at the fact that at present the English market is used as a dumping ground for German manufacturers, who, while obtaining good prices in their own country [behind tariff barriers], wreck the [open] market here with their surplus production'.

The Association's membership was gradually extended from the North to include Price's and Gibb's, of London, and Thomas's, of Bristol, but it proved ineffective. Complaints of underselling were heard, and contracts for forward sales also proved a problem. On 2nd May 1899 there was a lengthy discussion of outside competition. Non-members 'were taking advantage of the existence of a minimum price to undersell members of the Association'. It was therefore decided 'that for the time being a fixed minimum price should be abandoned and members . . . should take what steps they thought fit to meet competition'. The Association thereupon collapsed.

It was revived, however, at meetings in Manchester on 25th January and 6th March 1901, which were attended by several of Crosfield's directors and C. Haslam, their chemical sales manager, and by representatives of most of the main glycerine distilling firms in the country. These agreed to form an Association 'to regulate the price and conditions of sale of C.P. Glycerine', and to invite the co-operation of English makers not present and also of foreign makers. A basic price was fixed of 60s. per cwt. (naked) in 10-cwt. lots, with extras on small orders and reductions on larger ones. Agreement was also reached, as in the previous Association, on packaging and delivery charges, contracts, terms of payment, etc. These regulations applied to the home trade only.

J. J. Crosfield and C. Haslam were appointed joint honorary secretaries of the new Association. They were authorized 'to

commence negotiations forthwith with the continental manufacturers and to send over Mr. [Adolphe] Secretan of J. Crosfield & Sons Ltd. with this object'. As a result agreements were
reached in April with the French and with the German and
Dutch makers, whereby it was mutually agreed not to sell below
the prices fixed for C.P. Glycerine by the associated distillers in
each of their respective countries. Price lists were exchanged
and any alterations were to be sent by wire, Crosfield's acting
on behalf of the English Association.

This international co-operation worked happily during the
next twelve months, and at the Association's first annual meeting, on 19th March 1902, the Chairman (F. S. Timmis) declared
that he had never known an Association work so well. 'The
Trade was in few hands and ought to be profitable, and if
makers were not greedy but kept to their own customers, the
Association would hold together and be mutually advantageous.' A number of foreign makers attended this meeting and
joined in the discussion, which resulted in an agreed advance of
£4 per ton.

The trade remained stable throughout the following year and
no change in prices was made at the next annual meeting in
March 1903. It was agreed that no manufacturer should appoint
more than one selling agent for England and Wales, one for
Scotland, and one for Ireland. At the third annual meeting
in March 1904, Timmis, the Chairman, again referred to the
satisfactory working of the Association and also to the 'very
firm' prices for glycerine, 'owing to the large consumption of
dynamite, etc.' Again no change was made.

Throughout these years, however, it proved impossible to get
unanimity on export prices. Efforts in 1904 to reach agreement
with foreign firms, including visits to the Continent by Secretan,
Crosfield's representative, proved futile, 'owing to the diver-
gence of interests, and the number of foreign glycerine manufacturers who are not Members of the Convention'. Doubts
began to be felt about the wisdom of keeping home prices too
high in the face of cheaper foreign imports, and in October 1904
a reduction of £6 per ton was made. This produced protests
from the Vereinigte Chemische Werke, Charlottenburg, who
also complained of underselling in Germany, but the Association pointed out that they had been undercut in the home

market by Continental makers 'outside the Convention'. The German firm then gave notice of withdrawal from the agreement. At the same time, Watson's, of Leeds, resigned, followed by Lever's, and the Association broke up in February 1905.

The collapse came on a falling market for raw materials, when soap output was rising sharply and there was consequently an abundance of glycerine. Crosfield's output of glycerine rose considerably in the next two years, but at lower prices. During 1906, however, prices of raw materials leapt up again and soap output declined, so the Glycerine Association was re-formed in March 1907, with William Gossage as Chairman and C. Haslam as Secretary.[1] A basic price of 50s. 6d. per cwt. on 5-ton lots, packed in 10-cwt. drums, was agreed on, and agreement was also reached on terms of payment, contracts, etc. An advance of £2 per ton was made in May. In September it was reported that 'Mr. Secretan had attended a meeting of the Continental glycerine makers on July 30th', as a result of which an agreement between them and the English makers was now approved: 'Continental makers to sell in U.K. at English Convention prices and terms. English makers to sell in Germany, Holland, Belgium, Switzerland, Denmark, Luxemburg, Sweden, Norway and Finland at Continental Convention prices and on same terms.' Prices were now advanced by a further £2 per ton.

The surviving minute book ends at this point, and no other records appear to have survived, so that we do not know how long the revived Association lasted. But we have seen enough to appreciate that combination in this section of the glycerine trade was fraught with difficulties even greater than those in the soap trade, owing to international competition. Crosfield's, however, had done as much as, if not more than, any other firm to get co-operation.

Glycerine manufacture was a profitable sideline of almost all large soapworks. Crosfield's, however, were outstanding among soapmakers in their range of other chemical products, of which silicate of soda and caustic soda were the most important. Trade in these also came to be regulated by national and international

---

[1] Before the Association was formally re-established, there had been informal meetings, such as that of 27th July 1906 between Lever's, Crosfield's, Watson's, and Gossage's, at which Lever introduced his scheme for a soap combine.

agreements. In England, silicate manufacture was mainly in the hands of Crosfield's and Gossage's, between whom some sort of *modus vivendi* appears to have been established. Moreover, at the end of the century the two firms collaborated in negotiations with continental (mainly German) manufacturers of silicate for agreed division of markets and regulation of prices. Dr. Markel and Adolphe Secretan played leading roles in these negotiations, which resulted in the establishment of an international Silicate Convention or Association in May 1900.

Annual meetings of this Association were held in the following years, but outside competition from continental makers could not be overcome and the Association collapsed by the end of 1903. It was revived again, however, in 1907, when several outsiders were bought off and prices were again regulated. In the British home trade, alkaline 'glass' varied from £5 to £5 7s. 6d. per ton; prices for neutral 'glass' were 10s. lower. Solution in casks varied from £3 5s. to £4 15s. per ton, according to concentration; prices for solution in iron drums were fixed at lower levels. All these prices were free-on-rail Warrington, for ten-ton lots and upwards; extras were fixed for smaller lots. Export prices, f.o.b. Liverpool or Birkenhead, were generally 2s. 6d. per ton higher than in the home trade, but in certain markets, mainly in the Americas, they were much lower. There was also general agreement on rates of discount, brokerage, and agents' commission; not more than one agent was to be appointed in each country.

During the next three years the Silicate Association worked well, with Secretan as its secretary. Prices were kept up and at the regular annual conferences the makers congratulated themselves on the prevailing harmony. There was also an arrangement with the United Alkali Company, though this firm did not join. By 1911, however, outside competition in Europe was again causing serious concern.

There are only scrappy statistics of silicate exports during this period, but these show that Crosfield's honourably abided by their agreements with the continental makers. In some countries, such as Italy and Spain, where dissolvers had been erected, exports were mostly or even entirely 'glass', but to others, such as Greece, Roumania, Egypt, Argentina, and Uruguay, they were mainly or even entirely solution.

During this same period Crosfield's also participated in negotiations with various other English chemical manufacturers to regulate prices and output of caustic soda. The first reference to these is in the Board minutes for 24th September 1900, when J. J. Crosfield reported briefly on 'the efforts which had been made with the United Alkali Co. and other makers to arrange prices [of liquid caustic soda] for next year'. These resulted in an agreement, dated 1st October 1900, regulating prices and conditions of sale for 1901.[1] It was made between the United Alkali Co. Ltd., Castner-Kellner Alkali Co. Ltd., J. Riley & Sons Ltd., Schofields Ltd., and J. Crosfield & Sons Ltd. The prices for liquid caustic soda of 90°Tw., supplied in sellers' drums, were to range from £4 15s. to £5 per ton according to quantity bought; 80°Tw. to cost 10s. per ton and 70°Tw. 20s. per ton less than 90°Tw. Reductions were made for caustic supplied in tank wagons or in buyers' drums. Carriage rates were also fixed. Terms were net cash, payment within fourteen days (as in all later agreements). There was to be no poaching of each other's customers, but by a modification in April 1901 it was agreed that the business of combines, such as the Calico Printers' Association, should be free to all makers, at the agreed prices. Agents and travellers were 'not to undersell by allowances of any kind whatever or by giving part of commission'.

Brunner, Mond & Co. were not included in this agreement, but in June and July 1901 another was negotiated for 1902, between the United Alkali Co., Brunner, Mond & Co., the Castner-Kellner Co., and Crosfield's, covering both solid and liquid caustic soda. For solid caustic, prices for England ranged from £8 12s. 6d. to £11 15s. per ton, according to concentration and size of drums; higher prices were fixed for London and Scotland, on account of carriage. Brokerage was fixed at 2 per cent (another feature common to later agreements). For liquid caustic at 90°Tw. the contract price was £4 8s. per ton in the home market, with the same reductions as previously for lower concentrations and also for caustic supplied in tank wagons. Export prices (f.o.b. Liverpool or Tyneside) for both solid and liquid were 2s. 6d. higher. Specially agreed prices would be fixed for the large combines (Bradford Dyers' Association,

[1] All home prices in this and later agreements were 'free-on-rails Widnes', carriage to the customer being charged extra.

British Cotton & Wool Association, and Calico Printers' Association), and deliveries would be equally shared between the United Alkali Co., the Castner-Kellner Co., and Crosfield's. If necessary, prices might be reduced to prevent existing customers producing their own caustic soda. Undercutting by agents, brokers, and travellers, however, was banned as previously.

The associated companies were evidently parties to an international agreement, carving up and allocating world markets for caustic soda in the same way as for silicate. The above agreement on prices did not apply to the U.S.A., Canada, China, and Japan, and shipments to Europe and to Mediterranean ports, the Black Sea, and Levant were banned. All these countries were the preserves of the Solvay group. Later evidence, from the legal battle between Lever's and Brunner, Mond & Co. in 1917, shows that the latter had for many years had agreements with the Solvay group—'a large international group of manufacturers of alkali on the Continent of Europe and the northern Continent of America'—whereby they 'do not trade in the countries in which the Solvay group carry on their operations and vice-versa'.

Crosfield's agreed in April 1902 to limit their sales of liquid and solid caustic to 9,000 tons for that year. It was also agreed that if they were unable to sell this quantity, they might be allowed to reduce their prices slightly. The agreement was subsequently renewed for 1903, 1904, and 1905, with the same prices and output limitation. In September 1905, when it was renewed for 1906, clauses were included providing for investigation of alleged underselling, for which a penalty was imposed of 5s. per ton of the quantity sold in contravention of the agreement. In October 1906 it was again renewed for the following year. Earlier, in August, Crosfield's made a similar agreement with the United Alkali Co. regarding the sale of powdered caustic soda. This consisted of many pages, with long lists of prices, since the powdered product was sold not only in several different grades but also in different containers (barrels, drums, cases, and canisters), of many different weights, ranging from $\frac{1}{2}$ lb. to 5 cwt. Moreover, prices varied according to quantity bought. A few examples only can be given. In the home trade, bulk prices of 98 per cent powdered caustic ranged from £12 to £15 per ton, according to sizes of containers (drums and barrels) and orders; prices for 98 per cent powder in canisters similarly varied from $2\frac{1}{8}d$. to $3\frac{3}{8}d$. per lb. Bulk prices for 70 per cent powder were fixed at 15s. per ton less, and for 60 per cent at £1 15s. per ton less, than for 98 per cent, and prices for canisters were similarly lower. Different prices were fixed for London and also for export. No rebates were to be allowed to buyers.

This agreement was fixed for 1907, but was to be continued to the end of 1908 and then year by year, so long as the solid caustic soda agreement remained in force. The total quantity of caustic of all kinds—solid, liquid or powdered—which Crosfield's might deliver in 1907 was limited to 11,375 tons.

A number of meetings were subsequently held with representatives of the United Alkali Co. to discuss operation of the powdered agreement. Crosfield's had a large trade with bleaching, dyeing, and calico-printing firms in Lancashire, but a good deal was supplied at an agreed discount to other chemical firms, such as the East Lancashire Chemical Co., who resold it, with consequent problems of price maintenance. Another problem was to get agreed c.i.f. prices for foreign markets; this required agreement on insurance and freight charges to ports in many parts of the world.

In October 1907 new agreements were drawn up, increasing the bulk prices for 1908 by 10s. per ton for solid and powdered caustic, and by 5s. per ton for liquid. The ceiling on Crosfield's output remained unaltered. It was agreed in March 1908 that if Crosfield's exceeded this quota they would have to buy an amount equal to the excess from the United Alkali Co., while if they fell below it the latter would purchase from them an amount equal to the deficit. Thus, while they would be penalized for exceeding the quota, they would have a guaranteed market for that amount.

The agreements were revised slightly in November 1908 for 1909, mainly in relation to the export trade in powdered caustic, which was expanding considerably, especially to South Africa, India, Australia, and New Zealand, and was controlled by pages of detailed regulations. There was very little alteration in 1910, but in 1911 prices were put back to the level of 1907 and earlier years.

These agreements and the correspondence relating thereto provide evidence of a very effective combination in the caustic-soda trade. Price stability was maintained not merely by price-lists but also by restricting output. The correspondence reveals few differences between the associated firms, who appear to have co-operated very effectively. There is, however, a considerable difference between Crosfield's fixed quotas and their actual deliveries,[1] which calls for explanation; it is probably to be explained by differences in the basis of calculation, Crosfield's figures being actual tons, while the quotas were calculated as 70 per cent Na_2O.

With the great chemical firm of Brunner, Mond & Co., their most powerful associate in these caustic soda agreements, Crosfield's had long been on very friendly terms. John Crosfield remained a director of Brunner's till his death in 1901, and Crosfield's were for many years their best customer for alkali (soda ash). Eventually Brunner Mond's also came to supply Gossage's, Lever's, and many other soapmakers with alkali. In fact, according to the plaintiff's brief in the case of Associated Enterprises (Lever's) v. Brunner, Mond & Co. in 1917 they had

supplied . . . the greater part of the alkali used in the manufacture of soap in this country for a considerable number of years, and undoubtedly this supply of alkali to the soap trade has been a very substantial and profitable part of the defendants' business, but . . . the defendants were not otherwise associated with Lever's or Crosfield's or Gossage's than as suppliers to them of their alkali, and the defendants were not at this time in anywise interested directly in the soap trade, their business being confined to that of chemical manufacturers.

Brunner, Mond & Co. were not in a monopolistic position, for there were other alkali manufacturers, such as the United Alkali Co. (working the declining Leblanc process), the Castner-Kellner Co., and the Ammonia Soda Co., but by agreements with these firms, and also with the international Solvay group, prices for alkali were kept up in the same way as for caustic soda. Soapmakers, much less firmly combined, were in a weak bargaining position. Crosfield's, however, because of their intimate personal and business relations with Brunner Mond's, had been able to secure preferential terms. According to the above-mentioned brief of 1917, John Crosfield 'had secured for Crosfield's an agreement with the defendants [Brunner, Mond

1 See above, p. 204.

& Co.] that Crosfield's should always be charged [at least] 2/6*d*. per ton less than the price charged by the defendants to any other soapmaker'. This statement is supported by evidence from alkali contracts. On 10th November 1905, for example, Brunner Mond's contracted to supply Crosfield's with soda ash at £2 17*s*. 6*d*. to £3 per ton until 30th November 1915, and at £2 15*s*. to £2 7*s*. 6*d*. for the following ten years. But in a ten-year contract with Gossage's, made on 20th March 1907, the price was £3 3*s*. to £3 5*s*. 5*d*. per ton.

Although soda ash formed only a small fraction of total soap-making costs, these preferential terms gave Crosfield's an appreciable competitive advantage over other firms. Lever certainly found this situation galling, but he had to acquiesce in it when making a new contract with Brunner, Mond & Co. in 1907. At the same time he had to bind himself for nearly ten years not to manufacture caustic soda or carbonate of soda for general sale, though Crosfield's were operating a very profitable trade in caustic, and though Brunner Mond's gave no reciprocal undertaking not to enter the soap trade. In the following years, however, with rising prices of raw materials and fierce competition in the soap trade, Lever feared that Crosfield's preferential terms for soda ash and their flourishing chemical manufactures might enable them, as the 1917 brief explained, 'to act regardless of making a profit on soap'. This, as we have seen, is what Crosfield's were in fact doing from 1907 onwards.

Lever was not the sort of man to sit still in such a situation. In April 1911 he bought a large estate at Lymm in Cheshire, under which were salt deposits suitable for manufacture of alkali. His intention seemed obvious. Brunner Mond's at once took retaliatory action. As Sir John Brunner later pointed out to Lever, at a meeting on 30th November 1911, Brunner Mond's had previously never

even thought of entering the soap trade. He stated that what had induced them to do so was the purchase by Lever's of salt lands at Lymm, that Lever's had purchased a number of soap businesses, and that, excepting Crosfield's and Gossage's, there were not many left in the United Kingdom, and . . . as the supply of alkali to the soap trade was a large part of their business, and they viewed the possible loss of that market as a very serious business they had to act in self-defence.

Brunner Mond's therefore began negotiations for the purchase of both Crosfield's and Gossage's. Unfortunately, it has
proved impossible to find any contemporary documents relating
to these negotiations, but there is some interesting later evidence. George R. Crosfield has left the following brief account:

Roscoe Brunner, Chairman of Brunner, Mond & Co.,[1] alarmed
at Lever Bros. action in buying up brineland in Cheshire with the
indication that they were going to make their own carbonate of soda,
came to Warrington and said they must have a counter attack and
go into the soap trade. He proposed to exchange our ordinary shares
for Brunner, Mond shares, the Managing Directors of Crosfield's
to carry on, but as employees of Brunner, Mond & Co. My brother
[J.J.] and myself realized that it meant giving up our independence,
but the proposals were so advantageous from a financial point of
view, that we did not think, in justice to shareholders, we were right
to refuse, and the deal went through very speedily . . . In discussing
the deal . . . my brother had stipulated that the shares should not
be sold behind our back to Lever Bros. because of commitments
we had on the Continent with Messrs. Schicht who were in competition with Lever's.[2]

More important than the alliance with Schicht's, however,
was their strong antipathy to Lever and their desire to defeat
this prodigious rival, who, but a quarter-century earlier, had
started as a pygmy beside their Bank Quay works. They could
not achieve this alone, but Brunner Mond's massive support
might enable them to do so.

Later correspondence in 1920–1 between Sir William Lever
and Sir Arthur Crosfield (as he had become in 1915) reveals
that the latter had again opposed his brothers in these negotiations. In a letter of 26th May 1921 he wrote:

I would like to explain, as accurately as I can, exactly what
happened at the time B.M. & Co. bought their business. As I
happened to be in Warrington, staying at the Patten Arms Hotel,
I received an urgent message over the 'phone from Mr. J. J. Crosfield, asking if I would go to the works, as he wanted to see me on a

[1] Actually Sir John Brunner was Chairman at this time; his son Roscoe
did not become Chairman till 1918.
[2] Crosfield's had sold the Normann hydrogenation rights in Austria-
Hungary to Schicht's, who, in part return, provided them with technical
information on oil-refining, etc. (see above, p. 171); they also supplied
Crosfield's with soap-cooling machines. If Lever's acquired Crosfield's, they
would obtain this confidential information.

matter of first-rate importance. I declined to go the works but arranged to meet him at the Patten. He came there with Haslam and told me that, after some prolonged negotiations, B.M. & Co. had offered to buy our business and to give the ordinary shareholders nine £1 shares in B.M. & Co. for every ten £1 shares held in J.C. & Sons. I immediately asked my brother whether Lever Brothers might not be willing to pay us a higher price. He replied that Lever Brothers had not been consulted, and when I expressed my natural surprise that a transaction of such magnitude should be settled before both possible purchasers had been consulted, his answer simply was: 'Brunner's would not have stood it.' He went on to intimate that the whole thing had been negotiated confidentially with B.M. & Co.; that it would have been out of the question to . . . attempt to get any competitive quotation against them; that things had now been brought finally to a point, and he had come to see whether I agreed to the terms, as if I *did* agree, it would save them the necessity of making any alteration in our Articles of Association.

There was, of course, no mistaking the plain hint in the last remark . . . And so there was nothing for it but acquiescence.

In fact, however, not only was Arthur deprived of his directorship in March 1911, but the Company's Articles of Association were altered in June and July, whereby the transference of Ordinary shares to outsiders was prevented, without consent of the other Ordinary shareholders. J.J. and George were determined to prevent any sell-out to Lever's.

Sir William Lever also recalled, in a letter to Sir Arthur of 17th May 1921, that 'at that particular moment you [Crosfield's] had two prospective buyers, Lever Brothers and Brunner Mond, and it scarcely seemed to me business for Messrs. Crosfield to close with one buyer without ascertaining what price the other prospective buyer would be willing to pay. However, Messrs. Crosfield did not take that course; not only so, but I heard later that they made it a condition that Messrs. Gossage did not.' A short time previously, Lever stated, he had been approached by Gossage's regarding purchase of their business, and negotiations were going on when 'we were informed that Messrs. Brunner, Mond had purchased not only Messrs. Gossage's shares but [also] Messrs. Crosfield's'. The only excuse given by Gossage's was 'that they preferred Brunner, Mond's shares to Lever Brothers' '. Lever considered that the shareholders in both companies lost thereby.

Another factor which strongly influenced Brunner Mond's in their decision to purchase these two soapmaking firms was that Crosfield's held what they considered to be a master patent (Normann's) for hydrogenation. As Lever recalled in his letter of 17th May 1921, 'Brunner Mond [later] told me that they would never have entered the soap business at all only they were attracted by the patents for hydrogenation and believed that Messrs. Crosfield's had the exclusive right of hydrogenation for the United Kingdom'. In the words of the above-mentioned brief of 1917, Brunner Mond's

sought by the Normann Patent to secure a monopoly in the United Kingdom in the hydrogenizing of oils and fats . . . and thereby an ascendancy over Lever's and all other soap firms in the matter of the supply of oils and fats for soapmaking, which, coupled with the fact that the defendants B.M. & Co. themselves produced the other essential ingredient in the manufacture of soap, viz. alkali, would, they hoped, have placed them in a very strong and indeed unique position in the soap trade in the United Kingdom.

Hence Sir John Brunner declared in his Chairman's report to the Annual General Meeting of Brunner, Mond & Co. in May 1912, 'these two concerns [Crosfield's and Gossage's] will make soap cheaper than anybody else in the world before very long'.

The agreement for transference of shares was signed on 22nd November 1911. Crosfield's Ordinary shares, nominal value £300,000 (£250,000 paid up), were exchanged for Ordinary shares of Brunner, Mond & Co., nominal value £225,000 (fully paid up). Crosfield's shares had never been quoted on the market, but Brunner Mond's £1 Ordinary shares then stood at £4 17s. 6d., so that Crosfield's shareholders received the equivalent of £1,096,875. Only the Ordinary shares were sold, not the Preference shares or Debentures, whereas the whole of Gossage's capital was acquired by Brunner Mond's.[1]

Thus as an independent family business—for this is what it had remained even after conversion to a limited company—Crosfield's now ceased to exist. Why did the third generation of

[1] The price paid for Crosfield's and Gossage's together (£715,000 nominal value, £2,237,625 market value) was not, as Professor Wilson says, 'equivalent to Brunner's whole issued capital' (£2,789,650 nominal value), but was about a quarter of it. He has confused the nominal and market values.

Crosfields agree to this amalgamation? Many of the reasons we have already noticed: the pressure of competition and the losses in the soap trade, the need for more and more capital to finance developments such as hydrogenation, etc., and the general movement towards associations and combines. Lever's were swallowing up other soap firms, and amalgamation with their old friends Brunner, Mond & Co. was preferable to becoming subservient to Port Sunlight. The terms offered were financially attractive, and perhaps J.J. and George Crosfield were not too sorry to relinquish the family business. According to A. W. Tangye's private diary, J.J. was 'not greatly interested in Soap', but was 'an excellent amateur mechanic [on] lathe work, etc., [and a] great fisherman'. George, too, was a fine sportsman, fond of hunting and very active in the local Volunteers and National Service League. On the other hand, the firm's records suggest that J.J. was very diligent, keeping a specially close eye on the financial side of the business, while his brother George is recalled by Mr. Cliff Billington and Mr. Rex Furness as having been similarly active as technical director. During the previous fifteen years they—under Markel's inspiration, of course—had been responsible for achieving a vast expansion of the business, due mainly to vigorous technical research and innovation. Theirs was the very reverse of a stagnant family firm. Moreover, they did not now withdraw from the business, but remained on the Board in active management. They were not, however, to stay there very long.

CHAPTER XVI

THE LAST OF THE CROSFIELDS

THE most immediately evident consequence of the take-over by Brunner, Mond & Co. was an intimate association between Crosfield's and Gossage's—so close, indeed, that the two firms were soon referred to jointly as 'Crossage's'.[1] In this association Crosfield's were predominant. Five of their directors and managers—J. J. Crosfield, G. R. Crosfield, C. Haslam, R. F. Jones, and G. H. K. Kingdon—were immediately appointed to Gossage's Board, but no representatives of Gossage's joined Crosfield's Board. W. W. Gossage remained Chairman of Gossage's, but only as a figurehead, control being mainly in the hands of the directors from Crosfield's. Before long, in fact, the two Boards became virtually identical. In all matters the two firms collaborated very closely, agreeing on markets and prices, helping each other both with raw materials and finished products, exchanging technical information, and negotiating jointly with Lever's and other firms. In April 1913 we hear of 'arrangements for selling in the Home Trade so as to avoid competition as far as possible between Crosfields and Gossages'. A joint 'home soap sales department' was set up in Warrington. About the same time, Crosfield's export soap department was moved to Widnes, where the overseas trade of the two firms was jointly organized.

Brunner Mond's, of course, holding all the Ordinary shares of both firms, had ultimate control, but, in view of their inexperience of the soap trade and their long friendship with the Crosfields, they allowed them at first a great deal of independence. They did not even appoint a representative on Crosfield's Board, which remained unaltered, with J.J. and George Crosfield as Chairman and Deputy Chairman respectively. As time went on, however, Brunner Mond's acquired a tighter

[1] We shall not, however, trace the history of Gossage's, except in so far as it is linked with that of Crosfield's. The financial and trading accounts were still kept separate.

grip and the subordinate position of Crosfield's directors became more obvious, especially in top-level negotiations with Lever. Brunner's, it seems, had acquired Crosfield's and Gossage's not because they wished to enter the soap trade permanently, but to use them as a bargaining counter against Lever's threatened entry into alkali manufacture. Lever, on the other hand, regarded their take-over of Crossage's as a breach of an implied condition in the alkali contract of 1st October 1907 between Lever's and Brunner Mond's, that the latter would not enter the soap trade. He therefore considered himself released from his undertaking not to enter the alkali trade. In fact, however, neither Brunner Mond's nor Lever's really wished to poach on the other's territory: each firm was merely trying to safeguard and strengthen its position in its own sphere.

Immediately after the acquisition of Crossage's, Brunner, Mond & Co. opened negotiations with Lever's in an effort to reach an amicable understanding, and at the end of February 1912 it was agreed to hold conferences with a view to arriving at a 'working arrangement' for the home and export trades in soap. These quickly broke down, however, owing to competitive rivalry. As Sir Alfred Mond wrote to Roscoe Brunner on 27th March, 'the heads of the soap departments of Crosfields, Gossages and Levers have been fighting for years and will continue to fight and to make difficulties unless we decide not to permit them'.

Further meetings between Brunner Mond's and Lever's followed. It was proposed that if Lever's would enter into a new contract for soda ash and abandon any competition in the alkali trade, Brunner Mond's would sell to Lever's their shares in Crosfield's and Gossage's and agree never to compete in soap, oils, and fats. Crosfield's and Gossage's, however, were strongly opposed to such a deal, and Sir John Brunner therefore had to inform Sir William Lever on 20th May:

The transfer to Lever Brothers of our soap interests is now out of the question in view of the fact . . . that the directors of the two Soap Companies are against the proposal, and that we feel ourselves bound in honour not to throw them over.

The strength of Crosfield's opposition to Lever's is illustrated

246

by a letter from **Dr. Markel** to **F. W. Brock**, a director of Brunner Mond's, on 13th May 1912. He considered that 'we must do everything imaginable to force him [Lever] into seeing the necessity of making terms with us. . . . We must therefore concentrate our efforts on his weakest points and attack him with blow upon blow.' He suggested several lines of attack. They should try to 'prevent his getting cash', by undermining his forthcoming capital issue. They should attack him commercially, 'by advertising campaigns or by [reducing] prices'. Litigation would be another weapon: 'going for him on the ground of infringement of our [hydrogenation] patent rights'. 'Personal influences should be used where possible to get on his nerves. A. H. C[rosfield] might serve as the unconscious channel for such communications.' Finally, 'bear operations on his shares might be useful if on a sufficient scale to be noticeable, though I suggest this with diffidence.'

Some years later, in a letter of 13th August 1920, Sir Arthur Crosfield reminded Lord Leverhulme that in 1912 Crosfield's directors tried to persuade Brunner Mond's 'that if they would only smash the price of glycerine, they would be masters of the situation, as Lever Bros. would not be able to face the loss of profit on glycerine, added to the cutting of soap prices'. This statement is borne out by contemporary correspondence, which reveals a threat by Crosfield's and Gossage's to withdraw from the Glycerine Association and to reduce prices; but Brunner Mond's decided against such a course. Sir Arthur Crosfield considered that he had done much to counteract 'the one-sided sort of nonsense talked at Bank Quay' and to prevent open warfare between Brunner Mond's and Lever's, occupying as he did 'a unique position at the time, as the one man who happened to be on a friendly and confidential sort of footing with the Principals of both these great firms'. But Markel's above-quoted letter indicates that Sir Arthur was being used as a mere cat's-paw, and Lord Leverhulme pointed out to him, in a letter of 17th May 1921, that his interventions had only 'increased the prejudice against Lever Brothers and myself'.

In August 1912 another effort was made to reach agreement between Brunner Mond's and Lever's, but was again wrecked on the rock of Crosfield's opposition. J. J. Crosfield's final answer to Lever was contained in a letter of 24th September

1912: 'I see no great difficulty in a friendly working arrangement being come to and I should personally welcome it, but beyond this we are not prepared to go.'

Brunner Mond's could, of course, have sold the two soap firms over the heads of the Crosfields, but Sir John Brunner would not thus betray the sons of John Crosfield, his old friend and first chairman of Brunner Mond's. This honourable obligation was undoubtedly the main factor preventing Brunner Mond's from selling out to Lever's, but that they had other motives is indicated by a letter of F. W. Brock to Sir John Brunner on 22nd August, in which, while stressing their 'repeated promises' to the Crosfields, he also pointed out that retention of Crosfield's and Gossage's was perhaps 'the greatest security we can have against any [future] incursion by him [Lever] into the alkali trade'. And lacking knowledge of the soap trade, they depended upon the Crosfields for successful management of the business. Moreover, other personal factors were also important. As Sir Arthur Crosfield recalled, in writing to Lord Leverhulme on 26th May 1921, there was in Sir John Brunner's character 'a strain of vanity and pomposity which did not by any means make him the best man to arrange a settlement'. A. W. Tangye, in his diary, put the matter even more strongly. Differences between Brunner Mond's and Lever's were, he wrote,

much due to the bad feeling (& jealousy) of Sir J. T. Brunner who *hated* Lever (he had known Lever in the old days . . . when Lever was a very poor but pushing young man,[1] & the tales of that time should have been forgotten) & always spoke badly of him.

Thus there was as yet no possibility of Lever acquiring Crossage's. Lever accepted J. J. Crosfield's suggestion, however, for 'a friendly working arrangement' and met him, together with Haslam, at Chester on 1st October 1912, 'with a view to arriving at a mutual understanding as to prices, &c.' The question of bringing in other soapmaking firms was also discussed, and another conference, including Watson's and Knight's, was held in London on 10th October. In a letter of the 3rd, Sir John Brunner had suggested that Brunner Mond's

---

[1] Lever had never been 'very poor', but he had developed his great business from a small beginning.

and Lever's should jointly buy control of these two firms, but Lever, not surprisingly, rejected this proposal. (He was soon to acquire them for himself.) Brunner Mond's main object was to get a prolongation of Lever's alkali contract, and in addition to a working arrangement in the soap trade they offered a licence to use the Normann hydrogenation patent and a deal on Gold Coast palm-oil interests. But in a letter of 15th October Lever refused to enter into a new alkali contract and so the whole negotiations ended.

By this time a crisis was developing in regard to hydrogenation, as a result of which Crosfield's became engaged in a much bigger battle, involving the largest firms in the fats and soap trades not only of the United Kingdom, but also of Europe and the United States. Crosfield's, with their claim to a 'master patent'—that of Normann—were at the centre of this struggle. Their position, as we have seen, was challenged on all sides, by the rival patents of Erdmann, Bedford and Williams (Hydroil Ltd.), Wilbuschewitsch (the Bremen Besigheimer Oelfabriken, or B.B.O.), Testrup (Techno-Chemical Laboratories Ltd.), and others. They had, however, some powerful allies: Schichts (Austria-Hungary), Jurgens (Holland), and Procter & Gamble (U.S.A.), to whom they had sold licences under the Normann patent and also information regarding their secret processes, and who, therefore, would aid Crosfield's in maintaining their rights. In August 1911, for example, we hear of 'arrangements for watching and fighting competitive or piratical Patents between this Company and Jurgens'.[1]

Other patentees naturally turned to those oil, soap, and margarine manufacturers who had not been favoured with licences by Crosfield's. In December 1911 a 'working arrangement' was negotiated between the owners of the Wilbuschewitsch and Testrup patents for the sale of their hydrogenation rights in various countries. From the B.B.O. Company, De Nordiske Fabriker (De-No-Fa) of Frederiksstadt acquired the Wilbuschewitsch rights in Norway, and Van den Berghs for their plant at Zwijndrecht in Holland, while Lever's eventually, in February

[1] A further agreement was made with Jurgens on 17th January 1912, concerning not only joint patent actions, but also sale of licences, and permitting Jurgens to export hardened products for inedible purposes to a number of European countries, at a royalty of 10s. per ton. This agreement was further modified on 14th June 1913.

1913, secured the process in the United Kingdom, France, and various other countries. Earlier, in July 1912, Lever's had acquired from Techno-Chemical Laboratories a licence for the English patent, and in February 1913 they purchased both the English and foreign rights, at the same time as they acquired the Wilbuschewitsch rights. Joseph Watson's, Price's Candle Co., and Hydroil Ltd. held the shares in Ardol Ltd., which had secured the U.K. rights in the Bedford & Williams Patent. Crosfield's former chemist, Higgins, had also patented a fat-hardening process.

In August 1911 Crosfield's decided, with Jurgens' support, to oppose the Wilbuschewitsch, Testrup, and Higgins patents, as being infringements of their Normann patent. In December they brought an action in the High Court against Testrup and the Techno-Chemical Laboratories. Lever's realized the seriousness of the situation. As Horatio Ballantyne, their chemical consultant, later observed:

> Lever's might well have been placed in a serious predicament; they would, if the [Normann] patent were valid, have had to pay tribute to their chief competitor, Crosfield's, and many things in the soap industry might have been different today.

Brunner Mond's, already possessing a virtual monopoly in the manufacture of alkali, would also have monopolized hardened fats. Lever's, therefore, agreed to undertake the legal defence against Crosfield's, at the same time as they secured a licence under the Testrup patent. The importance of the latter to Lever is illustrated by the fact that he paid £10,000 for the English licence and £100,000 for the foreign rights.

Brunner Mond's tried, as we have seen, to make a deal with Lever over the Normann patent in October 1912, in their efforts to get him to sign a new alkali contract, but the negotiations failed. The Testrup case therefore came up for trial in February 1913. Crosfield's were confident of success and were looking forward to huge profits from hardened fats. Unfortunately, however, the Normann patent had serious deficiencies.[1] Crosfield's tried to maintain that it was a 'master patent', laying down the broad principles of hydrogenation, but Horatio Ballantyne had no difficulty in proving its insufficiency. Lead-

[1] See above, pp. 165–6.

ing chemists, he was able to demonstrate, could not, merely by following its vague and inadequate directions, succeed in hydrogenizing oils. Moreover, the years of trial and error at Crosfield's proved the same point. On 18th March 1913, therefore, judgment was given for the defendants and the Normann patent was declared invalid. The action cost Crosfield's about £12,500.[1]

This judgment was a grievously disappointing blow to Crosfield's. They had undoubtedly been the first firm to develop hydrogenation on an industrial scale, and some of their secrets had certainly been filched from them, but in relying on the Normann patent they were, from a legal point of view, resting on a broken reed. The Testrup judgment was rendered the more bitter by the fact that it was Lever's who had beaten them. They wished to go on fighting and at once gave notice of appeal; a separate action against Lever's was also pending. But Brunner Mond's recognized the futility of further litigation and that they could not now hope to overcome Lever's. As Lord Leverhulme recalled to Sir Arthur Crosfield on 17th May 1921,

What did bring us together was the action in the law courts on Hydrogenation patents. . . . Messrs. Crosfields were what is called 'cocksure' of winning the action, and Messrs. Brunner Mond shared in this confidence. It was a great shock to both when they lost and the patents which Lever Brothers had purchased were upheld. When this result was arrived at, Brunner Monds, through Mr. Brock, had a conversation with myself from which it was quite obvious that some arrangement between Brunner Monds and Lever Brothers with regard to Crosfields and Gossages would be welcomed by Messrs. Brunner Mond equally as with Lever Brothers.

These negotiations resulted in 'Heads of Agreement' signed on 7th May 1913, which laid down principles for detailed elaboration afterwards. A straightforward exchange of shares was not possible, since Lever was unwilling to give Brunner Mond's any foothold in his business, and Brunner Mond's were still bound by their promise to the Crosfields not to sell out to Lever's. These difficulties were overcome, however, by a complicated agreement of 5th June 1913, whereby Associated Enterprises Ltd. (controlled by Lever's) agreed to procure the

[1] Jurgens bore a proportion of the costs. This firm became involved in lengthier and costlier litigation defending its patent rights in Germany.

transfer of 800,000 of Lever Brothers' 15 per cent Cumulative Preferred Ordinary £1 shares to a bank or insurance company to hold in trust, while Brunner Mond's agreed to transfer to the same trustee the whole of the Ordinary shares in Crosfield's and Gossage's. Dividends on the shares in Lever's and in Crossage's would be paid to the trustee and divided equally between Brunner Mond's and Associated Enterprises Ltd. (The London County & Westminster Bank was subsequently selected as trustee.) Brunner Mond's agreed that the business of Crosfield's and Gossage's should be conducted for the mutual benefit of themselves and Associated Enterprises, and that they would not acquire any further interests in the soap trade. Lever's, for their part, now signed a new alkali contract with Brunner Mond's, from whom they would purchase all their supplies of soda ash at £2 7s. 6d. per ton until 1923 (the same price as for Crossage's); they also agreed not to sell any alkali or caustic soda outside the 'family'. At the same time they sold the Lymm salt lands to Brunner Mond's. All litigation between them was stopped. J.J. and George Crosfield accepted these arrangements with as good grace as possible, but Lever's victory rankled deeply in their hearts.

The way now seemed open for an international settlement in regard to hydrogenation. After the Testrup judgment, no one firm or group could monopolize fat-hardening. Protracted negotiations followed between Lever's, Crosfield's, Jurgens, Van den Berghs, Schichts, B.B.O., De-No-Fa, Procter & Gamble, and others. At first it looked as if all the various patents and processes would be pooled in a joint holding company, Hydrogenators Ltd., but rivalries proved too strong and Lever's eventually withdrew, after having acquired from B.B.O. a half-interest in De-No-Fa, which seriously threatened the continental interests of Jurgens and Van den Berghs. Crosfield's, however, together with Jurgens and Van den Berghs, went ahead with the formation of Hydrogenators in December 1913: of the 100,000 £1 shares issued, Crosfield's acquired a sixth and Brunner, Mond's a third. (Adolphe Secretan, of Crosfield's, was appointed commercial manager.) Schichts and B.B.O. soon joined, but Lever's remained aloof, having secured their supplies of hardened fats through the De-No-Fa and Port Sunlight plants. Moreover, they found that they could secure little practical advantage from Hydrogenators, since Crosfield's refused to pool their secret processes, which undoubtedly gave them technical superiority over Lever's in fat-hardening. On several occasions Lever tried to bargain with them on this point, but without success. He strengthened his position, however, by buying the remaining Bedford & Williams patent rights (for the U.S.A., Canada, etc.) from Hydroil in March 1914—his acquisition of half Watson's Ordinary capital in April 1913 having given him an interest in Ardol—and by negotiating an agreement with Procter & Gamble in May 1914 for the pooling of patents in a joint Hydrogenation Company, U.S.A. But Crosfield's refused to give Procter & Gamble permission to disclose their secret processes to Lever's.

Two rival groups emerged: Hydrogenators (including Crosfield's, Jurgens, Van den Berghs, and Schichts) and the Lever group (including Lever's, Watson's, and De-No-Fa, the two latter being really controlled by Lever's). Hydrogenators, with Giles Hunt of Crosfield's as secretary, went ahead with schemes for development in France, Russia, and various other countries, including a fish-oil business in Alaska. But now that fat-hardening plants had been successfully established by all the major oil-milling, soap, and margarine concerns, Hydrogenators gradually dwindled in importance, becoming (as the minutes of Jurgens' directors in January 1914 indicate) 'simply a connecting link for the buying conferences'.

The latter reference is to joint purchases and price-fixing of whale oil, the raw material mainly used in hydrogenation. Jurgens' archives provide evidence that as early as February 1912 Crosfield's, Jurgens, and Schichts, meeting at Emmerich, agreed that they should buy their whale oil in combination, or at any rate that they should agree on prices. These arrangements were soon extended to include all the leading buyers. World demand for whale oil considerably exceeded supply, so in order to prevent cut-throat competition, conferences were held and a 'Whale Oil Pool' was eventually formed, dividing each season's catch in agreed proportions at prices fixed annually. Thus at a conference on 25th November 1913 the following percentages were proposed: Jurgens 28·57, Crosfield's 19·05, Schichts 19·05, Lever's 33·33. Lever's succeeded, however, in raising the proportion of their group: by an agreement early in 1914 the Lever group, including Watson's and De-No-Fa as well as Lever's, was to have 45 per cent and the Hydrogenators group (as above) 55 per cent. There was, of course, some very hard and acrimonious haggling over this vital raw material. On one occasion, for example, Clarence Knowles reported to Lever's Policy Council that G. H. K. Kingdon, of Crosfield's, 'was most aggressive . . . and was really very rude to him'.

Similar differences occurred in relations between Crosfield's and Lever's in the soap trade. The negotiations in 1912 for a 'working arrangement' had broken down, but the agreements of May–June 1913, which gave Lever's a half-interest in Crossage's, provided better prospects for co-operation. Sir William Lever wrote to Sir John Brunner on 28th May 1913, expressing great pleasure at being associated in business with Brunner Mond's and suggesting that

by avoiding friction and unnecessary expenditure on advertising, and combining knowledge on the preparation of materials for the soapmaker, we may be able to serve the public better and supply to our shareholders a more remunerative and a more sound investment.

During the next two years there was a steady stream of correspondence, telephone calls, and conferences between Brunner Mond's, Crossage's, and Lever's concerning the soap trade. These covered such matters as the standardizing of the various qualities and packs of soap (many hundreds in number), arrangement of prices, discounts, bonuses, and credit, consultation on purchasing of raw materials, sales and prices of glycerine, and economies in advertising. In the home market there was a long tradition of discussion and agreement, through the Soap Makers' Association, though this was practically defunct: J. J. Crosfield told Sir William Lever on 8th April 1914 that he thought such an Association was unnecessary, since the soap trade was now dominated by Lever Brothers and their Associated Companies on the one hand and Crosfield's and Gossage's on the other.

A fair measure of agreement was reached in the home trade, though open warfare occasionally threatened. Rivalry remained very strong, however, in export markets, each side continually complaining of underselling by the other. Crossage's controlled nearly three-quarters of the total export trade, but Lever's competition was growing, especially in tablet soaps. There were no other rivals, British or foreign, of any consequence, so it seemed obviously sensible for them to reach agreement. Joint export conferences were regularly held, but often gave rise to recriminations, personal rivalries and suspicions. Lever sought to settle these differences, writing to J. J. Crosfield on 11th June 1914:

We are always ready to respect your trade in all markets and we have no wish to build up a trade in any way at your expense. I believe that there is room to more than double the present Export Trade in Soap by judicious exploitation of markets and by advertising. Cannot we agree on a policy in our Export Trade which will mean making new markets, making new uses for Soap in old markets, and reaping a much bigger increase for both of us than is possible under the present arrangement?

The outcome was a draft Export Pooling Agreement, which was lengthily discussed and amended during the next twelve months. Its basic purpose was to divide world markets (outside Europe) for household soap between Crossage's and Lever's, in agreed quotas and at agreed prices and terms, with penalties on excess sales. But ultimately nothing came of it. Lever's were particularly upset by Crossage's competition with 'Sunlight' in foreign markets by means of cheaper tablets, of lower quality and smaller size, such as 'Umbrella' and 'Telegraph', against which Lever's were forced to retaliate with 'Urn', etc. Export conferences were still held, but competition continued as strongly as ever.

In two overseas markets, however, co-operation proceeded much farther, to the extent of schemes for joint production and sale. Crosfield's had for some time been considering the establishment of a works in South Africa, but local competition was severe and Lever's were already established there, so in November 1913 they joined with Lever's in acquiring a controlling interest in the Natal Soap Works (established in 1906, with a capital of £10,000), Lever's shares being held in trust by Crosfield's. It was arranged that this works should manufacture Crosfield's and Gossage's soaps for South Africa, and Crosfield's sought to run the business in their own interests; J. J.

Crosfield pointed out to Lever in July 1914 that they were still competitors.

In China also, both Crossage's and Lever's were becoming increasingly interested. Here was a vast potential market, which was explored by C. H. Hamilton, Crosfield's export manager, in 1909 and again in 1912. He recommended establishment of a works there, but a few months after the settlement of May 1913 it was agreed that a joint company—the 'China Manufacturing Co. Ltd.'—should be formed, to take over the business there of Crosfield's, Gossage's, and Lever's. As we shall see, however, this project proved abortive and eventually led to further hostilities between Brunner Mond's and Lever's.

In another field, too, competition could not be restrained. Consultation in regard to buying raw materials could not gloss over the struggle for sources of supply. Lever's vast schemes in West Africa, the Congo, and elsewhere have been described in the *History of Unilever*. Crosfield's projects were on a smaller scale. They already owned Apol Ltd., and in 1912 they joined with Gossage's in financing Bulama Ltd., for the production of palm oil, but the scheme proved a total failure and Crosfield's lost over £7,300. Nevertheless, towards the end of 1914 they again joined with Gossage's and also with Brunner Mond's in establishing Palm Oil Estates Managers Ltd., to acquire and develop plantations in West Africa and elsewhere. Crosfield's held about a quarter of the total issued capital of over £125,000.

Despite these clashes of interest, Lever undoubtedly tried to work amicably with Crosfield's during this period. In letters to J. J. Crosfield he repeatedly stressed his desire to put an end to 'frenzied competition', while maintaining 'friendly rivalry', on agreed prices and terms. Lever's Policy Council minutes also prove his conciliatory attitude. When, for example, clashes occurred in the export trade, he 'felt that in view of the fact that we took one half of Gossages' and Crosfields' profits we should be prepared to give way'. He constantly urged co-operation, not merely on markets and prices, but on all business matters. In a letter of 14th April 1914, for example, he offered Crosfield's assistance in advertising and selling methods, and also suggested technical co-operation. Crosfield's, however, would not reciprocate, and Lever complained to F. W. Brock on 18th August 1914 that 'Lever Brothers' help, instead of being welcomed, is not desired'. One of Lever's chief disappointments was his failure to gain access to Crosfield's fat-hardening processes. The Policy Council minutes for 25th August 1914 reveal a suggestion by Lever for a combination of research laboratories, but he complained that although Lever's had thrown their works open to Crosfield's, the latter had not reciprocated. J. J. Crosfield, confident of his firm's technical superiority, especially in hydrogenation, carefully safeguarded (as he frankly told Lever on 21st July 1914) the 'information with regard to the manufactures of Soaps, which, as you know, from previous discussions, we regard as extremely valuable and are not prepared to divulge to any competitor'.

Lever's large financial interest in Crossage's gave him a strong motive for interference, but this aroused resentment on J. J. Crosfield's part. He wrote to Lever on 27th July 1914:

I have often thought in considering the respective positions of our firms, that you sometimes overlook what are the relative positions of this Company and your own. Through the agreement which you have with Messrs. Brunner, Mond & Co. your firm has an important interest in the profits of this Company, though you do not hold any part of its capital. This Company, on the other hand, has no knowledge officially of your agreement with Brunner, Mond & Co., nor any interest in the profits of Lever Brothers . . .

They must therefore 'compete to some extent with each other, though in a friendly way'. Lever, however, replying on the 29th, disapproved of this attitude, and asked,

. . . is it not a matter for Messrs. Brunner Mond to decide? I cannot think that they will wish there should be any competition as competition is understood between our respective firms, but that we should work together on lines that will give the most profit with the least anxiety and friction.

Lever, in fact, was bringing increasing pressure to bear upon Crosfield's through Brunner Mond's. Roscoe Brunner and F. W. Brock were appointed directors of Crosfield's in February 1914, and though they rarely attended Board meetings their voice was decisive upon an increasing number of high level matters, sometimes with little or no consultation with Crosfield's other Directors. J. J. Crosfield's mounting dissatisfaction at the way in which the firm was being treated as a mere pawn is illustrated by a letter to Lever on 26th August 1914. He complained that he had never heard of the proposed joint company in China until it had been arranged between Brock and Lever. He strongly objected to any sharing of hydrogenation secrets with Lever's: he 'would never be a party to our information . . . being given to you or anybody else without due recompense'. (He had stipulated £100,000.) And he again expressed strong views 'in regard to the indirect interest which you have in this Company'. Lever had conveyed the impression at a recent meeting that, by virtue of the agreement with Brunner Mond's, he had 'a right to a say in the directorate of this Company and at any rate some control over the Company'. But Crosfield pointed out that Brunner, Mond & Co. owned all their Ordinary shares and had 'sole control of this Company'.

Lever replied on 31st August that Brunner Mond's did not own Crossage's, but that the Ordinary shares were in the hands of a trustee, together with certain shares of Lever's, and that the business was to be run in the joint interests of Brunner Mond's and Lever's. Lever's therefore, had a legitimate interest, along with Brunner Mond's, in seeing that the business was run profitably. Unless Crosfield worked amicably with him to secure that end, his (Lever's) confidence would be withdrawn and he would seek changes in the directorate of Crossage's.

J. J. Crosfield's only answer was that they must agree to differ. He was annoyed by rumours that Lever's owned Crossage's and evidently feared that these might soon become reality. Other directors and managers of Crosfield's also shared his deep-rooted antipathy to Lever's, bred by long years of trade competition. Moreover, as Lever pointed out to Brock on 18th August 1914, they had 'a nervous dread' of losing their jobs if Lever's took control, despite the fact that Lever's had sixty-four Associated Companies 'and we never willingly part with a good man'. At the same time, however, Lever's subordinates also showed aggressiveness towards Crosfield's, and Lever found it difficult to restrain them. Personalities were undoubtedly as important as policies in creating difficulties.

Brunner Mond's found the Crosfields an increasing embarrassment. This was particularly so in China, where their agent, E. S. Little, had taken over control of Crosfield's business and was making arrangements for the establishment of joint works for the China Manufacturing Co. at Shanghai. In a letter to Little on 4th February 1915, Brock referred to 'pressure brought to bear upon Warrington' and to difficulties 'of a personal nature'. The Crosfields 'have given ample evidence that they resent any interference from anybody connected with us almost as much as from Levers'. But, he went on,

within the last week an incident has arisen which I think has shown our friends at Warrington that they cannot have the absolute freedom from our interference that they have been seeking. We have, I think, shown them that although we are ready to put up with a great deal in order to have the business proceed on pleasant lines, there is a point beyond which we will not go whatever happens.

Lever again complained to Brock on 27th February of 'an absence of candour coupled with some suspicion and distrust' on Crosfield's part, which was preventing business co-operation. As a result of these pressures, applied by both Brunner Mond's and Lever's, J. J. Crosfield finally sent in his resignation on 18th March 1915. Unfortunately, it has not been possible to find this letter, but it was referred to in the course of evidence in the action between Associated Enterprises and Brunner Mond's in June 1917, from which it appears that 'the letter all the way through shows he is conscious of and does not very much like the fact that the Company is being very much run over his head'. One of his objections was that the 'fat-hardening process should not be [made] available to Lever Brothers'. His brother, Major George Crosfield, who was then at the Front in France, also resigned by a letter of 9th April 1915, mainly from motives of family loyalty.

Further light is thrown on the underlying causes of the Crosfields' resignation in a letter of 23rd July 1915 by George Harley, Lever's solicitor, reporting a statement by Brock:

The two C's were regarded by you [Lever] and by B.M. & Co. as 'stumbling blocks' to a very close and intimate connection and that you and he had each . . . come impartially to the conclusion that the entire blame for this rested with the C's themselves. Having arrived at this conclusion he [Brock] aided and fostered . . . the idea of retirement and when the one C. joined the forces and intimated his preference for a military career, and the other C.—possibly for health considerations—began to think of retiring, he (Mr. B.) knowing that this would be to your liking welcomed the thought and did not press him to stay when he openly announced his intention. . . .

At a presentation made by leading members of Crosfield's staff on J.J.'s retirement, 'Mr. C. lost his head and . . . made some "nasty" remarks as to the positive danger of the C. business being controlled by your [Lever's] Co.'

In some reminiscences, written many years later, in 1948, George R. Crosfield stated that Brunner Mond's had broken their promise of 1911 by 'selling our shares to Lever Bros. in 1915'. But his memory was mistaken. There was no such sale of shares at this time. Brunner Mond's had not broken their promise, but they had been obliged, after Lever's victory in the Testrup case, to face facts and compromise with him. They could not allow Crosfield's to dictate policy to them. The Crosfields, on the other hand, proud of their firm's long history and accustomed to business independence, could not bend their necks either to Brunner Mond's or to Lever's. There could, therefore, be only one conclusion. In 1915, exactly a hundred years after Joseph Crosfield first started soapmaking at Bank Quay, his grandsons withdrew from the business.[1]

They left behind them a thriving and expanding company. During their last two or three years they had vigorously continued their earlier development schemes. Above all, they had greatly extended the fat-hardening plant on the Cheshire side of the river, including provision of numerous oil-storage tanks. Between January 1912 and August 1914 a total of about £105,000 was voted on this account. Moreover, the large increase in oil-storage capacity was mainly responsible for an increase in total stocks from £271,000 at the end of November 1911 to £787,000 three years later. This necessitated a much larger supply of working capital.

There were no further additions to the adjoining oil-extraction (oil-milling) plant, but extensions to the oil refinery (V.B. department) on the Lancashire side were planned. These were eventually cancelled, however, in favour of an entirely new plant, to cost £35,000, on the Cheshire side, next to the oil-mill. A three-storied extension to the soapery (£6,000) and another

[1] Their withdrawal, however, did not improve relations between Brunner Mond's and Lever's (see below, pp. 276–84).

(a)

(b)

14. Crosfield's works, 1913 (a) north of the river; (b) south of the river

to the soap export building (£4,500) were also planned, while more machines were introduced for crutching, cooling, drying, milling, scent-mixing, plodding, and stamping, at a total cost of several thousands of pounds. The growth of the wood-box section of the packing department necessitated an extension of the timber stores (£9,500). A new cask-making plant (£15,000) was also approved. Additional bag-making machines for 'Carbosil' and more printing machines were also installed.

Only minor additions were made to the caustic soda and silicate plants, but new evaporators and stills were approved for the glycerine department (over £19,000), and large additions to the cement works (£16,000). New electricity generators were also installed (£6,500), and more boilers and pumping plant (£19,000).

Increased manufacturing production necessitated improvements in the handling and transport of goods. The biggest development was a scheme for a new transporter bridge, connected to works railway facilities on the Cheshire side, so as to improve movement of goods across the river. The whole scheme was to cost about £35,000. During these years river traffic continued to be important, and the Company acquired another steamer and several barges, including a few small tankers for carrying oil. More steam cranes were installed on the wharves, more conveyors and elevators in the works, and a new locomotive and a number of tank wagons were purchased. Horse-vans were still being used for canvassing, but a motor-car and a motor-van were bought, and a garage was built at Whitecross, adjoining the Catholic Church and Joseph Crosfield's old house.

These years also witnessed the founding of the Centenary Institute. The existing accommodation for social purposes, such as dining- and dressing-rooms, gymnasium, etc., were inadequate and required for business purposes, so it was decided in 1914 that—to celebrate the firm's centenary—a new building should be erected, at a cost of £30,000, on land recently acquired in Baxter and Powys Streets, next to the joiners' and pattern makers' shops and engineers' offices. This was to contain a large assembly hall, with a stage, for concerts, dances, dramatic and operatic performances, etc., and also billiard rooms, club-rooms, and baths.

Capital for all these projects was raised by calling up the

outstanding 10s. per share on 50,000 Ordinary shares (bringing the total Ordinary capital to £300,000 fully paid up), and by raising an additional £500,000 of Preference capital. The existing 5 per cent Preference shares were converted to Pre-Preference ones, which now totalled £400,000; additional shares to the value of £100,000 were authorized, but not issued.

These ambitious projects were interrupted by the first World War, but a basis for further expansion had been laid. Production, trade, and profits were rising, and were to rise even more rapidly during the war.[1]

[1] The pre-war and war-time figures will be considered together in the next chapter.

PART IV

CROSFIELD'S IN THE AGE OF BIG BUSINESS, 1915–65

CHAPTER XVII

WAR AND COMMERCIAL RIVALRY

By the time the Crosfields left Bank Quay the world was already at war. At first, when the war was expected to be brief, 'business as usual' was the slogan, but as it dragged on and became increasingly 'total', the whole economy was seriously affected and had to be directed to the war effort. Shortages of capital, labour, and raw materials developed, prices rose, overseas trade was disrupted, and Government controls became more stringent. At the same time, however, production in many industries—particularly those essential to the war—increased remarkably, unemployment disappeared, wages and purchasing power rose, and profits soared to such an extent that complaints were made of 'war profiteering'.

Crosfield's, with their strong affiliations to the Volunteers or Territorials, and the National Service League, naturally supplied a large contingent to the Armed Forces. At the outbreak of war they were employing about 3,000 people, of whom about 500 were women. By mid-January 1915 over a quarter (665) of their male employees—managers, staff, and works personnel— had 'joined up', following George Crosfield's example, and the Board recorded 'their appreciation of this patriotic response to the call of King and Country'. The Company undertook to reinstate all those who enlisted and to pay half wages (or a minimum of 10s.) to their wives, and 1s. for each child under fourteen years. By the end of the war a total of 1,275 employees had joined the Forces, of whom 116 had been killed, while the Company had paid nearly £58,000 in war allowances.

This loss of manpower caused considerable difficulties, which could be only partially overcome by increased employment of women. Moreover, labour shortage increased the bargaining power of the trade unions and combined with the rising cost of living to bring pressure for increased wages. The Government had to intervene to prevent industrial disputes by means of compulsory arbitration. By the end of the war the soap workers' minimum weekly wage had risen to around £3.

In the early part of the war, fats and oils were abundant, due to the British blockade of Germany, and the Directors reported in January 1915 that the Company 'has benefited by lower prices of materials, and its policy of carrying large stocks has been of great assistance in overcoming the difficulties with regard to supplies occasioned by the War'. This stockpiling policy was continued throughout the war: stocks on hand rose from £787,000 on 30th November 1914 to £1,772,000 four years later. Fats and oils, however, were the source not only of soap, but—more essential in war-time—also of glycerine, used in manufacturing explosives. Oil-seeds were also required for margarine and cattle-cake, important for feeding humans and animals. Inevitably, therefore, though gradually, the Government intervened. In August 1915 glycerine was requisitioned at a fixed price, unaltered throughout the rest of the war. From the end of January 1916 Crosfield's works came under the control of the Ministry of Munitions. Next month all whale oil (for fat-hardening) was requisitioned by the Ministry, to be distributed in the following proportions—Lever's 47·4 per cent, Crosfield's 31·6 per cent, and Watson's 21 per cent—the three companies agreeing to treat such oil so as to produce the maximum quantity of glycerine for munitions. (The proportions were subsequently altered to 40 per cent, 35 per cent, and 25 per cent respectively.) Early in 1917 rigid control was established over all fats, oils, oilseeds, and their products, including soap, margarine, and oilcake. Other materials, such as paper, were likewise brought under Government restrictions. Crosfield's participated in the Government-inspired Soap Makers' Federation and Oil Seeds Products Association, created in the summer of 1918, for the purpose of regulating these industries.

Early in the war the Government imposed restrictions upon capital issues, with the result that Crosfield's were unable to raise any additional resources by flotation of shares. This factor, combined with control by the Ministry of Munitions, resulted in the delayed completion, or postponement, or even abandonment of pre-war investment schemes. Most of the extensions to the fat-hardening plant were completed, but the building of the new V.B. plant (oil refinery) was stopped. The extension of the soapery was not even started, while that of the export soap building was not completed until after the war. Most of the additional glycerine plant was installed before the war, but completion even of that had to be postponed. The new cement works were left half-finished. The building of the new cask-making plant was eventually stopped and the machinery sold. Completion of the transporter bridge was badly delayed. The Centenary Institute was not opened until after the war.

Nevertheless, war-time profits and bank loans enabled the Company to proceed with some capital construction during the war: a new oil-pressing plant (£35,000), started early in 1915; a new electric power-house, with generators, etc. (£26,500), begun towards the end of that year; more steamships, tankers, and barges (nearly £22,000); additional pumping and water-treating plant; more boilers; more railway wagons; the firm's first fleet of lorries (gross value £25,000 at the end of 1919); more elevators for fuel, sand, etc.; and a few soap-milling, bag- and box-making and printing machines. At the same time, several of the pre-war projects, such as the transporter bridge, were slowly brought towards completion, while early in 1918 temporary extensions to the V.B. plant, at an estimated cost of £62,000, were begun in Pochin's former buildings. Moreover, considerable investments were made in the Natal Soap Works, Palm Oil Estates Managers Ltd., and the China Soap and Candle Co. (Investments in allied companies had risen to over £178,000 by the end of 1918.) The firm also extended its landholdings at Bank Quay, with an eye to post-war development.

Despite difficulties, therefore, the Company greatly expanded its production, trade, and profits during the war. Home sales of soap increased from an annual average of between 21,000 and 22,000 tons in 1912–14 to about 29,000 tons in 1918 (after reaching a peak of nearly 32,000 tons in the previous year).[1] 'Perfection' sales rose from about 11,000 to nearly 13,000 tons, 'Pinkobolic' from 2,000 towards 4,000 tons. There are no surviving figures of export tonnages, but there is little doubt that

---

[1] These figures, which do not include Erasmic soaps, are taken from a letter by Lord Leverhulme to C. F. Huffam, 5th August 1921. A note-book of pre-war statistics at Crosfield's gives figures nearly a thousand tons per annum higher for the years 1912–14.

these also rose substantially. The Government encouraged production of soap in order to get as much glycerine as possible for munitions, and although the home market expanded considerably, further outlets had to be found abroad.

Trade grew much more in value than in volume, due to wartime inflation.[1] Home soap sales rose from £505,000 in 1913 to £1,388,000 in 1918, the most dramatic increases occurring in the last two years of the war; exports expanded from £178,000 to £361,000. But these increases were mainly a reflection of those in the costs of raw materials, which, after falling during the first year of the war, rose sharply thereafter, until Government control was imposed early in 1917. Tallow rose from £34 per ton in 1913 to £72 in 1918; copra from £29 to £46; palm oil from £30 to £46; whale oil from £21 to £63. Soap prices, however, rose to an even greater extent, though mostly in the last eighteen months of the war. 'Perfection', for example, went up from 3½d. before the war to 5d. by May 1917 and then soared to 9d. by June 1918. It was only in the last year of the war, therefore, that inflated profits were made. Indeed, after rising from about £61,000 (less than 9 per cent on sales) in 1913 to £105,000 (14 per cent) in 1914, total soap profits (both home and export) declined to £72,000 (6 per cent) in 1917, but then leapt to £346,000 (20 per cent) in 1918.[2] Crosfield's, along with other soapmakers, were criticized by the official *Report on the Soap Industry* in 1921, for raising prices and profits unduly towards the end of the war, but one must remember that there was a heavy Excess Profits Duty.[3]

Another factor tending to increase profits during the war was the cessation of 'frenzied' advertising. In the spring of 1915, for example, by mutual agreement between Lever's, Watson's, and

[1] Unfortunately, there was another change in accounting procedure in 1913, whereby *net* sales revenue only (after deduction of selling expenses) was entered in the annual trading accounts, and there are no surviving nominal ledgers for these years from which to discover gross sales. The sales figures in this chapter cannot, therefore, be properly compared with those of earlier years, but they do clearly indicate the growth of Crosfield's trade during the war.

[2] The conversion of the soap department's previous heavy losses (see above, p. 194) into substantial profits was mainly due to a change in accounting, whereby credit for spent lyes was now given by the crude glycerine department. These profits, and those of other departments given below, are net of depreciation, interest on capital, and general expenses.

[3] See below, p. 273.

Crosfield's, presents for soap wrappers were abolished. Crosfield's annual advertising expenditure, which had averaged nearly £50,000 in 1913–14, fell to below £6,000 in 1917–18.

The Erasmic Company, on the other hand, intensified its selling and advertising pressure. Despite difficulties in regard to supplies of essential oils, bottles, fancy boxes, etc., its total turnover rose from £117,980 (exports £19,232) in 1913 to £558,909 (exports £100,657) in 1918. This was largely due to higher prices, but output of Erasmic soaps also increased, from 1,367 tons in 1915 to 2,038 in 1918. Soaps still formed the bulk of the Company's trade, but perfumery and toilet requisites were of increasing importance; by the end of the war they formed about a fifth of total sales. Trading profits, which had been below £6,000 in 1913, rose to nearly £44,000 in 1918. But this was less than 8 per cent on turnover, since the large increase in sales was only achieved by very heavy selling and advertising expenses. In the home trade, for example, selling expenses (travellers, discounts, carriage, etc.) rose from about £10,000 annually before the war to nearly £50,000 in 1918, and advertising (mainly in the press) from about £7,000 to nearly £31,000. There was a similar increase in expenditure in the export trade. Just before the war, in 1913, a subsidiary company had been established in France—the Compagnie Erasmic, Paris, with an issued capital of 2,500,000 francs (later increased to 4,000,000), held by the parent company—to market Erasmic products more effectively in the French market. This progressed favourably during the war, but was hampered by difficulties in getting supplies over to Paris; a factory was therefore acquired to manufacture locally.

Crosfield's sales of 'Carbosil', 'Persil', 'Feather Flakes', and 'Glitto' stagnated during the war. Total deliveries of these products remained around 10,000 tons until 1918, when they rose to 11,600. 'Carbosil', of which 9,500 tons per annum were sold in 1912–13, still predominated, but its sales revenue declined from nearly £56,000 in the latter year to below £43,000 in 1914, at about which level it remained during most of the war; it leapt up, however, in 1918 to over £63,000.[1] 'Persil' was still relatively insignificant: sales declined from 564 tons (£19,379) in 1913 to 215 tons (£12,144) in 1918. Sales revenue from

[1] All these sales figures are net of selling expenses.

'Feather Flakes' rose from £2,333 in 1914 to £4,621 in 1918, and that from 'Glitto' shot up from practically nothing to over £17,000 in 1916 (there are no figures for 1917–18), but demand for both these remained very limited. The war-time cessation of advertising in the household soap and powders trade made it impossible to expand sales of such new products.

Profits on all these products tended to fall. In fact by the end of the war all except 'Carbosil' were losing money. Profits on the latter declined from £16,000 in 1914 to less than £10,000 in 1917, but then, like soap profits, they rose sharply to £23,000 in the following year. 'Persil' profits grew to nearly £5,000 in 1915, but then fell away and a loss of nearly £3,000 was suffered on this product in 1918. In the last three years of the war, losses were recorded on both 'Feather Flakes' and 'Glitto' —several hundred pounds annually on the former, several thousands on the latter.

These small losses on flakes and powders cannot have worried Crosfield's directors unduly, however, when compared with the huge profits being made on other products. Their oil extraction, oil treatment (fat-hardening), and oil-refining (vegetable butter) departments were the most profitable of all. Brunner Mond's now reaped where Crosfield's had sown. There was an enormous increase in the demand for these products, mainly because of the war-time stimulus to both the soap industry— producing glycerine—and margarine manufacture, which expanded rapidly due to the shortage of butter. Crosfield's remained suppliers of refined oils to the margarine companies, and of vegetable butters ('Veberine', etc.) to the bakery, confectionery, and chocolate trades. At the same time, of course, they provided themselves with oils for soapmaking.

Tonnage figures have survived only for the fat-hardening plant, the output of which rose from 8,348 tons in 1912 to 19,623 tons in 1914, and then to 27,306 tons in 1917, though it fell in 1918 to 24,314 tons. Figures of sales revenue show the soaring prosperity of all these departments. These figures, unfortunately, are not only net of selling expenses, but also include departmental transfers. (Extracted oils were for the most part transferred and consumed internally, but outside sales of hardened oils expanded considerably, while refined oils, of course, were mostly sold.) Sales revenue of the oil-extraction plant, which was only £8,000 in 1913, shot up to £141,000 in 1914 and then to £587,000 in 1918. Even more remarkable were the corresponding figures for hardened oils—£86,000, £417,000, and £1,710,000—and for refined oils (vegetable butters)—£140,000, £154,000, and £1,034,000.

These enormous increases in sales revenue were accompanied by large increases in profits. The oil-extraction plant made little or no profits before the war, but in 1915–18 they rose to an average of £23,000 annually. Much more striking were the increases in profits on hardened and refined oils, the former rising from an annual average of £15,000 in 1912–13 to one of £102,000 in 1917–18, and the latter from £20,000 to £163,000 over the same period.

Crosfield's chemicals also provided substantial war-time profits, mainly due to inflation. Output of caustic soda remained around the pre-war figure: the annual average, which had been 16,108 tons in 1912–13, was 16,257 in 1914–18 (but only 14,275 in 1918); works consumption (liquor only) averaged 4,216 tons. Rising prices, however, raised sales revenue from £129,000 in 1913 to £203,000 in 1918,[1] and profits from £34,000 to £63,000.

Silicate production similarly stagnated during the war. The annual average (calculated as 'glass') rose from about 10,500 tons in 1912–13 to 11,333 tons during the war, but output was only 9,829 tons in 1918; works consumption averaged 1,765 tons a year. As a result of war-time inflation, however, sales revenue rose from £59,000 in 1913 to £100,000 by 1918, and profits from £11,000 to £50,000.

There are no surviving figures of Crosfield's war-time glycerine production, but it certainly increased substantially, along with that of soap. Governmental control of glycerine prices, however, checked the rise in sales revenue and profits. Sales revenue of distilled glycerine rose from £105,000 in 1913 to £304,000 in 1916, but then declined to £251,000 in 1918; profits, though growing from an annual average of only £2,000 in 1913–14 to £19,000 in 1915–18, were very modest by comparison with those of other departments.

Cement production was stopped during the war, due to the drop in building activity, and waste lime from the caustic soda

---

[1] Chemical sales are net of selling expenses, but include departmental transfers.

plant had to be stored on the Cheshire side. The general pattern of Crosfield's manufacturing activities was not, however, seriously altered by the war. Production of glycerine and refined oils were even more important in war than in peace, and soap was still essential. But a few new manufactures were introduced for war needs. Large quantities of acetone, which is a solvent for cellulose, were required to produce the 'dope' then used for varnishing and taughtening the fabric of aeroplane wings. The new oil-refinery buildings, which had been commenced on the Cheshire side of the river in 1914, were therefore requisitioned for the production of acetone from ethyl alcohol. A disastrous explosion, causing loss of life and serious injury, occurred in one of the buildings in 1917. This manufacture was under Government control and was not very profitable. (The allowance of profit for 1917 was only £152 and for 1918 it was £2,405). It was stopped at the end of the war.

A number of other chemicals, in short supply during the war, were also manufactured. Activated earths for oil bleaching, which had been purchased from Germany before the war, now had to be produced in this country. Research at Crosfield's indicated that the acid extraction of neutral fuller's earth, followed by washing and drying, would prove suitable. This led to large-scale production of 'Acsil', which continued after the war. This plant was also situated on the Cheshire side.

Crosfield's war-time prosperity can be measured by the enormous increase in their total sales and trading profits.[1] The former (net of selling expenses) rose from just over £1⅓ millions in 1913 to nearly £6 millions in 1918, the latter from £168,000 to £727,000;[2] but expressed as a percentage of total sales, trading profits remained around 12 per cent. To these was added a growing—though still comparatively small—amount of investment revenue. Until 1913 Crosfield's investments in railways, etc. had altogether brought in only £400 to £500 annually, but in that year, for the first time, the Erasmic Co. began to pay an ordinary dividend, maintained thereafter at 10 per

[1] Excluding those of the Erasmic Company. See above, p. 269.
[2] After charging all manufacturing and selling expenses (including advertising), depreciation, repairs, interest on capital, and general expenses. The comparable trading profits for 1907–12 were as follows: 1907, £7,747; 1908, £26,433; 1909, £65,099; 1910, £50,842; 1911, £46,608; 1912, £124,438.

cent (£4,576). This and dividends from the Natal Soap Works, the China Soap & Candle Co., and the West African enterprises raised Crosfield's investment income to just over £26,500 in 1918.

The rise in Crosfield's profits would have been much greater had it not been for the fact that considerable sums had to be spent out of revenue on constructional items due to the Government's restriction on capital issues. So-called 'repairs and renewals' rose from less than £50,000 in 1913 to about £114,000 in 1918. At the same time, the Company borrowed very heavily from the District Bank, not only to help finance their increasing stocks of raw materials, but also for building purposes. The balance sheet at the end of November 1918 showed an outstanding bank loan of nearly £561,000. Bank and other interest charges therefore rose from around £2,000 per annum in the years before the war to an average of £17,000 in 1917–18.

During the war, moreover, the Company had to make far heavier Income Tax payments, rising from less than £5,000 annually before the war to an average of £40,000 in 1917–18. Much more burdensome were the Excess Profits Duty assessments, which rose from £72,330 in 1915 to £396,810 in 1918, i.e. from about a quarter to more than half of trading profits.

Thus the amount available for appropriation was very much smaller than the latter figures suggest, and on this balance, of course, there were first charges of Debenture interest (£12,675) and Pre-Preference and Preference dividends (rising from £20,000 per annum in 1911–13 to £50,000 in 1915–18). Ordinary dividends (free of income tax) were then paid, as follows:

	%	£
1912	24	60,000
1913	30	90,000
1914	38	114,000
1915	27½	82,500
1916	22	66,000
1917	29	87,000
1918	29	87,000

These seem very handsome by comparison with those paid before Crosfield's were taken over,[1] but one must remember that Brunner Mond's had paid the equivalent of more than four

[1] 1909, 14%, £28,000; 1910, 12%, £25,032; 1911, 12%, £27,820.

times the nominal value of the Ordinary shares, and so were really getting only a modest return (5 to 6 per cent) during the war. Moreover, one must also take into account the general war-time inflation; in real terms, distributed profits were not nearly so high as in the years immediately before the war. On the other hand, however, substantial Reserves were built up out of war-time profits, which were distributed to the Ordinary shareholders after the war in the form of large capital gains. By the end of November 1918, these Reserves (General, Depreciation, etc.) totalled £744,000.

There had been no changes during the war in the authorized or issued capital, nor had the value of the Company's land, buildings, and plant been adjusted to take account of war-time inflation, but merely for additions less depreciation. Moreover, in 1913 all the goodwill (£100,000) had been written off against the General Reserve. At the end of the war, therefore, the Company's assets were undervalued, and the business was considerably under-capitalized. The most striking change in its assets, as listed in the balance sheets, was the huge increase in stocks.

	Total Assets	Land, Buildings, Plant, Machinery, etc.	Stocks on hand	Sundry Debtors	Cash and Investments
	£	£	£	£	£
30th Nov. 1913	1,556,556	680,005	558,399	244,490	73,662
30th Nov. 1918	3,546,998	813,895	1,772,290	692,785	268,029

Steps were taken immediately after the war to raise more capital. The profits which had been 'salted away' in the Reserves were now distributed as a tax-free bonus to the Ordinary shareholders (Brunner Mond's), who therewith purchased additional Ordinary shares. A total of £700,000 out of the Reserves was capitalized in this way: £300,000 in March 1919 and £400,000 in November 1919.[1] Thus the Ordinary share capital was increased to £1,000,000 (issued and fully paid). At the same time (March 1919), the Preference capital was increased by the creation of 3,000,000 new 6½ per cent Cumulative Preference shares, of which 1,000,000 were issued. The prospectus explained the reasons for this issue:

Since 1914 the expansion of the business has been continued

[1] The latter just after Lever's take over. (See below, p. 283).

274

without the Directors being able to issue fresh Capital. Further Freehold Land has been acquired, Buildings erected, and extensive new Plants installed.

Capital outlay has been incurred since 1st December, 1914, as follows:—

Land, buildings and plant	£273,722
Investments in allied companies	107,629
Other investments	50,177
Stocks	1,050,327
A total of	£1,481,855

This sum has been provided by Bankers' advances and Profits reserved in the Business. The new issue is required to pay off these advances, to provide for further extensions of the business of the Company, and to redeem the Debenture Issues.

The latter objective had been laid down by J. J. Crosfield as long ago as 1906. The moment now seemed opportune to extinguish this debt on favourable terms. Both the 4¼ and 4½ per cent Debenture Stock, totalling £290,000, had been issued at a premium, but now stood at a considerable discount, as money was much dearer, and the Company therefore offered redemption on the following terms: £85 of 5 per cent War Loan for each £100 of the former, and £90 of War Loan for each £100 of the latter.[1] This offer met with a mixed reception. Some Debenture holders protested strongly, but the Directors pointed out that stockholders would be getting the same income and a more marketable security, worth nearly £10 per cent more than the Debentures at prevailing market prices. With these arguments they carried the day at meetings of the stockholders in February 1919.

Thus, with new capital raised and old debts extinguished, Crosfield's were poised, so it seemed, for post-war expansion. Several major schemes were launched: a new melting-out house for the raw materials department in Pochin's Yard (£25,000); extensions to the cement plant (£16,625); to the pressing plant (£100,000, later reduced to £85,000); to the soap-milling department (£25,000); to the printing room (£20,000). At the

---

[1] £85 of War Loan was worth £80 15s., and £90 of War Loan was worth £85 10s., whereas the Company had originally received £106 for each £100 of Debenture Stock.

same time, vigorous advertising was resumed: £12,000 was sanctioned for 'Glitto', £10,000 for 'Perfection', £3,000 for 'Carbosil', and £2,000 for 'Persil'.

The firm's future, however, was still in the balance between Brunner Mond's and Lever's. It might have been expected that the Crosfields' departure early in 1915 would soon have been followed by a settlement of the differences between Brunner Mond's and Lever's. In fact, however, these became worse, and commercial squabbling continued throughout the war. Personal and economic motives, deeper and more powerful than the Crosfields' pride, were still operating to prevent a rapprochement. The Crosfields, it appears, had merely been used as scapegoats by Brunner Mond's. Lever, however, expected that Crossage's would soon fall into his grasp. According to Lever's Policy Council minutes of 25th August 1914, he had mentioned to Brock that 'in the event of a rupture we would be willing to take over the management of Crosfield's and Gossage's business'. And after the rupture occurred, he at once pressed for representation on Crosfield's Board. He had undoubtedly a good case: by the terms of the 1913 agreement, the Ordinary shares of Crossage's were held in trust, together with a large block of Lever's Preference shares, and the business was supposed to be run in the joint interests of Brunner Mond's and Lever's, yet while the former's share of profits under this arrangement was guaranteed by the fixed dividends on Lever's Preference shares, Lever's share was dependent upon the trading profits of Crossage's, from whose management, however, they were excluded. Only by a joint directorate, Lever maintained, could they work effectively together, without continual differences.

As long as the Crosfields were in the business, Lever had not pressed for representation, 'knowing as I did that our presence would have been a source of irritation to them', but the situation was now quite different. Brunner Mond's, however, rejected Lever's proposal. F. W. Brock was appointed Chairman and C. Haslam Deputy Chairman; Dr. E. F. Armstrong (who had been appointed to fill the gap created by Captain G. R. Crosfield's call to the Colours) and F. J. Burlton, the Chief Engineer, were appointed Directors, but no representation was granted to Lever's. Several reasons were given for this refusal. Crosfield's staff were very apprehensive of Lever's control, and Brunner Mond's were opposed to publicizing the links between themselves, Crossage's, and Lever's (so far kept secret), since such a large-scale combination might arouse public feeling and lead to anti-trust legislation as in the U.S.A. Lever's had no legal right to representation on Crossage's Board under the 1913 agreement, nor had they previously claimed any, and there was certainly no need for it now, since the Crosfields' resignation—due to Brunner Mond's insistence upon friendly relations with Lever's—had removed the main obstacle to the smooth working of the agreement. Brock also pointed out Crosfield's technical superiority over Lever's, especially in fat-hardening, and that they could not reveal secret information that would increase Lever's power of competition; besides, they were bound by agreements to Jurgens, who were rivals of Lever's in the margarine trade. Personal motives were also involved. At a meeting with Lever and others on 27th May 1915 Brock declared 'that being Chairman of Crosfield's he intended to be so, not only in name but in fact, and he intimated that sooner than see Lever's representatives on the Crosfield Board he would resign his Chairmanship'. Moreover, we have previously noted Sir John Brunner's attitude towards Lever, which, according to A. W. Tangye, was shared by other Brunner Mond directors.

Disagreement on this central issue led inevitably to conflict elsewhere, though meetings continued to be held on the home trade, export trade, and buying. Lever considered that 'Brunner Mond's are being won over to the policy of opposition to Lever Brothers, which has actuated Warrington from our first commencement in business'. He deplored the fact that, despite J. J. Crosfield's resignation, they were no nearer agreement.

The scheme for a joint manufacturing company in China was abandoned and the land already bought at Shanghai was divided. There was further dispute over the Natal Soap Works. Continued competition in the export trade caused endless wrangling, 'one side or the other continually underselling the other with a soap lower in quality and cheaper in price to that last put on the market' (Crosfield's 'Memorandum on the

Export Trade', 22nd September 1916). Crosfield's still refused to give Lever's information about their hydrogenation processes. Lever's were also disturbed by the fact that Brunner Mond's had taken shares in Hydrogenators and also in Palm Oil Estates Managers, and thus were extending their interests in oils and fats. A proposal for a joint works in West Africa fell through.

Relations worsened after Brock's sudden death in August 1916. He was succeeded as Chairman by Roscoe Brunner, who resigned, however, in October 1917. Cyril Haslam was then appointed Chairman, with Giles Hunt as Deputy.[1] At a private meeting on 3rd October 1916, Sir William Lever told Roscoe Brunner that he regarded Brunner Mond's staying in the soap trade as 'an unfriendly act' and that he wished to buy Crossage's shares in exchange for shares in Lever Brothers. But he was not prepared to pay so high a price as Brunner suggested. The latter pointed out that, having bought Crossage's in self-defence against Lever's, they 'continued to hold them as a definite policy of extending our interests outside Alkali'. All the old grievances were raked up, particularly regarding hydrogenation, Lever complaining bitterly of Crosfield's continued ill-will. But Brunner told him frankly that 'all my experiences of him [Lever] shewed him to be a person very inappreciative of the other man's point of view, always being ready to take and having little to give'. Lever concluded by saying 'that he could not stand the state of things which had lasted for the last three years, that he must go his own way, and carry out his own policy'.

The China question finally brought matters to a head. The negotiations with Lever having broken down, Brunner Mond's and Crossage's reached agreement with Price's Patent Candle Co. in May 1916 for the establishment of a 'China Soap and Candle Co. Ltd.', with a capital of £600,000, of which Crossage's would subscribe 70 and Price's 30 per cent. Lever's regarded this as a breach of the 1913 agreement, since Brunner Mond's would thereby be extending their soap interests, while Crossage's assets in China would be transferred to the new

---

[1] Hunt first came into association with Crosfield's as a solicitor in practice on the West Coast of Africa. After joining their secretarial staff in 1913, he rose rapidly to become Secretary in 1915 and a Director in 1916.

company, thus diverting profits from the pool and also benefiting another party, Price's, who were trade rivals of Lever's.[1]

Complicated legal exchanges followed, culminating in the trial of Associated Enterprises Ltd. *v.* Brunner, Mond & Co. Ltd. in the High Court in June–July 1917. The action was eventually settled out of court, however, by 'Heads of Agreement' signed on 12th July, whereby Brunner Mond's agreed to sell to Lever's half the Ordinary shares in Crosfield's and Gossage's for 500,000 of Lever's 15 per cent Cumulative Preferred Ordinary £1 shares, which were then quoted on the market at 40s. 3d. per share. Moreover, Lever's and Brunner Mond's were each to nominate a third of the directors of Crosfield's and Gossage's.

These terms were to be embodied in a formal agreement, a draft of which was submitted by Lever's in October. It was not returned by Brunner Mond's till February 1918, and then with serious alterations. It appears that Crosfield's and Gossage's were withholding information from Lever's regarding their business affairs and that restrictions were to be placed upon the directors nominated by Lever's, e.g. they would be refused access to Crossage's secret technical processes. Lever's therefore decided that no useful object would be served by further negotiations on the draft agreement and that the only way to settle matters was to go to the High Court again.

In March 1918 they commenced an action against Brunner Mond's, Crosfield's and Gossage's for declarations that they were entitled to an equal share with Brunner Mond's in all matters connected with the management of the business affairs of Crosfield's and Gossage's, and that the directors nominated by them were entitled to full directorial rights and powers. The action came up for trial in February 1919, when the judge indicated that in his view there had been no actual breach of the 'Heads of Agreement' and that the action was therefore premature. Lever's thereupon withdrew their claim, paying costs, and resumed negotiations with Brunner Mond's.

In a letter to Roscoe Brunner on 24th October 1917, Lever had again suggested that 'the best course for B.M. & Co. to

---

[1] Negotiations were opened for a take-over of Price's by Crossage's, but proved abortive. So did a proposal for a joint concern in Chile, like that in China.

take would be to sell the remaining half interest [in Crossage's] to Lever Brothers'. This proposal was mulled over in the next year or two and was dealt with at great length, and very shrewdly, by Giles Hunt in a letter of 15th October 1918 to J. H. Gold, secretary of Brunner Mond's. Hunt was in favour of selling to Lever's. He admitted that some of the directors of Crosfield's and Gossage's were against it, but pointed out that it was a matter solely for Brunner Mond's to decide, 'with a view to their best interests'. Moreover, directors and managers of companies taken over by Lever's had not generally suffered thereby. Possession of only half Crossage's shares gave Brunner Mond's 'no control of or possibility of affecting the Soap Trade for the purpose of attaining their own ends', whilst 'the sale of the shares might open a very convenient door to the negoti-ation of an entirely satisfactory Alkali contract'. Hunt empha-sized that the shares would be

best sold while Lord Leverhulme is alive. Experience leads one to believe that Lord Leverhulme is prepared to pay for hobby and ambition . . . Ambition on Lord Leverhulme's part to own the whole of Crosfield's and Gossage's is undoubtedly a strong motive with him. After Lord Leverhulme's death I doubt if the Directors of Lever Brothers would have the courage to purchase the shares, seeing the price which must be paid for them.

Moreover, Hunt considered that the shares should be sold now, while profits were 'unduly inflated' by the war. The future was uncertain and he doubted whether the businesses would be able to maintain dividends at the rates paid immediately before the war. In the export trade, for example, Lever's works in many Empire and foreign countries, together with American and local competition, would seriously undermine Gossage's and Crosfield's former superiority. In the home trade, profits were 'considerable now, but that is a state of things unprecedented and which is not likely to continue after the War'. Huffam had expressed the view that to extend the home trade profitably was almost an impossibility, in view of the strength of Lever's and their Associated Companies. Lever's had also acquired in the Congo and West Africa a strong advantage—'as producer, ship-owner and importer'—in supplies of raw materials. 'There is no shutting our eyes to the fact that Crosfields went into West Africa on too small a scale and were not sufficiently bold in their expenditure or, in the beginning, careful in the selection of their staff. We cannot consider Palm Oil Estates as in any way a set off against Lever's Congo'.

Hunt also reviewed Crosfield's prospects in chemicals and oils. He pointed out that the post-war position of glycerine would be insecure. The inflated war-time demand would fall, while ammonium nitrate might be substituted in explosives; industrial substitutes were also being developed. Profits on refined oils had been similarly inflated by the war; before the war margins had been reduced by competition, mainly from Germany. Although demand had grown greatly, so had refining capacity. No doubt there would be good profits from fat-hardening, but competition would increase and Crosfield's should not exaggerate their technical superiority.

To put the two businesses on a secure footing against Lever's, by extending the plant at Warrington and Widnes, building overseas works, etc., Hunt estimated that additional capital of at least £3,000,000 would be required.

There was, Hunt observed, a brighter side to the picture. The Erasmic Company was now flourishing, with profits seven times pre-war, thanks to an energetic advertising campaign. The Compagnie Erasmic (Paris) and the China Soap & Candle Co. had shown the advantages of establishing foreign works. The capital expenditure on the pressing and refining plants should also bear considerable fruit, even if profit margins had to be reduced. 'The Extraction and Pressing plant will be able to deal with 2,000 tons a month. The Refining plant with 3,500 a month, which should give a profit of £66,000 a year, while the Hardening plant at 3,500 tons a month may be expected to yield a profit of £84,000 a year.' Similarly, on the chemical side, 'Caustic and Silicate are satisfactory, but the former leaves no room for expansion, owing to the restrictions on output. The latter is susceptible of considerable expansion and that is now being considered.'

Finally, Hunt pointed out that, under the present arrangement, Lord Leverhulme would never 'move a hand to expand the Crosfield and Gossage business or to help in any way to increase the value of B.M. & Co.'s investment therein'. Moreover, the divided directorate would prevent effective management and perhaps lead to further litigation.

Haslam, Crosfield's Chairman, wrote brief comments on Hunt's letter, opposing a sale to Lever's, 'both from a personal point of view and in consideration of the benefit of the staff'. He referred to the repeated promises by Brunner Mond's not to sell out. The example of Watson's since their take-over was not encouraging. 'Lever will not help us to increase; he prefers to keep all increases to himself', i.e. Crossage's would suffer to the advantage of Port Sunlight. In exports, for example, 'Lever won't help—he'll rather hinder where he has works'. Haslam also appears to have taken a more optimistic view than Hunt of Crossage's future prospects. On the other hand, he agreed that if the businesses were to be sold, now was the time to sell. He also agreed that litigation was likely to continue.

Haslam's views were probably shared by most of the directors and staff who had been at Crosfield's for many years. Hunt, on the other hand, was a newcomer, unaffected by ties of tradition and sentiment, and a shrewd realist, who apparently saw the advantages of hitching his wagon to Lever's star. At the same time, there was much strength in his arguments for selling out. They were backed up late in October 1918 by detailed estimates of post-war profits, as compared with the likely annual return on the proceeds of selling Crossage's, showing a substantial margin in favour of the latter.

The question was lengthily debated between the directors of Brunner Mond's and Crossage's, but for the time being nothing was done. Then, in February 1919, as we have seen, the litigation between Lever's and Brunner Mond's came on for hearing and was terminated by Lever's withdrawing. The subsequent events are outlined in some notes by Giles Hunt, who clearly played a key role in the prolonged and delicate negotiations between Brunner Mond's and Lever's. He, indeed, appears to have been largely responsible for bringing them eventually to a successful conclusion, working skilfully upon Lever's, unbeknown to Brunner Mond's, and finally persuading Lord Leverhulme that it would be worthwhile to buy Crossage's for the high price asked. (He pointed out that dividends, though substantial, might have been higher, and that a good deal of the profits had been put to reserves, that heavy allowances had been made for depreciation, that the firm's capital assets were greatly undervalued in the balance-sheet, and that the latter now contained no allowance for the very valuable goodwill, trade marks, and patent rights.) It is significant that Hunt, for whom Lever had developed a high regard, became Chairman of Crosfield's in July 1919, when Haslam retired on account of ill-health. The death of Sir John Brunner earlier that month had facilitated a settlement with Lever's. On the other hand, Brunner Mond's had been approached by Jurgens with a view to forming an 'offensive alliance' against Lever's. Brunner's, however, preferred to establish friendly relations with their biggest customer.

An agreement was eventually signed on 8th October 1919, whereby Crosfield's and Gossage's at last passed completely into Lever's hands. For the whole of their Ordinary shares— £600,000 in Crosfield's and £300,000 in Gossage's—Lever's, in the guise of Associated Enterprises, were to pay £4,000,000, of which £1,000,000 was to be paid on 5th January 1920 and the remainder by annual instalments over the next five years. With Crosfield's, of course, Lever's also acquired the Erasmic Company and its French subsidiary, and Crosfield's holdings in the Natal Soap Works Ltd., the China Soap & Candle Co. Ltd., Apol Ltd., Palm Oil Estates Managers Ltd., and Hydrogenators Ltd. Moreover, Brunner Mond's agreed to transfer to Crossage's all their own holdings in the three last-named companies. At the same time, a settlement was reached between Brunner Mond's and Lever's in regard to their respective alkali and soap interests. Lever's and their associated companies agreed to buy from Brunner Mond's all their requirements of alkali,[1] at £4 10s. per ton until the end of 1920, and thereafter at an agreed price, or at 5s. per ton below the average realized price of soda ash delivered by Brunner's in the U.K. during that year (excluding deliveries to Lever's, Crosfield's, and Gossage's). Lever's and their associated companies, except Crosfield's and Gossage's, would produce caustic soda only for use in manufacturing their own soap and soap powders, and not for sale to any third party. Brunner Mond's tried similarly to restrict Crosfield's and Gossage's, so as to make a clear-cut division between soap and chemicals, but it was finally agreed that Crosfield's should be permitted to manufacture and sell up to

---

[1] Except in Europe and North America, where, however, each side undertook to give preferential treatment to the other.

12,500 tons of caustic soda per annum and any amount of silicate of soda, 'Carbosil', and 'Persil', while Gossage's were allowed similar rights in regard to the manufacture and sale of soda crystals, 'Aquamol', and silicate. As in earlier agreements, however, Crosfield's and Gossage's undertook not to export caustic soda, soda crystals, and 'Aquamol' to Europe, in order to safeguard the interests of the Solvay group. During the continuance of this alkali contract, Brunner Mond's agreed not to enter the soap trade.

Thus, after eight years of bitter rivalry and litigation, Lever's and Brunner Mond's had finally succeeded in drawing a boundary between their respective soap and soda empires. Crosfield's interests were still predominantly in fats, oils, and soap, and so they belonged logically to the Lever group. But they still held a substantial slice of chemical territory, for, as in 1910 (see above, p. 229), it proved impossible to separate their soda and silicate from their soap interests.

Unfortunately, there was a deplorable sequel to this agreement. Brunner Mond's had hoped to arrange a revised soda contract with the C.W.S. similar to that with Lever's, but failing in this they were obliged to continue supplying the C.W.S. at previous prices, unbeknown to Lever's. When this leaked out, in 1924, Lever's commenced proceedings in the High Court, claiming £1,000,000 for overpayment, and Brunner Mond's were forced to settle in November 1925. According to A. W. Tangye's diary, Lever's had paid '£1,000,000 more than we expected' for Crossage's, so matters were now all square and 'the Ghost of Lord Leverhulme [who had died on 7th May 1925] should have chuckled'.

THE pattern of the firm's manufacturing activities at the end of the war can be gauged from the following valuations of buildings, plant, and land for each of the departments at 30th November 1919. How near these figures were to true values, it is impossible to say. No account had been taken of war-time inflation; on the other hand these are the gross values, exclusive of depreciation.[1] The most striking feature is the great increase in the values of buildings and plant for oil-milling, hardening, and refining.

	Buildings £	Plant £	Land £
Soap (Household)	41,722	76,422	15,165
,, (Milling, i.e. Toilet) . . .	6,822	18,214	1,554
Export Soap (Warrington) . .	10,423	15,767	539
Carbosil	8,621	12,884	1,375
Persil	1,825	565	—
Stearine	937	4,552	1,199
Oil Extraction	17,205	31,308	754
Oil Pressing	10,621	41,683	—
Oil Treatment (Fat-hardening) .	36,542	85,345	1,409
Oil Refinery (V.B.)	16,529	31,435	1,329
Glycerine	14,467	53,268	4,646
Caustic	11,489	44,125	5,871
Silicate	5,318	18,498	3,278
Cement	9,159	20,921	559
Wharf and Warehouses . . .	17,732	5,786	1,956
Boilers and Fuel	8,617	99,116	4,731
Electric	11,500	36,166	542
Engineering	9,599	8,999	2,575
Packing	12,649	4,801	7,074
Printing & Litho	8,825	13,469	1,773
Cooperage	933	273	2,049
Cask-making	2,107	2,646	318
Locomotives	341	6,031	8,119
Wagons	—	9,603	—
Steamers & Flats (Lighterage) .	—	46,987	245
Motor Lorries, Cars & Cycles .	—	25,094	—
Motor Garages	2,800	55	2,456
New Transporter Bridge . . .	34,424	—	1,094
General Works	8,944	10,671	5,978
General Offices, Fire Station, etc.	21,602	4,685	3,217
Institute	34,084	2,208	2,517

[1] We have not included a number of plots of land, recently acquired and not yet developed; nor have we included tools and furniture.

CHAPTER XVIII

LEVER'S TAKE OVER
1919–29

LORD LEVERHULME had achieved one of his most cherished ambitions in acquiring Crosfield's, but it had cost him dearly. He had to pay an inflated price for a business whose profits had been swollen by war-time conditions and by the brief post-war boom. This boom broke, however, about six months later: markets collapsed both at home and abroad, prices came tumbling down, profits dwindled or disappeared, unemployment in Britain rose to two and a half millions by May 1921, and recovery was painfully slow in the following years. Leverhulme's business problems in these slump conditions were, as Professor Wilson has shown, seriously aggravated by his overweening optimism, especially by his acquisition of the Niger Company. Crosfield's were to suffer from his consequent financial difficulties.

On the other hand, one cannot but express astonished admiration at the immense energy and enthusiasm which, at seventy years of age and over, Lord Leverhulme still brought to business affairs. Indeed, the main interest of Crosfield's history between 1919 and his death in 1925 lies in a study of the effects of his take-over: the impact of his drive and personality, and how he tried to weld Crosfield's into the huge business organization of which Lever Brothers were the centre. By this time he was administering a vast empire, including soapworks, oil-refineries, plantations, and many other business interests throughout the world, yet somehow he found time to consider not only the major aspects of Crosfield's activities, but many of the minor ones as well. His phenomenal energy is evidenced by several fat volumes of surviving letters and telegrams, and references to innumerable visits, meetings, and 'phone calls, whereby he kept in constant touch with Crosfield's directors. Not merely did he examine and often revise yearly accounts, consider major proposals for capital expenditure and new products, and exercise general control over manufacturing, selling, and advertising policy; he also looked at monthly deliveries, studied comparative costs, commented upon particular advertisements, trade marks, and designs, and kept an eye on the firm's 'house organ' (*Crosfield's Flag*), the organization of its departmental councils and committees, and matters relating to social welfare. His special interests were financial and commercial affairs, and labour relations; on several occasions he confessed his ignorance of technical matters, but he showed keen appreciation of their importance.

The evidence relating to Crosfield's tends to confirm Professor Wilson's view that control of the vast Lever business was 'still a personal autocracy'. But it also suggests that Leverhulme was not entirely self-willed and tyrannical. He frequently took advice and criticism, for example, from Giles Hunt and C. F. Huffam, successive Chairmen of Crosfield's, and on several occasions when there were differences of opinion he gave way. He certainly recognized that he must have the willing co-operation of the Directors of associated companies. Thus on 7th April 1922 he wrote to Hunt, regarding a difference on 'Pinkobolic' advertising: 'It would be quite impossible for me to enforce an unwelcome policy upon any of our companies. So much depends on . . . our seeing "eye to eye". . . .' But he usually got his way, by powerful argument and by force of his immense personal prestige and experience. Occasionally, indeed, he was peremptory in his attitude, as in October 1921 when he countermanded proposals for additional capital expenditure: in view of the slump, he said, 'I must ask you on behalf of the ordinary shareholders [Associated Enterprises, Ltd.] to defer all further consideration of the same for the present'. But he was generally more flexible in attitude, preferring to offer 'help' and 'advice' rather than to dictate.

Lord Leverhulme also came to realize—contrary to the view expressed by H. R. Edwards, and to a greater extent than Professor Wilson has appreciated—that he must try to give some administrative coherence to his vast empire, and to achieve some 'rationalization' of the manufacturing and selling activities of the numerous associated companies.[1] Professor Wilson has

---

[1] H. R. Edwards, *op. cit.*, p. 170, n. 1, suggests that Lord Leverhulme had a typical 'founder mentality', with little idea of how to exploit the great

referred to the emergence during this period of Lever Brothers' Special Committee and Finance Committee, and of the various Group Boards and Export Trade Board. Leverhulme's correspondence with Crosfield's reveals that he was constantly wrestling with the problem of how to combine centralized control and integration with the maintenance of individual companies and internal competition. This problem was not easy of solution, considering the complex ramifications of the business, the amount of capital invested in existing plant, the possible loss of goodwill, the question of redundancy and the difficulties of trade depression. 'Rationalization' is easier in economic theory than in business practice.

The question of Crosfield's relationship with Lever's, and also with Gossage's, arose immediately after their take-over. All the existing Directors—Giles Hunt (Chairman), E. F. Armstrong, F. J. Burlton, C. H. Hamilton, C. F. Huffam, R. F. Jones, G. H. K. Kingdon, and H. Roberts—were retained, but, following the resignation of Roscoe Brunner and Emile Mond, three representatives of Lever Brothers were appointed: W. H. Lever (Lord Leverhulme's son), J. Gray, and J. L. Ferguson. These appointments aroused some feeling on Crosfield's Board. Giles Hunt had been given the impression, so he wrote to Lord Leverhulme on 2nd February 1920, that 'the entire direction and management of the business would be left, as it had been up to then, in the hands of the Board of Directors', but now Lord Leverhulme had not only appointed these additional Directors but had also 'named a number of Directors and officials of Lever Bros. as members of certain group [departmental] committees', which he wished to be established at Crosfield's. At the same time Hunt complained because he had not been given the Chairmanship of Gossage's as well as of Crosfield's, and he was also dissatisfied with Lord Leverhulme's proposed bonus scheme for himself and his co-Directors. He threatened to resign and go to Jurgens. Leverhulme therefore had to compromise. He could

---

business he had created. But Dr. Edwards has clearly never examined the Leverhulme correspondence. Moreover, he has overlooked the time factor: not until after the war, and after absorption of Crossage's and settlement with Brunner Mond's, was Leverhulme in a position to carry through his earlier schemes for cutting manufacturing, selling, and advertising costs (see above, p. 225). In his few remaining years he did begin to tackle the problems of 'rationalization'.

not concede independence to Crosfield's Board, 'without any help . . . from Lever Brothers or myself', and he pointed out the benefits of co-operation, but he agreed to withdraw Lever's Directors from Crosfield's committees. He insisted on separating Crosfield's and Gossage's and running them as 'two entirely distinct firms, exactly on the same lines as we worked Messrs. Pears and Messrs. Vinolia', but he mollified Hunt's disappointment by giving him a bonus of 2 per cent of Crosfield's profits, with a further 2½ per cent to be shared among the other Directors; at the same time he agreed to the purchase of Oughtrington Hall in Cheshire for £10,000 as a residence for Hunt. Crosfield's Chairman and Directors certainly did not suffer financially as a result of Lever's take-over.[1]

Hunt was strongly opposed to the splitting of Crosfield's and Gossage's joint export department, but Leverhulme insisted upon it, considering that friendly rivalry would be good for each business. Crosfield's therefore re-established their own export department, in the Liver Building, Liverpool; C. H. Hamilton having transferred to Gossage's (of which he was soon to become Chairman), T. Esmonde-Deane was appointed manager, with R. F. Jones still exercising directorial responsibility for the export trade. Competition still continued between Crosfield's and Lever's in foreign markets. There were complaints of underselling, for example, in August and September 1920, which necessitated a conference; Lord Leverhulme hoped that it would 'result in sympathetic working and absence of friction in future'. Six months previously, however, while welcoming co-operation in the West Indies, he considered that 'Gossages and Crosfields [should] have their own exclusive staff of salesmen and agents', and thought it 'would be madness to take any step that would tend to swamp the identity of Crosfield's and Gossage's in the export trade'.

Very soon, however, he began to modify these views. Thus in 1920–1 he came to favour the setting-up of a joint manufacturing and selling organization in China, and the China Soap Company Ltd. was eventually formed in February 1923; similarly

---

[1] Hunt's salary as Chairman was £5,000, plus bonus, with a guaranteed minimum total of £7,250. Other Directors had a flat rate of £3,000, plus bonus, with minimum guarantees varying from £4,250 to £6,250. One should add, however, that Directors subsequently appointed were not treated so handsomely!

in India, with the establishment of Lever Brothers (India) Ltd. in March 1922, and also in West Africa. In each case the capital was jointly subscribed by Lever's, Crosfield's, and Gossage's, and there was an agreed apportionment of the trade; in India, for example, Leverhulme proposed that Lever's should have 50 per cent, Gossage's 40 per cent, and Crosfield's 10 per cent, though Crosfield's would still have their own representative in India. Moreover, Leverhulme proposed in November 1921 that the joint committee set up for the China project should also 'consider the question of the organization in the export trade' generally, with a view to 'a broader and wider policy'. Here was the germ of the Export Trade Board, established in 1924, 'to obviate any undue competition between Companies, to facilitate the working of the Export business, and to increase the Export trade'. This was to lead ultimately to the formation, in 1928, of United Exporters Ltd.

In the same way, Leverhulme sought to achieve co-ordination in the sphere of raw materials. Thus Crosfield's interests in Palm Oil Estates Managers Ltd. and Apol Ltd. were taken over, to be merged into Lever's other West African interests. In November 1920 Giles Hunt referred to joint 'arrangements with regard to the purchase of West African produce'; his experience in that part of the world enabled him to give valuable assistance to the Niger Company, of which he became Chairman for a short time. In May 1923 we find Lord Leverhulme stressing to Kingdon the need for 'close contact between Warrington and Lever Brothers' Buying Department at Liver Building'; whereupon Kingdon informed him that 'the two staffs have been working satisfactorily together for some time . . . this association will be maintained, and if possible made even closer'.

The tremendous slump in 1920–1 caused Lord Leverhulme to devote much thought to the problems of excess capacity and how to operate the various manufacturing activities of the 'family' most efficiently in such circumstances. Some degree of 'rationalization' seemed sensible: that certain firms should supply the family's requirements of particular products, while other plants should be closed down. Visiting Warrington in May 1921, he found 'that both the Silicate Plant and the Caustic Soda Plant as well as [those for] the refining and hardening of fats were all practically unemployed and consequently were having to bear overhead charges which seriously cut into the profit'. He therefore had to consider how 'to keep the plant at Warrington fully occupied'. He soon concluded that the best solution would be for Crosfield's to produce some of the requirements of hydrogenated and refined oils, caustic soda, and silicate for Lever Brothers and associated companies, though he did not apparently contemplate any scrapping of plant. It had been agreed with Brunner Mond's at the time of the take-over that Crosfield's deliveries of caustic soda to Lever Brothers or associated companies should not be included in their agreed quota of 12,500 tons. Lever Brothers were also free to make their own caustic, and did produce liquid for their own soapmaking, but they did not manufacture solid or powdered; Lord Leverhulme felt that 'rather than put up a solid caustic plant at Port Sunlight it would be better to pass the business through Messrs. Crosfield's to keep your plant working at the maximum'. Silicate might be similarly supplied, especially as Crosfield's were found to have a comparative cost advantage.

The situation was complicated, however, by the problem of inter-company accounting (similar to that of Crosfield's own inter-departmental transfers). Leverhulme insisted that these products should be supplied to Lever Brothers at cost price, not at market price as Hunt suggested.

The sole advantage that would accrue to Crosfields and Gossages would, therefore, be the reduced overhead charges on the remainder of their oils and fats, or caustic soda or silicate of soda for consumption in their own works or marketed elsewhere resulting from the increased production made possible by Lever Brothers . . . It would be unsound to have one Associated Company or Lever Brothers making a profit out of any other [Associated] Company or . . . out of the Parent Company. I have always been very strict on this point otherwise a Company might look to be doing extremely well, then Lever Brothers suddenly withdraw their support and the Company does badly.

Clearly Lord Leverhulme—incorrigible optimist that he was —regarded these measures as temporary only, pending a return to active trade and full production. He does not appear to have had any long-term plans for drastic rationalization. A possible solution was to sell Crosfield's and Gossage's caustic and silicate departments to Brunner Mond's. The latter were certainly keen to buy; they had tried to make a clear-cut division between soap and chemicals during the take-over negotiations. On several occasions between 1921 and 1924 they broached the subject, but nothing came of it. There were clearly advantages in Crosfield's retaining their chemical plant, which saved the Lever 'family' from entire dependence on Brunner Mond's. At the same time, Crosfield's and Brunner Mond's remained on very friendly terms and co-operated closely in trade affairs. Thus they continued the joint regulation of prices and output quotas for caustic soda. Indeed, co-operation went even farther: in November 1923, for example, there was an agreement that Brunner Mond's would 'take over our selling arrangements for India and China in respect of Silicate of Soda, Caustic Soda and Glycerine'.

After the war, Brunner Mond's commenced silicate manufacture, but do not appear to have become very serious competitors of Crosfield's. International rivalry still continued, but friendly contacts were resumed between Crosfield's, Gossage's, and the major continental manufacturers of silicate, particularly in export markets.

Lord Leverhulme had for many years—long before he absorbed Crosfield's—urged the need for co-operation combined with friendly rivalry. This he interpreted as competition at agreed prices, i.e. competition in production costs, quality, packing, and selling. This policy was maintained within the Lever 'family' and was defined very clearly in November–December 1922, when he intervened in a dispute between the Erasmic Company and Gibbs regarding their competing brands of solidified dentifrice:

> . . . in the family the only competition possible is in novelty and quality . . . The price should be the same and the weight the same . . . I want us all to compete strenuously on everything except price. It is really such a poverty of imagination to be only able to compete on price and takes us back into the ruts of the very worst days of the soap trade forty years ago.

In the following January he returned to the same point in a letter to J. H. B. Wigginton, managing director of the Erasmic Company:

> Competition is going to be increasingly keen in my opinion.

Victory will not be to the toilet soap maker or perfumer who sells at the lowest prices but to the one who shows the greatest originality in ideas or the greatest intelligence in advertising and who most correctly catches the public taste.

He sought constantly to keep associated companies on their toes. Although Lever Brothers had now absorbed the major part of the British soap industry, there was vigorous competition in the early 'twenties from the C.W.S., the British Oil & Cake Mills (with their 'New Pin' soap), Bibby's of Liverpool, and the American Palmolive Company. In the edible fats trade there was the much more formidable competition of the Dutch makers, Van den Bergh's and Jurgens. Improved efficiency was clearly important, and so we find Lord Leverhulme frequently requiring comparisons between the manufacturing and selling costs of the various departments at Warrington and Port Sunlight. He was also compelled to recognize that internal competition could be wasteful. He therefore urged frequent visits between firms in the family, for sharing of technical information, and felt (in May 1921, when recommending a visit to Crosfield's and other works by Cecil Walton from Port Sunlight) that 'it would be a great help to the business as a whole if we could standardize on our methods in factory and workshop management'. He had written to Giles Hunt in the previous January regarding the research laboratory, 'which I understand it has been arranged by Mr. Buchanan and yourself should in future be a joint one as between Lever Brothers and Warrington instead of each having their own separate Research Laboratory'.

The desire for standardization and improved efficiency was also visible in the establishment in 1923 of a new factory control and costing system, brought from Port Sunlight by John Inglis, formerly chief accountant and then a director of Lever Brothers, who had just been appointed a director of Crosfield's: thus Bank Quay entered the Hollerith machine age. The same motive underlay the introduction of a works committee and departmental committees on the Port Sunlight model, and of Lord Leverhulme's co-partnership and social welfare schemes.[1]

In selling and advertising, too, there was a similar tendency towards central control and co-ordination. The United Kingdom Soap Makers' Association, which fixed prices, etc. for the

[1] See below, pp. 316–7.

home trade, was now dominated by Lever's. So, too, was the
Glycerine Association, which was resurrected immediately after
the war. Its organization was now tightened and the question
was raised (by John McDowell, Lever Brothers' secretary,
according to a letter by Lord Leverhulme to Giles Hunt in
June 1922) 'whether it would not be better to form the Glycerine
Association into a Limited Liability Company', because of legal
contractual difficulties. This pointed the way to the formation
of Glycerine Limited in January 1929. British glycerine producers continued to face strong competition from the continent,
but in autumn 1923 we read in Crosfield's minutes of 'satisfactory arrangements made with the Dutch makers for the
maintenance of prices', along the same lines as the pre-war
agreements.

Competition between Crosfield's and Gossage's for the silicate
requirements of the Lever family was settled by Lord Leverhulme in January 1923 by apportioning the trade between
them. The efforts of the two firms ought not, he told Giles Hunt,
to be wasted on internal competition, but 'had better be devoted
to outside business'.

In August 1921 Lord Leverhulme wrote concerning 'a project
for the sale by Lever Brothers, Limited, of [cattle] Cake and
Meal produced by Lever Brothers, Limited, and their Associated Companies'. Crosfield's were already selling a good deal of
their production to Lever's, but had recently concluded a very
unfavourable contract with Silcocks, the cattle-food merchants,
for which Hunt was soundly rated by Lord Leverhulme, who
regretted 'that the sale should be made without first obtaining
the opinion of Lever Brothers who . . . are much more in the
way of selling cake than Crosfields and whose interest it is to
advise you to the utmost of our ability and knowledge on the
subject. We are always glad to help all we can.'

Lord Leverhulme, it is clear, kept a very sharp eye on Crosfield's trading activities, commenting upon monthly deliveries,
prices, profit margins, etc. He was assisted, of course, by Lever
Brothers' representatives on Crosfield's Board, and by the
Group Board, whereby Crosfield's came under the general
surveillance of J. L. Ferguson. Leverhulme took a particularly
strong interest in advertising matters. Not only did Crosfield's
directors have to discuss general advertising policy and ex-

penditure with him, but their advertising department had to confer on the details of press, poster, and other advertisements with Lever Brothers' experts, particularly John Cheshire. Lord Leverhulme himself frequently commented upon particular advertisements, handing out praise or condemnation. In June 1921, for instance, we find him applauding an 'excellent' advertisement for 'Persil'—'The little circle around the word "Persil" is a stroke of genius'—adding, characteristically, 'I hope there is a sufficient profit on this article'. Advertisements must be arresting, he emphasized in a crushing comment in July 1920:

I have had good opportunities of observing in driving about London the advertising effect of the Erasmic and Perfection posters. I do not think you will get value out of these posters. They are very beautiful and very artistic but they do not arrest attention. In fact, it was not until my attention was called to them that I saw them and I must have been driving past them for a few weeks and had never seen them.

He sent some advertisements from the American magazine *Life* as examples to follow. On several occasions he similarly expressed his personal reactions.

He took an especially keen interest in the launching of new products, such as Crosfield's proposed scheme for refined edible palm oil, and likewise for dyes, in 1921. He repeatedly emphasized his belief in the policy of selling proprietary branded goods. He suggested trade marks and commented on proposed packs, with an astonishing eye for detail of design, colour, etc. Similarly, he asked in June of that year that on a forthcoming visit to Warrington all the 'Erasmic' packs should be displayed for inspection by himself and Cheshire. (He had commented upon their appearance at the recent Chemists' Exhibition.)

But obviously Lord Leverhulme could not control all the details of advertising policy. He therefore began to devise measures of central control. This, however, was apt to cause friction. Crosfield's co-operated happily with Cheshire, but when a new man, C. F. Plowman, was installed in Lever House early in 1922, with the duty of 'advising and assisting' on advertising, Hunt and Huffam soon began to complain of his excessive interference, and a conference had to be arranged to smooth matters out. Eventually, towards the end of 1923,

Ernest Walls was placed in central control of all advertising (as Crosfield's were informed by Lord Leverhulme on 19th November), because there had been 'too much overlapping and confusion in the past which has only led to wasted money and squandered efforts'. Henceforth no new advertising scheme was to be initiated 'without his knowledge and endorsement'. At the same time, John Cheshire would be 'responsible for arranging all Advertising Schemes in detail', securing space for press and poster displays, designing packages, etc.

Nevertheless, though advertising schemes had now to be approved and controlled by headquarters, competitive selling still continued. Crosfield's still pushed their numerous brands of soap against those of Lever Brothers and other associated companies. But the writing was on the wall. Should outside competition become more serious, there would inevitably have to be more rationalization and centralization. Moreover, Lord Leverhulme was gradually having to delegate more responsibility and to create formal administrative controls at Lever House. Another move in this direction was evident at the beginning of 1923, when L. H. Hartland-Swann, Chairman of the Icilma Company, recently acquired by Lever's, was given general oversight of the toilet trade. J. H. B. Wigginton, managing director of the Erasmic Company, was told by Lord Leverhulme to 'keep in close touch with Mr. Hartland-Swann on all matters connected with the toilet soap department and perfumery articles'. 'This', Lord Leverhulme explained, 'is all the more necessary as I am feeling myself that owing to pressure of work in so many directions it is impossible for me today to find the time to devote to this department of Lever Brothers' business.'

Moreover, in May of that year the 'Control Grouping' arrangement was reorganized. Companies were grouped by types of product instead of territorially. Crosfield's now came under Hartland-Swann, instead of J. L. Ferguson. Hartland-Swann, so Lord Leverhulme informed Crosfield's Chairman, 'is making a programme which will enable him to be in personal touch with yourself and all other Companies under his group at least once a month and he will welcome at all times any visits or letters from yourself.'

It was in financial affairs that Crosfield's dependence was

most marked. All large items of capital or advertising expenditure had to be approved by Lord Leverhulme or by Lever Brothers' Finance Committee, and Lord Leverhulme exercised vigilant control over the annual accounts and distribution of profits. There is no doubt that his financial difficulties (described in the *History of Unilever*) caused him to 'milk' the associated companies. Crosfield's, for instance, were charged up to £250,000 annually for 'management expenses'; they were pressed to loan all their available cash balances to Lever Brothers; they were repeatedly called upon to make advances to Lever's in anticipation of dividends, and even to declare dividends which (as Giles Hunt protested in January 1921) were 'in excess of what the Company would be justified in paying', and which involved the risk of inadequate allowances for depreciation and reserves. They were also under heavy pressure to invest in Lever's issues of Preference shares, into which their loans were generally converted, instead of being repaid. During the slump such investments were no doubt sensible, 'it appearing [according to Crosfield's Board minutes in November 1922] that there was no chance of the Company being able to use the whole of the Capital to advantage in trading'. Lord Leverhulme pointed out in April 1924 that Lever's 20 per cent Preference shares, yielding 10 per cent on the purchase price, were providing 'the biggest return . . . that is possible' (see also below, p. 315). Nevertheless, Crosfield's Directors became very concerned at the increasing size of their holdings, and finally dug in their toes in autumn 1923, when they would have had to borrow from the bank in order to purchase more shares; Lord Leverhulme therefore relented.

By the end of 1925, however, the book (cost) value of Crosfield's holdings of Lever's Preferred Ordinary shares had risen to £1,713,121. On the other hand, Lever Brothers had in 1920 taken up £599,000 of Crosfield's issue of Preference shares. They were to a considerable extent 'taking in each other's washing', since the raising of additional capital from the public had been made difficult by the slump and by misgivings about Leverhulme's financial dealings, particularly in regard to the Niger Company. Crosfield's large holdings of Lever's shares prevented them, as Giles Hunt repeatedly pointed out, from raising more capital for their own expansion. At the same time they were instructed by Lord Leverhulme to cut back on building and repairs from mid-1920 onwards. One cannot resist the conclusion that, as the Crosfields, Haslam, and others had feared, the firm was being exploited for the benefit of Lord Leverhulme's multifarious schemes. On the other hand, no doubt, taking a broader view of the whole business, he would have justified the transfer of resources from one part of it to another—to the development, for example, of West African supplies of raw materials, or to the acquisition of food businesses, which in the long run were to pay handsome dividends.

Moreover, Crosfield's did continue to expand during this period. In spring 1920 the authorized (or nominal) capital was doubled to £10,000,000 by creating £2,000,000 more Ordinary shares and £3,000,000 'A' Cumulative Preference shares, but none of the former were issued and only £1,500,000 of the latter, with dividend fixed at 7½ per cent. Thus the Company's issued capital now consisted of £1,000,000 in Ordinary shares and £3,400,000 in Preference shares. With these additional resources, there was another dramatic burst of expansion in land, buildings, and plant during the post-war period.

For some years previously, the Company had been acquiring many additional bits and pieces of land and property surrounding the works. By piecemeal purchases, totalling about £20,000, from 1914 onwards they acquired leasehold land and cottages across Liverpool Road, in the Thewlis Street, Powys Street, and Baxter Street area—on which joiners' shops, engineers' offices, and the Centenary Institute had been built—and freehold land and property including cottages at Quay Fold and the *Bowling Green* inn, the *Railway Tavern* (near the railway bridge), the adjoining Bank Quay (Westwell's) coalyard, and the remaining cottages in Factory Lane. For sums totalling £6,000 to £7,000 they also secured both freehold and leasehold rights to the Whitecross House and adjoining property and to premises at the corner of Sankey Street and Parker Street, over the railway bridge, where they established motor garages. It was Company policy, wherever possible, to acquire freehold: thus they purchased in 1918 for £2,755 the freehold of the former Bank Quay Glass Works, Glasshouse Row, and Factory Lane property, previously leasehold.

To these relatively small purchases several major acquisitions were added. A considerable area—the site of the former Bank Quay Foundry—was secured south of the Garston railway. In 1913 the Company had acquired for £4,700 the freehold of part of this land, on which H. D. Pochin & Co.'s chemical works were built, and in 1919 for £18,000 they bought the leasehold. (They had for some years sub-leased part of this land, on which the V.B. plant had been erected.) Pochin's were given a twenty-one-year lease of the area on which their acid plant stood, but in 1922 Crosfield's paid £4,000 for the unexpired term. Meanwhile, in 1916 they had bought adjoining leasehold property (previously sub-leased by the firm) from the Pearson & Knowles Coal & Iron Co. for £10,000.

At the same time the Company extended its holdings north of the Garston line by acquiring the land and buildings of Robinson, Son & Co.'s glassworks. The freehold was secured in 1918 for just below £4,000, and the leasehold and premises for £41,000 (part of the land having been sub-leased since 1915). The glassworks, however, continued to occupy a portion of the site on a yearly lease.

In 1920 Crosfield's paid £6,000 for leasehold property in Academy Street, and also rented adjoining premises, for use as a box-making factory. At the same time they bought the freehold of the Arpley Meadows land (covering nearly eighty-five acres)—previously leased as a source of clay for the cement works—for a total of £25,000. A much more dubious venture was the purchase in the same year of the Dinbren Estate and Pentrefelin works, near Llangollen, for a total of £29,000, with the intention of acquiring supplies of lime more cheaply. (Hunt stated in October 1922 that the firm was consuming 225 tons per week.) The scheme eventually proved a failure: the quarries and works had to be handed over to Lime Firms Ltd., of Llandebie, South Wales, from whom Crosfield's purchased most of their lime, and the estate was sold in 1925 for £13,500, after Giles Hunt had received another ticking-off from Lord Leverhulme.

At this point the historian of Crosfield's can heave a great sigh of relief, for most of the firm's acquisitions of land and premises had now been completed. Emerging from the plethora of deeds, dating back to the eighteenth century, and looking at the map, one can see how all these piecemeal acquisitions had

gradually built up into the firm's modern site—a large con-
solidated area of land, comprising practically the whole of
Bank Quay, between the great loop of the Mersey and Liverpool Road, as well as across the river.

On the newly acquired land, the Company proceeded, in the
years after 1918, to erect a number of new buildings and plant.
The development schemes stopped by the war were now resumed, and fresh ones were started, several of them before
Lever's took over. The oil refinery (V.B. plant) on the Cheshire
side was completed by the end of 1921, together with the new
pressing plant and cake warehouse. Another addition to the
growing complex of buildings across the river was a plant,
costing £20,000, for producing the oil-bleaching material,
'Acsil'. The cement works, re-opened just before the end of the
war, was extended at an eventual cost of over £21,000.

On the Lancashire side, the biggest undertaking was the
erection of a new five-storied 'Erasmic' building—the present-
day Powders building—on the eastern part of the land acquired
from Robinson's glassworks company. The original estimate for
this building and plant, early in 1920, was £175,000, but its
construction was delayed by the slump and the consequent
restriction on capital expenditure; it was not completed until
the middle of 1923. The space previously occupied by the milling and perfumery departments could now be utilized for an
extension to the soapery and for a new four-storied tablet
building, with additional warehousing accommodation for soap
on the ground floor; these cost altogether well over £100,000.
The tablet building was situated between the existing soap
warehouse, printing and paper stores building, which was also
extended (£20,000), and the soap export building, just completed—all of them extending to Factory Lane, on the other
side of which the saw-milling and timber-storage premises were
now grouped. In addition, there was the new melting-out plant
in Pochin's yard (£20,000) and more electricity generating
capacity (£40,000).

The erection of these new buildings was accompanied by a
steady stream of orders for new plant: more pans, frames, etc.
for the soapery; more boilers; more stills for the oil-extraction,
refining, and glycerine plants; more kibbling (cake-cutting)
and mealing machinery for the oil-mill; more machines for

15 (*a*) Erasmic building, external view, 1923

15 (*b*) Erasmic building, internal view, 1923

making and printing packets, bags, tins, cartons, and boxes; more packeting, filling, and wrapping machines for powders; more conveyors and elevators; more storage tanks; more steamers and barges, railway wagons, lorries (including the first tankers), motor cars and vans. Annual expenditure on land, buildings, machinery, and plant averaged £227,000 in 1920-1, but fell to £105,000 in 1924-5. All this tremendous constructional activity required a large engineering department, which was employing about 650 men in spring 1923—probably more in 1920-1—and about 530 a year later. The total number of the Company's employees in 1924 was 3,300, of whom 1,100 were women and girls.

Building slackened off somewhat in the following years. Capital expenditure totalled £195,000 in 1926, but averaged only £61,000 annually in 1927-9. Nevertheless, there were some important developments and improvements: the wharf warehouse was reconstructed, new silicate and caustic plants were erected, and 'Persil' manufacture was extended on the top floor of the printing building.

The post-war years therefore witnessed a considerable increase in the firm's assets, as the following figures demonstrate:

	Total Assets	Land, Buildings, Plant and Machinery[1]	Stocks on hand	Investments and Loans	Debtors	Cash
	£	£	£	£	£	£
30th Nov. 1919	4,277,388	899,855	1,915,884	587,945	678,034	195,670
30th Nov. 1929	5,693,286	1,532,103	984,515	2,702,569	337,135	67,125

The most striking feature of these figures was not, however, the increase in land, buildings, and plant, but that in investments and loans, mainly to associated companies. We have previously noted the huge growth of the Company's holdings of shares in Lever Brothers. Those in Apol Ltd., Palm Oil Estates Managers Ltd., and the Natal Soap Works Ltd. had all been exchanged

[1] After allowing for depreciation, the Reserve for which was increased from £352,483 to £805,504 between 1919 and 1929. For comparison with earlier years, the Depreciation Reserve should be added to the above figures to obtain the book (cost) values.

for such shares. Nearly half the Lever Brothers shares were sold in 1927, but an equivalent amount was invested in De Lever's Zeep Maatschappij, of Vlaardingen. Crosfield's still held the shares in the Erasmic Company, and in 1925 had also bought those in its French subsidiary. Moreover, in 1920-1 they had acquired a large proportion of the Ordinary capital of J. & E. Atkinson Ltd., the well-known perfumery and soapmaking firm. They had also bought shares in various associated companies overseas, as Lever's set about reorganizing the export trade. Thus they had secured shares in Lever Brothers (India) Ltd. in exchange for their goodwill and assets in that country. Likewise they had exchanged their shares in the China Soap & Candle Co. Ltd. for those of the China Soap Co. Ltd. and Candles Ltd., and had also acquired a holding in the West African Soap Company Ltd. More recently they had bought a block of shares in United Exporters Ltd. Their only sizeable outside investment had been the purchase in 1919 of £100,000 of Government 4 per cent Funding Loan, sold in 1927-8.

The striking increase in the Company's investments contrasts with the large reduction in stocks. The slump caught Crosfield's with very large stockpiles, built up during the war and the post-war boom. These had to be heavily depreciated on account of the huge fall in prices. Tallow, for example, which had shot up to an average of nearly £87 per ton in 1919, fell to £37 per ton in 1922, recovering to just over £45 in 1925; copra fell from nearly £57 per ton in 1920 to £25 in 1922 and then rose to about £29 in 1925; the figures for palm oil were £70, £33, and £40 respectively; whale oil dropped even more dramatically from £83 per ton in 1920 to £31 in 1921, recovering to £39 in 1925. Prices of raw materials thus fell by more than half in the depression of 1921-2, and did not recover very much in the following years. By heavily writing down and using up stocks, Crosfield's readjusted their position, but not without difficulty. In the later 'twenties, prices of raw materials began to fall again, though more gently, and by 1929 were at about the 1921-2 level. These lower prices, of course, meant lower manufacturing costs, so Crosfield's were fairly well off during these years.

Soap prices continued to rise sharply in the immediate post-war inflation. The *Report on the Soap Industry* by the Standing

Committee on Trusts at the beginning of 1921 severely criticized Lever Brothers for keeping soap prices too high, but they soon followed raw materials downward, as demand fell during the slump and outside competition increased. 'Perfection', for example, which had risen to 1s. per lb., together with 'Sunlight', etc., in the early months of 1920, dropped to 6½d. per lb. before the end of 1922. From then onwards, however, soap prices were fairly stable, so that, with costs of raw materials falling, profit margins were substantially improved.

In the home soap trade, Crosfield's were getting an average of about £79 per ton in 1919–20, but by 1923 about £49. Prices declined more gradually thereafter to £45 in 1929. Sales tonnages dropped heavily, even in the boom of 1919, to 23,000 tons, well below the 1917–18 figures and not much more than in 1913; but high prices kept up revenue and profits at £1,703,000 and £303,000 (over £13 per ton) respectively.[1] In the slump of 1920–1 tonnages dropped to little more than 18,000. They then recovered to an average of well over 20,000 in the years 1922–7, but dropped to about 19,000 annually in 1928–9. Sales revenue, on the other hand, slid almost continuously downwards, with prices, and was only £876,000 in 1929, little more than half the 1919 figure. Profits also collapsed to £106,000 (£5·7 per ton) in 1920, but—since prices of raw materials fell even further than those of soap—gradually recovered in the following years to an average of £170,000 annually (£8·5 per ton) in 1926–9.[2]

The export trade also made a good recovery. Prices followed a falling trend similar to that in the home trade, though on a lower level, and sales likewise declined, from an annual average of 13,500 tons (£898,000) in 1920–1 to 9,000 tons (£410,000) in 1922, but then recovered to well over 15,000 tons (£570,000) in 1927. Profits fluctuated much more than in the home trade, and margins were lower. A profit of £85,000 (£6 per ton) in 1919 was followed by a loss of £24,000 in 1920, but as trade recovered profits rose rather unsteadily to £52,000 (£3·4 per

---

[1] All the sales figures given in this chapter are for *gross* sales extracted from the nominal ledgers. For comparison with the war-time figures (see above, p. 268), *net* home soap sales in 1919 were £1,327,000, net exports £648,000.

[2] Profits figures are also taken from the trading accounts in the nominal ledgers.

ton) in 1927. From 1928 onwards Crosfield's soap exports were taken over by United Exporters Ltd.

The toilet trade suffered similarly from the post-war depression. Sales of milled soaps (mostly 'Erasmic'), after rising to nearly 2,300 tons in 1920, dropped to around 1,500 in the next few years. The Erasmic Company's turnover fell from £716,000 in 1920 to an annual average of £384,000 in 1922–4; exports were especially hard hit. Little profit was made in the early 'twenties. In 1925–7, however, sales recovered to average £435,000 annually and net profits to £43,000; though trade fell off in the next two years, it remained fairly profitable.

The Lever combine's dominating position in the soap trade did not prevent a renewal of the pre-war advertising campaigns. Outside competition from the C.W.S., the British Oil & Cake Mills, and Bibby's, together with internal competition between members of the Lever combine, brought about a rapid increase in Crosfield's soap advertising expenditure, except for a severe cut in the slump of 1921. By 1924–5 it had reached £68,000 annually (well over £3 per ton), but in the later 'twenties expenditure was reduced to a yearly average of about £32,000 (well below £2 per ton). It was concentrated, as previously, on 'Perfection' and 'Pinkobolic', but did not prevent a steady decline in their sales. Those of 'Perfection' fell from nearly 13,000 tons in the *annus mirabilis* of 1918 to below 6,000 tons in 1929; 'Pinkobolic' from 3,700 to 2,800.

'Erasmic' advertising was similarly increased, to about £57,000 annually in 1925–9. Expenditure on export soap was also gradually raised, from £2,250 in 1919 to over £11,000 in 1927, but was still comparatively small, well below £1 per ton. In overseas markets, reliance was still primarily upon agents and representatives.

The difficulties of the post-war trade in hard soaps contrasts remarkably with the rapid growth of 'Persil' sales. These had stagnated—even declined during the war—since the original purchase of the patent from Henkel's in 1909. After the war, however, the figures began to soar rapidly. Sales rose, without ever faltering, from a mere 449 tons (£40,319) in 1919 to 9,464 tons (£746,206) in 1929. 'Persil' prices, which had averaged about £92 per ton in 1919–20, declined gradually to just below £79 per ton in 1926, at which level they remained throughout the later 'twenties. Raw materials, however, fell to a much greater extent, while costs were also cut by manufacturing improvements. Profits therefore rose from £8,610 in 1919 to £258,549 in 1929; from 1923 onwards they averaged around £24 per ton, or nearly 30 per cent on sales, despite high advertising costs.

A revolution was occurring in Crosfield's soap trade. While sales and profits of hard soaps were declining, 'Persil' had risen, almost from nothing, to become much the most profitable part of the business. The main reason for the rising demand for 'Persil' and other similar soap powders was the improved detergence and labour-saving convenience of these 'oxygenated' products, compared with earlier washing powders, soda, or hard soap. These advantages were brought home to housewives by a vigorous advertising campaign in the press, on posters, by vans and canvassing teams, by prize competitions, etc. Crosfield's travellers now covered the country by motor car, while the old horse-vans were replaced by motor-vans for canvassing. 'Institutes' were opened in large towns, to which the public were invited to bring clothing for free demonstrations of 'Persil' washing, while mobile laundry vans toured the smaller towns and villages. Advertising costs rose from £4,099 (£6 per ton) in 1920 to £87,547 (£11 per ton) in 1928.

The growing demand for 'Persil' necessitated greater productive capacity. It was therefore decided in 1921 to transfer its manufacture from the 'Carbosil' block to the former Stearine building (the present control laboratory for the Synthetic Fluid Catalyst Plant); the packing department was in the adjoining premises partly occupied by Robinson's glassworks. At this time, the 'base' mixture, consisting of soap, soda ash, and silicate, was reduced to small lumps in crutching pots, followed by weathering and cooling for four or five days in the wharf warehouse; perborate was then added, followed by more weathering, after which the mixture was fed to Kek grinding-mills. The resultant powder was then bagged, weathered, and eventually sent to the packing department. All these processes involved much time and handling. Much hand labour was also required in the packing department, though a number of packet-making and filling machines were introduced.

From 1925 onwards, however, after Sidney Newall became

manager of this department, a period of vigorous development began. He saved time and labour on the previously prolonged weathering and cooling processes, firstly by blowing cold air into the crutching pots, so that perborate could be added straightway to the base, and secondly by feeding the mixture into a new type of mill, where it was ground in a powerful current of air, which swept the resultant powder through a Rema separator for grading the particles. After a period of weathering, this powder was then ready for the packing machines. The first 'Rose' combined packeting, filling, and wrapping machines were introduced in 1925–6. For these Newall devised an improved automatic filler (patented by the firm), the first prototype of which he made at home and then brought to the works in a taxi! At the same time, more 'Rose' packing machines were installed. By 1929 output had risen to such an extent that it was necessary to move both making and packing to new premises, on the top floor of the printing building.

The competition of 'Persil' and other new washing powders brought about the gradual decline of the older product, 'Carbosil'. Sales fell from 11,756 tons (£231,144) in 1920 to 6,537 tons (£132,809) in 1929, although advertising was increased from about £2,500 (£0·2 per ton) in 1919 to a yearly average of £15,000 (£2 per ton) in 1926–9. Nevertheless, prices were well maintained, actually rising from £16 per ton in 1919 to £21 in 1921 and then staying around that figure. Profits therefore remained very substantial, rising from £21,790 (£2·1 per ton) in 1919 to £70,928 (£7 per ton) in 1923, but then gradually falling to around £40,000 (about £6 per ton) annually in 1928–9.

'Feather Flakes' did not prove a success. Sales slowly rose to nearly 700 tons (£42,000) in 1929, but fizzled out in later years. As a competitor to Lever's 'Lux', these flakes were a complete flop—not surprisingly, since nothing was spent on advertising them. It would seem that they were allowed, almost literally, to dissolve away. 'Glitto', on the other hand, a rival to 'Vim' as a scouring powder, after losing money in 1919–20, became a great success, backed by a vigorous advertising campaign. Sales rose from 1,783 tons (£61,144) in 1919 to 3,451 tons (£166,461) in 1927, though they began to fall gradually thereafter. This rise was paralleled by an increase in advertising expenditure from about £10,000 (£5·7 per ton) in 1919 to over £24,000

(£7 per ton) in 1928. At the same time, prices jumped from just over £34 per ton in 1919 to between £47 and £48 in 1921, and then tended to rise slightly in the following years. As a result, profits steadily increased to a yearly average of over £64,000 in 1925–9, nearly £20 per ton or 40 per cent on sales.

It is interesting to compare the rise of 'Glitto' with the decline of 'Carbosil'. In each case there was a comparable increase in advertising expenditure, but the one was in increasing public demand, while the other was not. Evidently advertising does not always pay—the product must be what the public wants; people are not so gullible as critics of advertising often suggest— but it is doubtful whether any new product, whatever its merits, could succeed without it, as the fate of 'Feather Flakes' suggests. On the other hand, it would appear that the demise of a sound, established product, like 'Carbosil', may be long delayed by sustained advertising, even though superior products may have come on to the market; the public do not quickly change their tastes and habits.

Both hard soaps and powders had benefited from the steep fall in the prices of raw materials, but Crosfield's oil-milling (extraction and pressing), oil treatment (fat hardening or hydrogenation), and oil-refining (vegetable butter) plants suffered severely thereby. Giles Hunt's cautious post-war estimates were, it turned out, wildly optimistic. The great drop in tallow prices caused the demand for hardened oils almost to disappear, except for small amounts of edible hardened nut oils. At the same time, trade depression, combined with loss of their highly profitable war-time markets and increasing competition, brought about a catastrophic decline in output and sales of refined edible oils (vegetable butters). The oil-milling plant, though producing mainly for internal consumption, was also, of course, seriously affected by the slump in the soap and edible fats trades. The latter was particularly hard hit, as Lord Leverhulme discovered at the end of May 1921:

The whole of Crosfields' edible fat plant is lying idle; the English Margarine Company, who used to be their biggest customers, have deserted them now that Jurgens has acquired that business.[1] Planters

[1] During the war Crosfield's had sold large quantities of refined oils, mainly palm-kernel oil, to this company at Broadgreen, Liverpool, but it was acquired by Jurgens early in 1920.

Margarine Company are not requiring any or likely to require any under the new arrangement for Planters taking over Lever Brothers' Refinery at Bromboro Port.[1] There is a loss on Crosfields' refining plant standing idle of some £20,000 a year in depreciation and overhead charges . . . The matter is therefore urgent.

As we have seen, Lord Leverhulme tried to help Crosfield's by providing outlets within the Lever combine for some of their production, but the trade figures show that he was able to do very little to check the steep decline in sales. Prices tumbled down: at the bottom of the slump, those of hardened and refined oils, and also of cake and meal, had fallen by more than half. The trading accounts are complicated, as in earlier years, by inter-departmental transfers, but the picture of slump is plain enough, contrasting sharply with the great war-time prosperity. The newly built oil-pressing and oil-refining plants began their working lives in the direst difficulties, while the long and costly development of hydrogenation bore disappointing fruit.

The production of the oil-extraction plant was almost entirely for internal consumption; outside sales were negligible. Output increased from about 7,500 tons in 1919 to over 8,000 in 1920, but then dropped to practically nothing in 1922—when the plant was apparently standing idle—and was only 2,000 tons in 1923. There are no surviving figures for extracted oils in the later 'twenties, but a fair idea of the plant's activity can be gained from the sales of the cattle-meal by-product. These fell from 7,995 tons (£92,141) in 1919 to 6,030 tons (£38,185) in 1921, prices dropping from £11·5 to £6·3 per ton. In 1922 meal sales were negligible, but recovered to 5,754 tons (£55,049) in 1925; prices also rose to £9·6 per ton. Losses, however, outweighed profits in the early 'twenties. Matters did not improve in the second half of the decade. Meal sales dropped to only 1,178 tons (£5,135) in 1926, and prices to £4·4 per ton. They rose to 3,252 tons (£32,878) in 1928, and prices to over £10 per ton, but the slump from 1929 onwards was to bring catastrophe.

The pressing plant experienced somewhat better fortunes. Here again, outside sales of oil were almost negligible, generally below 200 tons annually, except in 1921, when they rose to

---

[1] Lever's had entered the margarine business, through establishment of Planter's, at the beginning of the war, and their new factory at Bromborough, next to Port Sunlight, was completed just before the Armistice.

1,385 tons (£63,103). Oil output figures are only available for the early 'twenties. After rising from around 7,500 tons in 1919 to nearly 11,000 tons in 1920, they fell back gradually to just over 8,000 tons in 1923. Cattle-cake sales rose from 8,551 tons (£94,173) in 1919 to 13,314 tons (£113,642) in 1920, then declined to 11,200 tons (£60,046) in 1923. The drastic reduction in sales revenue was mainly due to the slump in prices, from £11 per ton in 1919 to £5·4 in 1923. A loss of nearly £14,000 was suffered in 1921. One can appreciate Lord Leverhulme's annoyance at the unprofitable contract with Silcocks.[1]

Cake sales shot up to over 19,000 tons (£112,000) in 1926, but prices remained unprofitable at less than £6 per ton. In the following years, moreover, though prices recovered to around £8 per ton, sales steadily declined to below 7,000 tons (£60,000) in 1929 and fell almost completely away in 1930. On balance, cake (like meal) was being sold at a loss. One must remember, however, that the main purpose of both the pressing and extraction plants was to provide oil for the soapery and refinery.

The oil treatment (hydrogenation) plant, on the other hand, had enjoyed huge war-time sales, in addition to providing hardened fats for internal consumption. These outside sales, however, as we have seen, rapidly dried up after the war, while internal consumption was also seriously reduced, especially by curtailment of the refinery's output. Even in the boom year of 1919, production fell from over 24,000 tons in the last year of the war to below 15,000 tons; but much worse was to follow. Sales dropped from 6,268 tons (£521,713) in 1919 to practically nothing in 1921, when the hardening plant was apparently at a standstill. Prices crashed from £87 per ton in 1920 to less than £33 per ton in 1923. Internal consumption also dropped, from over 8,000 tons in 1919 to zero in 1921, and averaged only 3,500 tons annually in 1922-3. Trading profits fell from over £110,000 in 1918 to £57,000 in 1919 and then practically disappeared in the slump.

The later 'twenties were equally unprofitable. Outside sales of hardened oils rose to 1,661 tons (£70,403) in 1925, with prices over £42 per ton, but they had almost disappeared again by 1927. In the later 'twenties, prices slid downwards once more to about £35 per ton in 1929, and though sales picked up to about

[1] See above, p. 294.

3,000 tons (£105,000) in that year, a loss of £6,000 resulted. There are no surviving figures of internal consumption for these years, but it was probably in the region of 5,000 to 6,000 tons per annum.

The oil-refining (V.B.) plant was in similar straits. In the brief post-war boom, sales rose to the colossal figure of 22,573 tons (£2,120,163) in 1919, but in the slump prices plunged from £114 per ton in 1920 to around £54, and sales likewise to an average of 6,700 tons (£361,000) in 1922-3. Whereas profits had been over £295,000 in 1919, a loss of £44,000 was suffered in 1921. Prices remained low in the later 'twenties, and although sales recovered to 11,573 tons (£631,364) in 1925, they then gradually fell away to 2,337 tons (£185,359) in 1929, while profits dropped from over £28,000 to only £5,000.

Crosfield's struggled to get out of the slump by developing new vegetable butter (edible fat) products. 'Vebol', refined edible palm oil, was first produced in 1921—'Acsil' being used as the bleaching agent—and was sold in barrels to Planter's and other margarine makers, and also to biscuit manufacturers. Later (from 1928 onwards) it was sold direct by travellers' vans to the fish-frying trade in northern England and Wales. Another edible fat, 'Bisco', was brought out in 1923 for the baking and confectionery trades, but does not appear to have been successful. At the same time, sales of the older products, such as 'Veberine', 'Kaynut', etc., still continued through Oldfield's of Liverpool. Crosfield's also began to sell cattle-meal and cake directly to farmers, by lorry transport, as well as to such trading firms as Bibby's and Silcock's.

Their chemical products also suffered from the post-war slump, but far less severely than oils and fats. Faced with the decline of the household soap trade, Crosfield's Directors decided to push ahead with expansion of their chemical manu-factures. Dr. E. F. Armstong appears to have been the main driving force behind the Company's efforts to maintain their technical superiority in these fields. During the 'twenties, how-ever, the trading figures were not very encouraging.

Glycerine production, of course, was geared to that of soap, but Crosfield's began to 'import' crude glycerine for refining—indeed they had previously done so to some extent—to supple-ment the quantities produced from their own spent lyes. Their crude output fell from 1,715 tons in 1919 to 1,045 in 1921, but gradually recovered to 2,274 tons in 1927, though falling somewhat thereafter. Distilled production dropped from 2,789 tons in 1920 to 1,024 in 1921, but rose in the following years to 3,452 in 1929. Distilled prices collapsed, however, from an average of £126 per ton in 1920–1 to £81 in 1925, and then, after a good recovery in 1926–7, dropped even further to £71 in 1928. Sales values, therefore, crashed from £348,176 in 1920 to £131,079 in 1921, and though they recovered in the following years, reaching £291,195 in 1926, were only £229,432 in 1928, despite the rising tonnages. In 1929, marketing arrangements were placed in the hands of Glycerine Ltd. Profits figures are bedevilled, as previously, by crude glycerine transfers, but there seems little doubt that they were substantially lower at the end of this period than at the beginning. Not surprisingly, therefore, one finds little evidence of capital expenditure on plant improvements during these years.

The Company's caustic soda manufacture was not in a much happier position. Total output figures survive only for the early 'twenties. They show a decline from 15/16,000 tons in 1919–20 to below 11,000 tons in 1921, but a quick recovery to over 16,000 tons annually in 1922–3.[1] Internal consumption fell from 4,431 tons in 1919 to 3,285 in 1921, but rose to 4,045 in 1923, at about which level it appears to have remained in the later 'twenties. Sales tonnages also, after falling from 12,088 in 1920 to 7,308 in 1921, soon recovered and settled at 12,000 to 13,000 tons. Increased orders for powdered caustic necessitated an extension of the tin-box making department in 1922, while the firm's first tanker lorries were acquired at about this time, 'to cope with the demand for Caustic Liquor'. But falling prices gradually reduced sales revenue and profits. Prices rose from £26 per ton in 1919 to £28·6 in 1920–2 and did not begin to fall until 1923, but they then declined continuously to £18·6 in 1928. Sales values, therefore, after dropping from £346,000 in 1920 to £210,000 in 1921 and jumping up again to £355,000 in 1922, then fell away gradually to £235,000 in 1928. Profits, too, declined. After an average annual profit of £48,000 in 1919–20, there was a loss of over £8,000 in 1921, and though profits

[1] All caustic output—liquid, solid, and powdered—was calculated as 70 per cent Na_2O.

quickly recovered to £49,000 in 1922, they subsided in the following years to an annual average below £7,000 in 1926–8.

One must remember, however, that in addition to providing caustic soda for internal consumption, Crosfield's plant was also supplying an increasing amount to Lever's and associated companies at cost price (see above, p. 291). Eventually, in 1927–8, Crosfield's Directors managed to secure the erection of a new caustic plant, and to persuade Lever's to close their own causticizing plant at Port Sunlight. A new and cheaper process, the Mount process, was introduced from America, whereby waste lime was eliminated. Caustic soda was still produced by the soda ash–slaked lime reaction, but the spent lime (calcium carbonate) was converted to quicklime by burning in a rotary kiln, and was then slaked and used over again, in a continuous process.

This new process, of course, brought about the closure of the cement plant. The latter had always been a mere ancillary to the caustic manufacture, and had never been very profitable. As H. G. Rushton reported to Lord Leverhulme in April 1923:

Cement is being sold at a loss, but the sale of cement allows the Company to get rid of its waste lime from the caustic soda plant, and it pays them to sell the cement at a loss rather than have to deal with the waste lime.

Now that waste lime was no longer being produced, however, the cement plant was redundant and was scrapped about four years later. Cement sales had fluctuated considerably in the 'twenties: supply was determined entirely by the caustic manufacture, demand mainly by the state of the building trade. After the re-opening of the works towards the end of the war, sales boomed to nearly 18,000 tons (£88,000) in 1920, then dropped to less than 9,000 tons (£33,000) in 1922, but rose again to nearly 25,000 tons (£78,000) in 1925. Similar but less pronounced fluctuations occurred in the later 'twenties, annual output averaging just over 17,000 tons; but the plant continued to suffer losses of around £4,000 almost every year.

The silicate department was also in the doldrums. Production had been held down during the war, but in the post-war boom it rose to the unprecedented figure of 15,000 tons in 1920.[1] The

---

[1] All tonnages calculated as 'glass'.

slump, however, brought it down to an average of about 8,500 tons per year in 1921–3. Internal consumption dropped relatively little, fluctuating between 1,700 and 2,000 tons during the 'twenties. Sales, however, which had soared to 13,138 tons (£293,116) in 1920, dropped heavily in the following years, to a low point of 5,925 tons (£96,627) in 1923, average prices falling from between £22 and £23 to £16 per ton. Sales tonnages gradually recovered in the following years to about 8,000 tons annually in 1928–9. But since prices sank to £15 per ton, sales revenue struggled to only £122,000. Profits were very modest: after reaching £74,000 in 1920, they fell to an annual average of £12,000 to £13,000 between 1921 and 1929.

Nevertheless, in 1927–8 a new silicate plant was built, on the modern site, south of the Garston railway. This was motivated by the prospects of increasing sales for silicate adhesives in the making of corrugated paper, fibre-board, etc., large-scale manufacture of which was now rapidly developing. The Company had some years earlier spent several thousand pounds on storage tanks for such adhesives. In the home trade, Gossage's remained their chief rivals, but at the beginning of 1929 an agreement was finally reached on the division of that trade—on the basis of the previous five years' sales—whereby Crosfield's were to have 46½ per cent and Gossage's 53½ per cent. This agreement included references to sales within the 'family'—to Port Sunlight, Home Associated Companies, and the Thames Board Mills (in which Lever's had a substantial interest)—as well as to outside firms. Exports were also growing: in 1929 nearly 3,500 tons were exported, mainly liquors.

The gloom of the post-war slump in chemicals was relieved by some scintillating scientific-technological achievements, particularly by Dr. T. P. Hilditch (chief research chemist) and H. J. Wheaton (manager of the caustic and silicate plants), leading to the production of sodium-alumino-silicate, the first commercially available 'synthetic' zeolite or base-exchanging compound, used for purifying and softening water, and sold under the trade name 'Doucil'. It was manufactured by mixing solutions of silicate of soda and sodium aluminate, to produce a gel, which was then dried, washed free from soluble salts, re-dried, and crushed to granular form. Its softening action was due to exchange of its sodium base for the calcium, magnesium, or other bases of insoluble salts contained in hard waters, thus producing soluble sodium salts. It could be 'regenerated' simply by passing a solution of common salt (sodium chloride) through it, thereby replacing the sodium base and displacing the calcium, magnesium, etc., as soluble chlorides. It gradually came into use both for domestic and large-scale municipal or industrial water-softening. Messrs. Boby & Co. of London were eventually appointed the sole selling agents. (The American patent rights were sold to a specially formed company controlled by the Philadelphia Quartz Company.) Production began on a small scale in 1922, with sales of about 3 tons, increasing to 234 tons (£18,603) in 1925, when the trading profit was £11,147. Sales dropped off, however, in the following years and were only 163 tons (£11,672), with a profit of £4,139, in 1929.

Another achievement was the production of 'silica gel', a granular, micro-porous material, eminently suitable for absorbing water vapour and other organic or inorganic vapours or gases; such vapours could be recovered simply by heating the material. It could also be utilized as a catalyst support, in view of its high porosity and immense surface area. It was prepared by neutralizing silicate of soda with dilute sulphuric acid, the product being washed, dried, and finally packed in air-tight drums. It was marketed under the brand names 'Gasil' and 'Sorbsil'.

Another use for silica gel, as a filtering material for refining mineral oils, was developed by the Dee Oil Company, who trade-marked it as 'Quepric'. All rights in this product were acquired by Crosfield's in 1926, for £5,000 plus a ten-year royalty. In 1928 Crosfield's appointed the Kestner Evaporator & Engineering Company, of London, as their sole U.K. agents for the sale of silica gel, on a commission of $7\frac{1}{2}$ per cent. But total sales (including 'Gasil', 'Sorbsil', and 'Quepric') were little more than ten tons (less than £1,000) in 1929. These new products, however, together with 'Acsil' and 'Doucil', mark the beginning of Crosfield's modern manufacture of a wide range of silicate derivatives, in addition to silicate of soda itself. They were under the management of H. J. Wheaton until the middle 'thirties, when C. Billington took over.

Another innovation, 'Rocket' dyes, launched in 1921–2, proved a failure, despite Lord Leverhulme's personal interest and the assistance of Lever's advertising experts. Only eleven tons (£4,180) were marketed in the first year, though advertising expenditure totalled nearly £15,000, and even smaller amounts were sold in the following years, when advertising was practically stopped.

The post-war pattern of boom-slump-recovery is clearly visible in the Company's general trading accounts. Profits soared in the brief boom of 1919–20, crashed in 1920–1, gradually recovered in 1922–4, and then remained comparatively stable in the later 'twenties.

Gross Trading Profits

	£		£
1919	893,734	1925	541,976
1920	487,861	1926	520,014
1921	185,058	1927	651,399
1922	397,165	1928	593,415
1923	497,337	1929	570,169
1924	597,163		

In 1919–20 the Company had to make provision for Excess Profits Duty of about £254,000 annually, but in the ensuing slump received substantial refunds, totalling about £350,000 by 1923, without which it would probably have been unable to pay Ordinary dividends. The slump in profits was attributable not only to the falling-off in the Company's trade, but also to the necessity for writing down stocks, due to the huge drop in prices of raw materials. Thus at the end of 1920 'Stock adjustments' totalling £276,000 had to be made; fortunately, £100,000 had been provided for 'Stock contingencies' out of the previous year's large profits. In the following years, with more stable prices, the situation became relatively easy.

Investment income, meanwhile, increased enormously, from £33,958 in 1919 to £377,787 in 1929. This was due, of course, to the massive growth of the Company's investments in Lever's and associated companies. The yield on these sank to about 3 per cent in 1920, but recovered in the following years to a fairly steady average of around 12 per cent in 1925–9. In the latter year, this income was about two-thirds as large as the trading profits.

The Company's *net* profits and Ordinary dividends ceased, after absorption by Lever's, to have much significance (and we shall not, therefore, reproduce them), since the parent company took large slices out of trading profits in the form of 'management fees' or 'advisory and service charges'. Subsidiary companies, such as Crosfield's, received an increasing amount of help from Lever (later Unilever) House, but the management or service fee was not charged on a purely cost basis; it was also determined by consideration of trading profits, taxation, and the parent company's general position. Moreover, the Preference shareholders—requiring dividends of £227,500 annually from 1921 onwards, and concerned for the general welfare of the Company—had also to be considered. The charge on Crosfield's was therefore apt to vary considerably: in a slump it might be reduced, or even remitted, but in good years it was sometimes more than the Ordinary dividends. In addition, large Reserves were accumulated, out of which in 1928 the Ordinary shareholders (Lever's) were paid £500,000 as a tax-free capital bonus, thereby increasing the Ordinary capital to £1,500,000, at which figure it was to remain until after the second World War.

It is clear that after the Company had emerged from the crisis of 1920–1, its trading position became fairly prosperous. The losses in oil-milling, hardening, and refining, and the small profits on chemicals, were far more than counterbalanced by the gains on soaps and soap powders, especially by the soaring profits of 'Persil' and 'Glitto', and also by the steady increase in investment income.

The post-war slump placed a great strain on labour relations. Lord Leverhulme, however, believed strongly in material incentives to increased production. We have already seen how he placated opposition on Crosfield's Board by payment of high salaries and bonuses. The departmental or group councils, which he introduced at Warrington at the end of 1919, were linked with this bonus scheme; though the lion's share went to the Directors, the scheme also gave managers and assistant managers a pecuniary interest in helping to increase profits. The same principle underlay the wider 'Co-partnership' scheme, introduced at Crosfield's in 1922. Professor Wilson has explained the objects of this scheme in the *History of Unilever*. Together with the 'Employees' Benefit Fund'—making insurance provision for sickness, unemployment, retirement, and death—this was an attempt, in days before the Welfare State was fully established, to give employees some sense of security, of participation in profits, and of loyalty to the firm.

None of these ideas, however, was new to Bank Quay. Crosfield's had for some years had their own bonus scheme, or 'Employees Participation Fund' (mainly for managers), a Sick & Funeral Society, and a Benevolent Society, and the firm had paid pensions and retirement allowances, and followed an enlightened social welfare policy. Lord Leverhulme's scheme, moreover, had some objectionable features. 'Co-partnership' was really a disguised bonus scheme, and the bonuses and other benefits were arbitrarily determined, depending upon loyalty and efficiency. Employees lost all of them if they left the firm, or if they went on strike, so that the Co-partnership and Benefit schemes could be, and were, used to weaken trade-union solidarity. On the other hand, there is no doubt that Lord Leverhulme did believe, though patriarchally, in 'prosperity-sharing', and that he was right in recognizing that these benefits were dependent upon increasing productivity. Nor is there any doubt of the great personal interest which he took in such matters, though as Dr. Armstrong pointed out to him in October 1919, the problem of social welfare 'here in a crowded town is very different from that which you have so successfully solved at Port Sunlight'.

Crosfield's Flag, a quarterly house journal started at his instigation in 1920, was a vehicle for his ideas. He frequently contributed articles (which also appeared in the journals of other associated companies), in which the main emphasis was upon the virtues of hard work, diligence, enthusiasm, loyalty, service, etc., so as to increase productivity and raise living standards— as opposed to a trade-union policy of 'ca' canny'. Capital and Labour, he constantly emphasized, had common interests, they were 'in the same boat', and must therefore 'pull together'. He often commented upon features in the *Flag*, expressing particular approval of photographs of long-service employees and the records of the Recreation Club. There was still a vigorous social life at Crosfield's, with sporting activities of all kinds, dances, whist drives, and socials, works band, operatic and dramatic society, debating society, boy scouts and girl guides, etc., for which the Centenary Institute now provided accommodation.

The post-war years, however, were marked by increased labour difficulties. Trade-union organization was now stronger at Crosfield's, and the immediate post-war inflation produced pressure for increased wages. In the ensuing slump, however, the trade unions were forced on to the defensive and the soap-workers' minimum wage was brought back to about £3 per week by the end of 1921, with further reductions to follow. (Hours of work were about the same as pre-war.) Not merely were wages reduced, but there was a good deal of weeding-out of inefficient labour. The wage-earners were not, however, the only ones to suffer from the slump: Ordinary dividends were reduced, directors' bonuses were severely curtailed, and managers' salaries were cut in 1922 by a total of £5,000 per year.

Dr. Armstrong, of Crosfield's, was chairman of the Soap and Candle Trades Employers' Federation, and his correspondence with Lord Leverhulme during these years reveals a strongly anti-union attitude. In March 1921 Lord Leverhulme wished to break up the Joint Industrial Council, but Armstrong considered that 'if we render it largely innocuous it would be better tactics to keep it alive', for the sake of public opinion and to avoid the possibility of a Trade Board. Both agreed on the need for ending 'Government interference' in wages-bargaining. On the other hand, Lord Leverhulme considered that it was 'not only generous but wise' for Lever's and associated companies to pay 3s. per week above the union rates. In this way, and by the Co-partnership and Benefit Schemes, they would retain the loyalty of the men and weaken the unions. Thus in February 1924 they increased wages to £2 16s. per week without consulting the unions. Their employees, Armstrong considered, were 'well contented' and probably would not come out on strike if ordered to do so. By this time he had come round to the view that the J.I.C. was 'useless', and he wondered whether they should continue meeting the trade-union leaders, whom he referred to as 'communists', but whom he considered had little influence. He was perturbed, however, by the general labour situation in the country and would welcome 'a long and un-successful strike in such an industry as the Coal trade', whereby public opinion would be turned against Labour, rendered 'truculent and aggressive' by the creation of the first Labour

318

Government. His hopes were soon to be fulfilled in the General Strike!

Armstrong left Crosfield's, however, in 1925 to become managing director of the British Dyestuffs Corporation Ltd. Meanwhile, some long-familiar faces had gone from the Board: H. Roberts, R. F. Jones, and F. J. Burlton had retired, C. H. Hamilton had moved to Gossage's, and Giles Hunt, the Chairman, had died prematurely in 1923, being succeeded by C. F. Huffam. The latter and G. H. K. Kingdon were now the only surviving pre-war directors. Kingdon succeeded Huffam as Chairman in 1926. Several younger men were promoted to the Board: W. T. Kipps, who, starting in the general office in 1895, had eventually become manager of the chemical sales department; W. P. Harris, who had come to Crosfield's in 1913 from James Keiller & Sons, to manage the selling side of the soap and powders trade, but who died in 1925; J. H. B. Wigginton, who came to the Erasmic Company from Harrod's of London in 1914, and was made managing director of that Company after A. V. Baxter's untimely death in 1921; R. E. Huffam, continuing the family connection with Crosfield's, successor to Armstrong as Technical Director; and J. Allan, the chief chemist, already a director of the Erasmic Company. Several, if not all, of these had impressed Lord Leverhulme with their ability. Lever's first representatives on Crosfield's Board—the Hon. W. H. Lever, J. L. Ferguson, and J. Gray—did not stay very long; nor did A. C. Knight, who followed, and H. G. Rushton took little active part. J. Inglis, on the other hand, was to remain for many years and to play an important role in shaping the Company's future. Under these new men, Crosfield's were to be merged more completely into the Lever and (after 1929) Unilever organization.

CHAPTER XIX

RATIONALIZATION WITHIN UNILEVER
1929–39

UNTIL 1929, despite absorption by Lever's, Crosfield's manufacturing and selling activities had undergone remarkably little change. Lord Leverhulme had, as we have seen, imposed commercial controls, with the object of achieving some co-ordination of buying and selling within the Lever 'family', and he had also controlled capital expenditure, but he had still left a considerable degree of independence to associated companies and had done very little towards 'rationalizing' their manufacturing activities. The slump of 1920–1 had caused him to worry about excess capacity and idle plants, and he had examined comparative costs, partly with a view to concentrating manufacture of particular products in the most efficient plants, but he had not proceeded far with this idea. Associated firms were still mostly left to produce their former range of goods, and to sell them in competition with each other.

At Bank Quay, this range had become very wide indeed during the first quarter of the present century. Crosfield's, in fact, were like three firms rolled into one, each with three major sections. There were, firstly, the oil-milling, hardening, and refining plants; secondly, the soapworks, with departments for household, toilet, and powdered products; and thirdly, the chemical plants, producing glycerine, caustic soda, and silicate with its derivatives. These manufactures were, of course, closely inter-connected and had been developed for reasons which were thoroughly sensible while Crosfield's were an independent firm, saving them from undue reliance upon outside sources for raw materials and utilizing by-products. But the Company was now part of a much bigger business, in which it was unlikely that the constituent works would be able to survive as separate, self-contained, and competing entities.

In 1929 Lever Brothers and their associated companies were amalgamated with the Dutch group established by Jurgens and

Van den Berghs, to form the vast Unilever business, and this amalgamation coincided with the onset of world economic depression, which, as Professor Wilson has shown, greatly accelerated the trend towards cost-reducing 'rationalization' of both manufacturing and selling. The Dutch group had already made considerable progress in this direction, but within the Lever family there was still much excess capacity, with many old, small and relatively inefficient works, and an excessive number of competing products and sales staffs. Lord Leverhulme had held the view that it would be unwise to swamp the identity of the individual firms and that efficiency could only be maintained by preserving a certain amount of internal competition. Many in Unilever still held this view, while local loyalties remained very strong. Rationalization would require the writing-off of capital assets, closure of factories, scrapping of plant, redundancy of employees, and possible loss of trading goodwill. After 1929, however, drastic reorganization was necessitated by the merger with the Dutch, by the severity of the trade depression, and by the rapid growth of outside competition, especially from Hedley's, acquired in 1930 by the American rivals, Procter & Gamble.

Rationalization would inevitably have serious effects on Crosfield's, and would arouse some fears and dislike. The old feelings of local pride and independence—the old rivalry with Lever's and Port Sunlight—were still deep-rooted, and Crosfield's could hardly be expected to welcome increasing control from Unilever House, compulsory reshaping of their structure, loss of certain manufactures and of independent research activities, and the merging of their sales organization into centralized agencies. It would take some time for the realization to sink in that 'Crosfield's' were really not Crosfield's any more, that their future—for better or for worse—was now bound up with that of Unilever, of which they were part, and that the interests of the whole must have priority over those of the parts.

Crosfield's, as J. J. Crosfield had proudly asserted and as later comparative statistics confirmed, had surpassed Lever's in manufacturing efficiency in several departments. Their efficiency, closely associated with their strength in research, would stand them in good stead during the process of 'rationalization', when decisions were being taken on closing down factories and plants and concentrating production. But for how long would it be possible for Crosfield's to carry on so wide a range of manufacturing activities, against the trend towards specialized groups or divisions within large combines?

Fortunately, Geoffrey Heyworth, who was the driving force behind the rationalization of the Unilever soap trade in the 'thirties, had been Chairman of Crosfield's in the late 'twenties and had acquired great respect for their technical expertise and tradition. Moreover, he was succeeded as Chairman by John Inglis, a shrewd tactician, who, while recognizing the necessity of rationalization, skilfully manœuvred to maintain a strong position for Crosfield's in the new manufacturing and trading structure. The old Crosfield directors had now all gone, and Inglis and the other new men who were guiding the Company's fortunes were loyal Unilever men; but they strove, nevertheless, to keep the Crosfield flag flying.

The seeds of 'rationalization' had been sown even before the Unilever merger. There had been, for example, the recent creation of the Sales Executive Committee, which was 'to be responsible to the Board for the sales policy of the soap companies in the Family', with the purpose of reducing internal competition and fighting outsiders. In the export trade, co-ordination had been carried much farther, with the formation in August 1928 of United Exporters Limited, managed from Lever House, to control the export of soap and other products (but excluding heavy chemicals), so as to end the former friction between Lever's, Gossage's, and Crosfield's. These three supplied the capital for the new company, and export manufacture was still carried on at Port Sunlight, Widnes, and Warrington, the products being supplied to Exporters at cost price. Lever's guaranteed to Gossage's and Crosfield's dividends equal to their average annual export profits for the years 1923-7. This arrangement was modified by a 'pooling' agreement in April 1931, which included other soap firms in the Lever group, but its underlying principles remained the same: Crosfield's still manufactured for export, but the trade was handled by Exporters, in whose profits (or losses) Crosfield's shared in an agreed proportion. At the same time, Crosfield's still retained their goodwill and trade marks abroad, which were taken over by specially formed subsidiary companies in such countries as India, China, Nigeria, South Africa, and the Dutch East Indies.

The formation of Glycerine Limited in January 1929 was based on the same principle of divorcing selling from manufacturing and placing it under central control, in the hands of a specialist company, thereby reducing competition and saving on costs of administration and distribution. Similarly, research and advertising were now more strongly controlled from the centre. Undoubtedly there were great economic advantages in such centralization, but there were also some drawbacks. Crosfield's spirit of pioneering research seems to have suffered somewhat, and loss of independence may perhaps have stifled initiative in other fields.

But centralization was inevitable and was accentuated after 1929. Perhaps the most critical sector was the purchasing of raw materials, with prices falling heavily in the slump till 1934, and again from 1937 to 1939. Whale oil, for example, fell from nearly £33 per ton in 1929 to between £11 and £12 in 1934, and then from £18 to £14 in 1937–8. Clearly amalgamation could not prevent falling prices, caused by world over-production of raw materials in relation to demand. Unilever's manufacturing firms stood to gain from cheaper fats and oils, but the business had important interests in the production of these raw materials in Africa and elsewhere, and also had to make long-term contracts with whale oil and other producers, with consequent risks of heavy losses on a falling market. Buying was therefore centralized and Crosfield's now secured their supplies through Unilever (Raw Materials) Ltd.

In the same way, control over the manufacturing and selling operations of associated companies was more tightly centralized through three executive bodies, responsible for oils and fats, soap, and margarine, under the general supervision of Unilever's Special Committee. Rationalization schemes resulted in the closing down of various oil-mills and edible fat factories, which were operating at uneconomically high costs, but Crosfield's still retained, for the time being at any rate, their oil-milling, hardening, and refining plants. The oil-milling (pressing and extraction) plants, however, were placed in extremely difficult circumstances, not only by the trade slump and enforced reduction of output, but also by repeated failure of the illipe nut crop during the 'thirties. The pressing plant was mainly engaged on palm kernels, crushings of which fell from 16,426 tons in 1931 to 11,689 tons in 1934; it then had to be closed down from the spring of 1936 until the outbreak of the second World War. The extraction plant, dependent upon the illipe nut crop, stood idle for most of this period, except in 1931 and 1936, when tonnages of nearly 4,000 and 6,000 respectively were extracted. Output of oils, meal, and cake were thus reduced almost to nothing in 1937–8, and Crosfield's had to obtain their requirements of crude oil from other Unilever mills, mainly from Selby.

The oil-hardening plant, on the other hand, experienced better fortunes. Output (mainly of treated whale and palm oils) fluctuated considerably, but the trend was generally rising, from 14,307 tons in 1931 to peaks of 28,153 tons in 1933 and 39,871 in 1937, principally due to increasing demands from Port Sunlight and Bromborough. Special hardened technical oils, such as 'Crescol', were also developed. But output was falling in 1938–9, after enlargement of the hardening plant at Bromborough, and would have fallen much farther but for the Government's precautionary stockpiling.

Professor Wilson has described the difficulties of the edible fats trade in the 'thirties, with falling output and prices, due mainly to the abundance of cheap butter. In this situation, Crosfield's refinery was working at only about a quarter or a third of capacity, though output did rise from 5,000 tons in 1932 to an average of 8,700 tons annually in 1935–8. The main lines were now 'Margol' (refined hardened whale oil) and 'Vebol' (refined palm oil), the latter proving particularly successful in northern fish-frying shops, as well as in the confectionery trade; output of the older products, 'Veberine', 'Kaynut', etc., stagnated. The average price of 'Vebol' dropped from about £55 per ton in 1929 to £28 in 1934, and after recovering somewhat in the following years, fell back to £30 in 1939. Despite the adverse circumstances, however, profits on these edible oils rose from almost rock bottom in 1931 to £59,000 in 1936, but both output and profits were falling in 1937–8. Significantly, moreover, it was reported in 1938 that production costs at the Zwijndrecht factory in Holland were 50 per cent below those at Warrington, mainly due to larger-scale operations. (The comparative outputs were then 3,000 and 230 tons per week.) Constant efforts were made to reduce costs, but the plant was burdened by high overheads on a production far below capacity, while the Oil Mills Executive was naturally unwilling to spend large sums on technical improvements. With equipment becoming increasingly outdated and in need of replacement, future prospects for the oil-milling, hardening, and refining plants were not very bright.

Crosfield's continued throughout this period to be primarily manufacturers of soaps and soap powders, but lost their remaining independence in the rationalization programme pushed through by the Home Soap Executive. Professor Wilson has outlined this programme, as explained by Geoffrey Heyworth (who had just relinquished the Chairmanship of Crosfield's) to a conference of managers in 1931. Its main principles were more starkly revealed, however, together with some of the snags involved, in a case drawn up by Lever's for opinion of Counsel at about the same time. It was pointed out that although Lever's had for some years held the Ordinary share capital of associated companies such as Crosfield's, Gossage's, Knight's, and Watson's, 'the five Companies have so conducted their respective businesses of Soap Manufacturers as to be in direct competition with one another in this sense that each . . . manufactures products of a similar type to those manufactured by the other four and endeavours to sell as much of its products as possible, whether or not by so doing it takes trade from the other Companies in the Group'. Examples were given of the competing products in laundry and carbolic soaps, flakes, powders, and scourers.

The system of each Company having its own factory and competing lines is not the most economical that could be devised, and Lever's have been considering how some scheme of rationalization could be introduced which would have the effect of reducing the total cost of production of the five Companies and the total cost of administration and distribution . . .

The scheme of rationalization would take one or more of the following forms:—

(a) Discontinuance of manufacture of one or more lines in a particular class and concentration of selling energy upon the remaining lines in the class;

(b) Closing one or more of the factories which are owned by the four Associated Companies, and the factory which would be the first to be closed would probably be that of Gossage's at Widnes; (c) Eventually, possibly, the liquidation of one or more of the Associated Companies.

Such a scheme of rationalization would of necessity be harmful to one or more of the Companies as an individual entity, but it would not be put into operation unless it were thought that the corresponding advantages to other entities in the Group would be greater, and that the ultimate result . . . would inure to the benefit of Levers as manufacturers themselves and as the holders of the equity in the other Companies.

These words inevitably recall the fears expressed years earlier by the Crosfields and Gossages, and though the Crosfields and Gossages had long since departed, their successors on the Boards at Warrington and Widnes still felt grave misgivings at these proposals, which might well mean ultimately the end of their companies. Lever's had, indeed, toyed with the idea of acquiring from these companies 'the whole of their assets and undertakings', but were deterred by the high cost of stamp duties, the difficulties regarding trade marks, the possible loss of goodwill, and the problem of the outside Preference shareholders. Instead, they proposed the creation of a special company—under Lever's control—to acquire the Ordinary capital of the four concerns and exercise 'full powers of management' over them. But this raised the difficulty of getting the Directors to delegate their legal responsibilities, as well as objections from the Preference shareholders. Lever's were not, therefore, able to carry through quite so rigorous a rationalization scheme as they had proposed, but despite local opposition, especially from Gossage's, they did achieve most of their practical objectives, whilst preserving the legal identity of the individual companies and safeguarding the outside shareholders. On economic grounds, there could be little argument against such reorganization.

Crosfield's came out of the rationalization process comparatively well: indeed, they gained substantially from Gossage's demise. They and Lever's shared the soap export trade previously carried on from Widnes. Gossage's carbolic soap, 'Bodyguard', and their famous blue mottled soap were now manufactured at Warrington. 'Glitto' manufacture was transferred to Port Sunlight, but marketing was still through Crosfield's.

Crosfield's also took over the whole of Gossage's silicate manufacture. Gossage's, however, though the Widnes factory disappeared, did not cease to exist as a company; it still had capital assets, trade marks, and goodwill, it still participated in marketing arrangements, its Directors' and Board meetings were still held, and it still paid out dividends; but its administration was now at Warrington.

Another important casualty at this time was Hudson's, of Bank Hall (Liverpool) and West Bromwich, whose well-known soap powder was from 1935 onwards produced by Crosfield's. At the same time, however, Crosfield's lost the manufacture of 'Erasmic' products, toilet soaps, etc., which were transferred in 1933 to Port Sunlight, though directorial management remained at Warrington until 1946. The Erasmic Company had never been a great financial success, having to face very strong competition, and its turnover had been gradually dwindling during the 'twenties; the slump of the early 'thirties resulted in losses or small profits. But the loss of Erasmic was a blow to Crosfield's pride, and not an encouraging portent for their household soap manufacture. The blow was softened, however, by increased production of soap powders and silicate, and by generous provision for the small number of redundant employees by pensions and lump sum payments.

Other works, mostly small and uneconomic, were also closed, and the soap trade was shared rationally among the larger survivors. In July 1933 an agreement was made between all the firms in the Lever soap group for 'more economical working of their respective businesses by . . . interchange of manufacture', i.e. for reciprocal manufacture of each other's products. A firm might be 'a producing company' or 'a purchasing company', or both. Crosfield's, for example, might be required by any associated company to make some of its products, to be supplied at net cost, and to be sold under its trade mark or name. The Erasmic Company, on the other hand, was simply a purchasing and selling company.

At the same time, marketing was rationalized, by reducing the number of competing brands, defining spheres of operation, and cutting sales staffs. Thus in August 1932 an agreement was made between Crosfield's and Christopher Thomas & Bros., Ltd., appointing each other reciprocally as selling and distributing agents for soap products in certain specified areas, with provision for 'pooling' profits. Thomas's became, in fact, a subsidiary company of Crosfield's, who acquired the whole of the Ordinary capital. Crosfield's also made agreements with other associated companies for sale of certain of their products for particular purposes in particular areas, e.g. in April 1932, with T. B. Rowe & Co. Ltd., for sale of 'Metso', 'Carbosil', 'Persil', etc., to launderers, dyers, and cleaners, etc., in Great Britain and Northern Ireland. (Subsequently Gossage's, and later Watson & Gossage's, were given this agency in the north, Rowe's retaining the south.)

Eventually, it may be added here, in December 1945, a general agreement was made among all soap companies in the Lever group for reciprocal selling and distributing of each other's products, corresponding to that for reciprocal manufacture.[1] Thus, while preserving the identity, trade marks, and goodwill of the individual companies, and overcoming the legal difficulties previously mentioned, complete flexibility was achieved in both manufacturing and selling, under the overall control of the Home Soap Executive. The trend was clearly towards specialization. Crosfield's, for example, were tending to become specialized manufacturers of soap powders (and also of silicate, etc., as we shall see), but were being relieved to some extent of marketing. United Exporters had taken over their export soap and 'Vebol' trade, and in 1940 the trend towards specialized marketing companies led to the formation of Crosfield, Watson & Gossage Ltd. (operated from Warrington), for dealing with the home soap trade of these companies. Another parallel development was the creation of specialized transport agencies, such as Speedy Prompt Delivery Ltd. and Distributors and Transporters Ltd., whereby Crosfield's motor vehicles were taken over, though still operated from Warrington.

These interlocking manufacturing and selling arrangements, combined with changes in accounting procedure, make it impossible to provide continuity in presentation of Crosfield's trading operations. On top of the existing problem of inter-departmental transfers, there is imposed the even more complicated one of inter-company accounting, affecting chemicals as well as oils and fats and soap products. Since these were

[1] See below, pp. 349-50.

generally supplied to associated companies at cost price, they make sales and profits figures somewhat misleading. Production figures, however, give us a realistic picture of what was happening at Bank Quay. Total output of soaps fell during the slump to just below 23,000 tons in 1932, but then rose to over 28,000 in 1935. It fell again in the later 'thirties, however, to below 22,000 in 1938, though recovering to nearly 25,000 in 1939. As manufacturers of household soap, Crosfield's were clearly declining. Output of 'Perfection' fell from about 6,000 tons annually in 1928-9 to little more than 4,000 in 1938-9—just over one-third of the 1913 figure—while 'Pinkobolic' dropped from nearly 3,000 to 1,700 tons. On the other hand, production of textile and industrial soaps, in which Crosfield's were tending to specialize, rose from 2,700 tons in 1931 to 7,500 tons in 1939. But there was a marked decline in exports (through United Exporters) from about 14,000 tons in 1929 to an annual average of only 8,000 tons in 1937-9.

At the same time, prices were falling. The 'Perfection' pound tablet, for example, which had stood at $6\frac{1}{2}d.$ during the late 'twenties, dropped gradually to $4\frac{1}{2}d.$ by 1935, where it remained till the war. Crosfield's were getting £51 per ton for this soap in 1929, but less than £34 in 1939. Sales revenue, therefore, fell dramatically.[1] Gross home sales of 'Perfection', for instance, declined from £292,000 in 1929 to £143,000 in 1939, despite increased advertising expenditure, rising from £23,000 (£4 per ton) to £36,000 (£8 per ton). The Company's soap exports dropped from £305,000 to £120,000. Unfortunately, there are no separate figures of total home soap sales, nor of profits, which are combined with those of soap powders, but there is no doubt that their hard soap trade was in parlous condition. Household soaps generally were in declining demand, while sales of toilet soaps, powders, and flakes were increasing, due partly to rising living standards, partly to the superior convenience and detergence of the newer products. At the same time, outside competition was becoming much fiercer, especially from Hedley's, who were capturing more and more of the market.[2]

[1] The sales figures for Crosfield's soaps and soap powders given below include those sold in the area of C. Thomas & Bros. Ltd. Only in the case of 'Persil', however, were these very significant.

[2] See H. R. Edwards, *Competition and Monopoly in the British Soap Industry* (1962), chap. 9.

What Crosfield's lost on the swings, however, they more than gained on the roundabouts. The decline of their household soaps and the loss of 'Erasmic' toilet manufactures were more than counterbalanced by the continued rise in their production and sales of powders. Output of 'Persil' went up year by year from 9,767 tons in 1929 to 26,555 tons in 1939, and was gradually overtaking Lever's 'Rinso'. Moreover, from 1925 onwards, throughout this period, the retail prices of the two 'Persil' packs were maintained at 3½d. (5½ oz.) and 6d. (9½ oz.), though Crosfield's prices were slightly reduced, from around £79 to between £73 and £74 per ton. Gross home sales (including Eire) therefore soared from £746,000 in 1929 to £1,996,000 in 1939. There are no separate export figures, but these also appear to have been rising. The agreement with Henkel's on division of overseas markets for 'Persil' was maintained throughout the interwar period, with some modifications.

The expansion of sales was largely attributable to vigorous advertising. Expenditure on 'Persil' in the home market rose from about £80,000 (over £8 per ton) in 1929 to nearly £351,000 (£14 per ton) in 1938. Advertisements continued to emphasize its oxygen action in whitening clothes, and then, in 1934, there appeared the first of the white, off-white comparisons which have become so well known. This advertising, despite its rising cost, certainly paid dividends. Unfortunately, there are no separate figures of 'Persil' profits after 1931, but in that year, in the depths of the slump, they were nearly £496,000, or about 35 per cent on gross home sales of £1,133,000.

Crosfield's soap powders department was greatly expanded from 1935 onwards by their taking over the manufacture of Hudson's famous product, output of which averaged about 11,500 tons annually in 1936–8. 'Carbosil' production, on the other hand, steadily declined from about 6,700 tons in 1931 to 4,400 tons annually in 1938–9, despite advertising expenditure increasing from about £13,000 per annum (£2 per ton) in the late 'twenties to about £23,000 (between £6 and £7 per ton) in the late 'thirties. It clearly could not compete against the improved washing powders. Sales of 'Glitto' also gradually declined, from 3,037 tons in 1929 to 2,563 in 1939, although advertising expenditure was raised from £21,000 (nearly £7 per ton) to £29,000 (£12 per ton); it was being gradually superseded by Lever's 'Vim'. The prices of these products, however, were well maintained.

Surveying the Company's trading operations in soaps and soap powders as a whole, we can see how the effects of the slump and the decline in household soaps were outweighed by the rapidly increasing demand for powders, especially 'Persil'. Gross sales (home and export) of all these products fell from £2,259,000 in 1929 to £1,752,000 in 1932, but quickly recovered and reached £2,611,000 in 1939. Profits increased from £540,000 in 1929 to £871,000 in 1939.[1]

The great increase in production of 'Persil' and the transfer of Hudson's soap powder involved considerable capital expenditure, which was also necessitated by important technical developments. We have previously noted the great improvements introduced in the late 'twenties, under the management of Sidney Newall. In 1929 'Persil' manufacture had been transferred to the top floor of the printing building. Increasing output, however, soon demanded more space. In 1933-4, therefore, following the removal of 'Erasmic' manufactures to Port Sunlight, the former Erasmic building became the modern Powders building, to which 'Persil' making and packing were transferred, together with 'Carbosil', followed in 1935 by Hudson's soap powder, for which additional plant was erected. In 1936 ten new 'Rose' machines for packing 'Persil' in cartons—in place of the fifteen existing units packing it in wrapped skillets—were purchased, together with the necessary printing and carton-making machines; a similar change was effected for Hudson's powder in 1938-9. In the latter year another revolutionary development occurred, with the installation of plant for producing powders by the 'blowing' or spray-cooling process, i.e. by high-pressure spraying of the liquid soap bases into blowing (cooling) chambers.

All these improvements, on which a quarter of a million pounds were expended between 1929 and 1939, resulted in much lower costs and greatly increased profit margins. Comparatively little, however, was spent on the soapery, which produced the soap bases for 'Persil', etc., in addition to hard

[1] These sales and profits figures are for Crosfield's area only. Including the area of C. Thomas & Bros. Ltd., sales in 1939 totalled about £3,000,000 and profits £965,000.

soaps. Nevertheless, some outstanding innovations in soap-making were made at Crosfield's during these years. The various soapmaking processes—boiling or saponification, washing, fitting, and lye treatment—were still basically unaltered from the late nineteenth century. There were now forty to fifty soap pans, but these included many old ones, and the operations were still dependent on traditional skills of hand, eye, and taste. During these years, however, Crosfield's began a revolution in soapmaking operations, often leading the way with their various innovations.

In 1929 a process for neutralization of the spent lye with acid oils was introduced, whereby the small percentages of excess alkali and dissolved soap were extracted and returned into the soapmaking processes. Later on, a similar method was applied to extraction of soap from wash waters or soapstocks (neutralizing residues) from the oil refinery. In 1930 a jet-saponification process was successfully developed, in which controlled feeds of oil and caustic liquor were pumped through a specially designed steam jet to produce a continuous stream of 'self-saponifying' emulsion. This replaced the old batch soap-boiling operation—saving time, steam, and labour—and provided the starting point for modern methods of continuous production. It was generally introduced into the soapery in the 'thirties, together with soap-pan gauges, which gave more accurate quantitative and qualitative controls and higher glycerine yields. Another development was the introduction of centrifuges for purification of 'nigres' after the fitting operation. In 1939 all these various innovations were drawn together in a pilot plant for continuous soapmaking and glycerine extraction, including counter-current brine washing in a tower. Unfortunately, however, the outbreak of war put a stop to these developments.

Endless experimentation also went on with soap 'boils'. Less and less tallow and hardened whale oil were used, more and more palm oil and palm-kernel oil, which together formed three-quarters of total oils and fats consumption by 1938–9. Chemical experiments were also made to improve the stability, lathering, and other properties of 'Persil'. More and more labour-saving automatic machinery was introduced in soap cutting and packing. Efforts were also made to improve plant lay-out. The most notable occurred in 1934–5, when a 'concentration and reorganization' programme costing over £12,000 was carried through. It was pointed out that 'during the hundred years or more that Crosfield's had been manufacturing soap the factory had grown by means of scattered buildings, either erected or adapted to meet its increased trade'. The result was a sprawling and inefficient lay-out, of mostly out-dated buildings, with an 'expensive and cumbersome system of steaming and pumping', and 'high operating costs'. It was therefore decided to concentrate production in fewer rooms, more closely integrated.

Another portentous innovation during this period was the early development of 'synthetic' or soapless detergents, upon which Crosfield's carried out research in conjunction with Unilever's Central Technical Research Department. Rex Furness, reporting on progress during 1933–4, stated that polyglycerol esters, or polyesters, of fatty acids had been successfully produced at Warrington and converted into shampoo powders in Watson's spraying plant at Leeds. Several patents were taken out and subsequently a large pilot plant was designed by Gordon Duff, but unfortunately Crosfield's were not permitted to proceed with it. This research work did, however, point the way to the post-war revolution created by non-soapy detergents.

Crosfield's glycerine department was very busy in the 'thirties. Increasing quantities of spent lyes came from their own soapery, as a result of the growing output of soap powders, and the production of crude glycerine rose from 1,963 tons in 1931 to 2,825 in 1939. At the same time, more and more crude glycerine was brought to Warrington for distillation or refining. The works report for 1934 stated that tanks had been erected 'for the storage of Crude Glycerine, both from Associated Companies and outside sources, purchased on our behalf by Glycerine Limited', thus enabling the crude glycerine to be transported in road and rail tank wagons, instead of in drums as previously. In fact, Crosfield's themselves produced only a third of the crude glycerine used, more than half coming from associated companies and about 10 to 15 per cent from outside firms, chiefly the C.W.S. and Boots. Output of distilled glycerine rose from 3,619 tons in 1931 to 5,794 tons in 1939. It was marketed, as previously mentioned, by Glycerine Ltd., from whom Crosfield's received credits, rising from only £3,300 in 1929 to

£108,000 in 1937, but then suddenly reduced to only £4,700 annually in 1938–9.

Continual efforts were made to improve the efficiency of this department, and the glycerine yield from spent lyes was raised considerably, but, as in the case of the soapery, the buildings and plant were getting old. The 1934 works report complained that it was 'now many years since any appreciable amount of money was spent on developing this [the Crude] Department, and its present condition is one which is quite unworthy of the important position which it holds in our Glycerine manufacture'. During the following years, however, considerable sums were expended on retubing evaporators and repairing the boiler installations.

Comparatively little was spent on the new caustic plant, apart from regular replacements of pots, retubing evaporators, etc. Output rose from about 20,000 tons in 1929 to 33,000 tons in 1938, chiefly as a result of increasing sales to associated companies. Under the 1919–20 agreements with Brunner Mond's (which had since become the I.C.I. Alkali Division), as we have seen, such sales were excluded from Crosfield's sales quota of 12,500 tons. After the erection of the new plant, therefore, supplies to other firms in the 'family' increased rapidly from 3,352 tons in 1929 to nearly 14,000 in 1931, reaching nearly 16,000 in 1938. Crosfield's own consumption, mainly in the soapery, rose gradually from about 3,700 tons to 4,800 tons, while outside sales remained steady around the 12,500 quota. The convenience of tank transport, by rail and road, caused a marked shift in home sales from solid and powdered to liquid caustic, though the former still predominated, especially in the export trade. Exports declined, however, from over 3,000 tons in 1929 to 2,000 in 1939.

Prices of caustic soda had to be reduced in the slump. Home prices dropped from an average of £14 per ton in 1929 to about £11 in 1937, recovering somewhat thereafter, while exports (mainly of solid and powdered) fell from £29 in 1929 to just over £18 in 1935, but recovered to nearly £25 in 1939. Supplies to the 'family' were at cost price, so that departmental profits were modest, rising from about £8,000 in 1929 to £38,000 in 1933, but then falling gradually to £8,000 in 1938.

In the late 'thirties Crosfield's caustic manufacture once

again became a counter in big business bargaining, between Unilever and I.C.I. After the 1925 settlement, relations between these giants of the soap and alkali industries had been good. Crosfield's and I.C.I. continued to agree on prices, as well as quotas, and in 1930 it was arranged that I.C.I. should act as agents for the sale of Crosfield's caustic in most of their export markets. But I.C.I. not unnaturally cast envious eyes on Crosfield's increasing sales to the Unilever soap group, and in the late 'thirties renewed their efforts to bring about the closure of the caustic plant at Warrington. Finally, by an agreement of 6th April 1939, they achieved their aim. Crosfield's at once ceased to manufacture caustic soda—the redundant workers being compensated with pensions and lump sum payments—and the plant, after maintenance as a 'shadow' plant during the war, was eventually scrapped. It was agreed that they should draw their own and Unilever requirements of caustic soda from I.C.I.,[1] at a price arrived at by comparison of Crosfield and I.C.I. costs, with provision for future alteration on a cost clause basis. Thus the Lever group got caustic soda on very favourable terms, I.C.I. had gained a large market, and Crosfield's, though they had lost their caustic manufacture, would remain intermediaries for supply to Lever Brothers and associated companies and were also allowed an annual quota from I.C.I. to third parties of 9,250 tons in the U.K. and 2,250 tons overseas (I.C.I. still acting as their commission agents in agreed export markets). The immediate effect of this agreement was a sharp rise in Crosfield's caustic sales from below 27,000 tons (£314,000) in 1938 to nearly 34,000 tons (£427,000) in 1939, but since this increase came mainly from sales to associated companies, especially overseas, profits remained at a mere £8,000.

Similarly close relations with I.C.I. were maintained in regard to silicate of soda, and in 1930 I.C.I. became Crosfield's agents for the sale of silicate (as well as of caustic) in most of their export markets. Internationally, Crosfield's continued their good relations with the larger silicate manufacturers, but control of export prices proved difficult in what was still a competitive market.

[1] Except in the U.S.A., Canada, and Europe, for the same reasons of international business diplomacy as previously mentioned.

This department of Crosfield's manufactures expanded pro-digiously. With the new plant built in 1927, production rose from less than 10,000 tons in 1929 to a peak of 31,000 in 1937, falling somewhat thereafter. After closure of Gossage's works in 1932–3, Crosfield's became their manufacturing and distribut-ing agents and output at Warrington more than doubled. But Gossage's still retained a trading interest, with their own trade marks, etc., and under a 'pooling' agreement were to receive 52 per cent of net profits on total silicate sales.

The great bulk of silicate output was sold. Crosfield's now used only very small quantities in hard soaps, but much more in powders and chemicals, so that their internal consumption rose from about 2,000 to 3,500 tons during this period. Their sales to associated companies rose from 1,570 tons in 1929 to 8,693 tons in 1932, but then stabilized at around 7,000 tons. An important new customer in Unilever was the Thames Board Mills, who built their modern factory on the Arpley Meadows, sold to them by Crosfield's at the end of 1936 (clay therefrom being no longer required after closure of the cement works). A mutually advantageous relationship was established between the two firms: Crosfield's supplied the Thames Board Mills with silicate adhesives—around 3,000 tons annually in 1936–9—and in return they obtained paper board for packing.

Average prices of silicate in the home market fell from £13 per ton in 1929 to £9 in 1932, but quickly recovered to between £11 and £12 in the following years. Export prices, however, dropped more heavily, from about £19 in 1929 to below £8 per ton in 1937–8, partly due to a shift from liquor to glass, as more dissolvers were installed abroad. Home sales grew more rapidly than exports. The former rose from 4,334 tons (£56,394) to 18,177 tons (£230,380) between 1929 and 1939; the latter from 3,422 tons (£66,036) to 6,574 tons (£56,644). In the home trade, tank transport caused a swing (as in the case of caustic) towards the liquid product, sales tonnages of which were about five times those of 'glass' in the late 'thirties. From 1933 on-wards small amounts of soluble powders (including Gossage's 'Keepeg') and powdered glass were also sold. The competition from starch adhesives in the late 'thirties led to the develop-ment of silicate-clay mixtures, later branded 'Claysil'. The in-creasing demand for liquid silicate adhesives necessitated new dissolving and evaporating plant, but it was decided in 1937 to erect this plant not at Warrington but at Bow, in East London, on the site of the old soapworks of Edward Cook & Co. Ltd. It came into operation in April 1938. Glass supplies had to be transported from Warrington—nearly 7,000 tons in 1939—but it was considered more economic to do this and to build the necessary dissolvers, etc., rather than to continue transporting liquors (about 60 per cent water) to the large and growing metropolitan market; on balance there would be a considerable freight saving, while ready-made stocks would be available to provide a better service to customers in that area. There was, of course, a consequent reduction in liquor output from the Warrington plant, from 20,679 tons in 1937 to 13,405 in 1939. Departmental profits, however, continued to rise. From £17,348 in 1929 they increased to £78,151 in 1939,[1] despite cost-price sales within the 'family'.

Constant effort was made to reduce costs in the silicate plant, e.g. to prolong the life of furnaces by water-cooling their walls, but by the end of this period Crosfield's had been surpassed technologically by I.C.I. and the Philadelphia Quartz Company, both of whom had built new plants, replacing the old batch-process furnaces with the modern continuous type; a continuous dissolving process was also developed. Crosfield's were allowed to inspect these plants, but not until after the war were they able to build their own.

This technical collaboration illustrates the friendly relations between the major manufacturers of silicate, who preferred commercial co-operation to cut-throat competition. In July 1938 an agreement was negotiated with I.C.I., and the two firms agreed on exchange of technical information and mutual exploitation of patent rights. This was followed in August 1940 by renewal of the silicate export quota and agency agreement with I.C.I.

During this period, Crosfield's greatly extended their range of silicate-based chemical products. They began to produce small quantities of potassium silicate for various industrial purposes— despatches grew from 77 tons in 1934 to 869 in 1939—but sodium silicate formed the basis of their expanding trade in

[1] The latter figure included profits on 'Metso' (see below, p. 339), sales of which, however, were only about one-sixth (in value) of those of silicate.

industrial chemicals. We have already noticed their development of 'Acsil', 'Doucil', and silica gel ('Gasil', 'Sorbsil', and 'Quepric'). The 'Acsil' plant was closed down in the early 'thirties, since it required major repairs and the Fullers Earth Union was able to supply activated earths for palm-oil bleaching at slightly lower costs. Production of the base-exchanging material 'Doucil', on the other hand, gradually rose, as demand grew from municipal, industrial, and domestic water-softening plants. Output was boosted particularly by a large order from the Norsk Hydro-Elektrisk Company, of Oslo, in 1935, for use in manufacturing nitrate of soda. This necessitated the erection of a new plant costing £8,000, including improved processes for drying, crushing, and screening. Total sales (home and export) rose from 163 tons (£11,672) in 1929 to 614 tons (£41,679) in 1935. They then declined, however, to 170 tons (£11,974) in 1939, despite the erection in 1937 of a new plant for making a more robust 'high-silica' Doucil, by precipitation and pressing, in addition to the earlier 'whole gel' process.

The new product was intended especially for acidic waters, but by that time the Permutit Company was marketing a much cheaper material, a carbonaceous zeolite obtained by sulphonation of granulated coal. At the same time, increasing competition was felt from even cheaper Australian greensand. Crosfield's themselves had already been carrying out research into the development of sulphonated coal as a base-exchanging material, patents being taken out in 1935 and 1937 by Rex Furness jointly with the Company. Semi-large-scale production, using oleum (fuming sulphuric acid) in tetrachlorethane, was begun in 1938, and just before the war plans were prepared for a large-scale plant, which eventually came into operation in 1941. (Experience in this field was also, as we shall see, to lead to some unexpected but very important results in the post-war production of synthetic detergents.) The product, at first called 'Doucil A.C.' (Activated Coal), but trade-marked as 'Soucol' in 1939, was not only much cheaper to produce than either 'whole gel' or 'high-silica' Doucil, but also more resistant to acidic waters. In 1939 an agreement on both patents and prices of base-exchanging materials was concluded with the Permutit Company.

The various brands of silica gel—'Gasil', 'Sorbsil', and 'Quepric'—did not prove very successful commercially. A new plant costing £3,000 was erected in 1930, when combined sales rose to 94 tons (£11,194), but they fell almost completely away in the next few years and were still only 45 tons (£6,424) in 1939. An amended agreement in 1934 with the Kestner Evaporator & Engineering Company, Crosfield's agents for the sale of silica gel in the U.K., refers not only to its use as a filtering agent in oil-refining and generally for absorption of water vapour or organic vapours, but mentions particularly its possible use in dehydration and purification of coal gas (with recovery of by-products), purification of exhaust gases from internal combustion engines, water treatment, and in domestic drying cabinets. But not much success was achieved in any of these fields during the 'thirties. By the beginning of 1937 silica gel showed 'so little prospect of ever being really worth while' that Crosfield's were considering closure of the plant. It was to be saved, however, by the war and by successful post-war developments.

Much the most successful of Crosfield's new ventures in industrial chemicals during this period was, appropriately, in the field of alkaline detergents. Since the 1860s silicate had been used in their soaps, and more recently in 'Persil'. Now it was to be made a cleanser in its own right—as sodium metasilicate pentahydrate. Sodium silicates are compounds of soda and silica in varying proportions. By increasing the soda content detergency is increased, but there were difficulties in preparing the product for commercial use. These difficulties were now overcome in a patent process, developed by the Philadelphia Quartz Company, 'for the manufacture of crystallized hydrates of sodium metasilicate', in the form of a dry free-flowing powder. This American Company, with whom Crosfield's had long had friendly relations, freely handed over the British patent rights in this new product—'Metso' became its registered trade mark—as Crosfield's had previously given them the American rights in 'Doucil'.

The 'Metso' patent was acquired in 1931. This powerful alkaline cleanser proved extremely successful as a general industrial detergent. But it could not fulfil all specialized demands, so from it was developed a large family of similar 'tailor-made' detergents for particular purposes. These metasilicates were used for laundry work, for scouring operations in textiles, for cleansing bottles, cans, etc. in the food and drink trades, and for all kinds of industrial degreasing. Their number and specialized functions were continually increasing, reaching six by the end of 1939. Their sales rose rapidly from 114 tons (£1,423) in 1931 to 3,117 tons (£45,866) in 1939. A new plant for their production, costing £7,500, was erected in 1936.

Crosfield's also produced relatively small quantities of sodium hexa-metaphosphate and other polyphosphates, for inclusion in these 'Metso' compounds and also in soaps and powders; 'Aquamol', Gossage's equivalent of 'Carbosil'; and sodium aluminate for water treatment. Research work, under the direction of Rex Furness, was constantly going on into ways of improving these chemical products and of developing new ones, while considerable ingenuity was shown by the engineers, under Gordon Duff, in devising plant for their manufacture. In these respects, Crosfield's were fully living up to their established reputation in industrial research and development.

Summing up the Company's trade in chemicals (excluding glycerine), we can see that gross sales leapt up from £416,000 in 1929 to £623,000 in 1933, following transfer of Gossage's manufactures, but they then tended to stagnate at an average annual figure of £633,000 for the years 1933–8, about a sixth of the Company's total sales. Chemicals profits, which had jumped from £31,000 in 1929 to £109,000 in 1933, similarly stagnated in the following years and actually fell to around £88,000 annually in 1937–8, less than a tenth of total trading profits.[1] This was mainly due to declining profits on caustic soda, an increasing proportion of which was being supplied to associated companies at cost price. A jump in total chemicals sales to £803,000 in 1939 was mainly attributable to the caustic soda agreement with I.C.I.

Looking at Crosfield's general trading position, it is evident that 'Persil' was easily their most important product, providing nearly half of total sales revenue in 1939 and an even higher proportion of total trading profits—three-fifths in 1931 and probably more in the following years. Their hard soaps had declined, while their oil-milling, hardening, and refining de-

---

[1] Moreover, Crosfield's had to pay over half their silicate profits to Gossage's (see above, p. 336).

partments were in great difficulties. On the chemicals side, their caustic manufacture had been ended, but silicate production and profits had risen substantially, their alkaline detergents ('Metso', etc.) showed great promise, and some interesting possibilities had been opened up (e.g. 'Soucol') by their research department, though demand for 'Doucil' and silica gel ('Sorbsil', etc.) had so far proved disappointing.

Crosfield's suffered, along with other associated companies, from the general financial stringency within Unilever during this period. They raised no further capital and there was a marked slackening-off in their physical growth. No more land was acquired; indeed some, such as Arpley Meadows, was sold. Few new buildings were erected and plant developments— compared with those of the first quarter of the century—were mostly minor, except for 'Persil' and other powders, which were housed in the vacated 'Erasmic' building. 'Erasmic' manufactures had gone, the cement works had been scrapped and the caustic plant closed. Thus, after allowing for depreciation, the book value of the Company's land, buildings, and plant declined from £1,532,103 at the end of 1929 to £1,110,564 at the end of 1939. It is probable, however, that their actual value was somewhat higher, for a valuation at the end of 1930 showed a surplus of £132,000 over the book value at that date; but this was not included in the balance sheets during this period. Capital expenditure averaged £58,000 annually between 1929 and 1939—with a low point of £31,000 per annum in 1933-4— only a fraction of that in the early 1920s and before 1914. It did not, in fact, keep pace with depreciation, for which, however, substantial provision was made.[1]

The Company was seriously affected, as in 1920-1, by the sharp decline in the prices of raw materials after 1929. Stocks had to be written down heavily, their value in the balance sheets falling from £985,000 at the end of 1929 to £305,000 at the end of 1934. As prices recovered, stocks rose to £435,000 at the end of 1937, but then declined, with prices falling again, to £319,000 two years later.

The most striking feature of the balance sheets, however, is

---

[1] A Depreciation Reserve of £542,000 on the revised (1930) book value had been built up by the end of 1939. The General Reserve had also been increased from £211,000 to £450,000.

the continued growth in investments in subsidiary and allied companies. These were changed kaleidoscopically, but the overall effect was a very large increase, from £2,702,569 at the end of 1929 to £3,991,670 at the end of 1939. By the latter date, in fact, they were over three times as great as the Company's investment in its own land, buildings, and plant. Christopher Thomas & Bros. Ltd. had been added to the Erasmic Company and J. & E. Atkinson as subsidiaries. The previously large holdings in Lever Brothers and United Exporters Ltd. had been sold, along with those in Lever Brothers (India) Ltd., Candles Ltd., the West African Soap Company, etc., but shares had been acquired in other allied companies, such as the Niger Company, the Olympia Oil & Cake Company, Jurgens Ltd., and Distributors and Transporters Ltd. Crosfield's, in other words, were being used increasingly to provide resources for other parts of the Unilever business rather than for their own development.

The overall distribution of capital investment was, of course, in the hands of the Unilever Board and Special Committee, and Crosfield's had to fit in with their far wider development plans. Crosfield's could not themselves have absorbed all their surplus capital in developments at Warrington, but more might perhaps have been profitably invested there.

Despite the economic difficulties of this period, Crosfield's trading accounts present, on the whole, a pattern of steadily increasing prosperity. They suffered comparatively little from the general slump between 1929 and 1933. Their gross trading profits[1] rose, in fact, from £579,000 in 1929 to £844,000 in 1931, and though falling to £714,000 in 1932, they rose rapidly thereafter to an annual average of £993,000 in 1935-6. They fell slightly in 1938, but leapt to £1,085,000 in 1939.

Their investment revenue, however, was more seriously affected by variations in general economic activity, and fluctuated considerably. It dropped heavily from £378,000 in 1929 to £127,000 in 1932, then rose to £405,000 in 1936, fell again to £284,000 in 1938, and then recovered to £379,000 in the following year, averaging 10 per cent per annum on capital invested in 1935-9. A better return would probably have been

---

[1] Including payments under the pooling arrangements with Thomas's, Gossage's, United Exporters, and Glycerine Ltd.

obtained on additional investment in new buildings, plant, and research at Bank Quay.

Increasing output, sales, and profits were achieved with a declining labour force. The total number of works employees (males and females), excluding management, fell from 2,309 at the end of 1931 to 1,647 at the end of 1939, about half the figure of 1924. The reduction in the number of women and girls since the latter date is particularly striking: in 1924 there had been about 1,100, but their number had fallen to about 650 by 1931 and 350 by 1939. This reflects the decline of the hard soap trade and increased mechanization of wrapping and packing. The automatic 'Rose' machines were a striking example of such developments in the production of soap powders. There were innumerable other labour-saving innovations, especially in the handling and movement of goods, by improvements in plant lay-out, use of conveyors, etc. Constant efforts, in fact, were made to reduce costs by raising productivity. At the same time, the engineering department was considerably reduced, with the slackening-off in constructional activity.

Those at Crosfield's helm had to face some tricky navigational problems during these years. At the end of 1929 G. H. K. Kingdon retired from the Chairmanship and was succeeded by Geoffrey Heyworth, who soon moved on, however, to higher spheres, being followed early in 1931 by John Inglis. Inglis was to remain Chairman until nearly the end of the second World War, piloting Crosfield's skilfully through these very difficult years. Dr. C. W. Moore became Technical Director in 1930, in succession to R. E. Huffam, who also moved up the Unilever ladder; at the same time H. W. Pring joined the Board. John Allan retired in 1933 and J. H. B. Wigginton in 1936; G. A. Worsley, previously Company Secretary, was appointed a Director in 1939. W. T. Kipps remained on the Board throughout this period.

Most of these had given many years service to Crosfield's. Under their direction was a team of very able managers, who had also, for the most part, been brought up in the firm, including such as C. Billington, manager of the oil-mill and refinery and also of the Doucil and Gasil department; S. Newall, manager of the Powders department; W. R. Jackson, of the Hardening plant; G. A. Duff, the Chief Engineer; and R. Furness, of the Research department, to mention only a few. Moreover, Crosfield's were a rich source of directorial talent for other parts of the Unilever business: C. H. Hamilton, for example, had gone to Gossage's, F. Fox to Knight's, and E. Ball to Watson's, while Dr. C. H. Clarke and R. E. Huffam were to rise to the Unilever Board. From lower levels, too, Crosfield's supplied capable men for service elsewhere. Unilever undoubtedly gained a great deal from this infusion.

CHAPTER XX

WAR AND PEACE

1939–55

THE years since 1939 have witnessed changes at Bank Quay as profound as any in Crosfield's history. Many of them are still only taking shape and we are perhaps too near them to be able to make a proper appreciation of their significance. But for the most part they are the logical outcome of earlier changes, especially of the 'rationalization' schemes started after Lever's takeover and pushed through more vigorously in the 1930s, following the formation of Unilever. In that period, as we have seen, the firm's manufacture of hard soap was declining, and the oil-milling, hardening, and refining departments were in serious difficulties. On the other hand, output of soap powders was soaring remarkably and the shift towards chemicals, especially silicate of soda and its derivatives, was becoming more pronounced. On the other hand, the caustic soda plant had been closed by agreement with I.C.I. in 1939, and the cement by-product had been dropped ten years previously. Crosfield's range of manufacturing activities was inevitably narrowing. They were also controlled by central authorities such as the U.K. Soap and Oil Mills Executives, while research work had been brought under the supervision of the Central Technical Department. At the same time, centralized Unilever buying and selling agencies had been created for oils, soaps, and other products, and similarly for transport. The establishment of Crosfield, Watson & Gossage in 1940, for marketing soap products in the home distributive trade, paralleled the earlier formation of United Exporters Ltd., while Glycerine Ltd. had served the same purpose in another field. A new selling company, Industrial Soaps Ltd., was soon to take over another section of Crosfield's trade. Thus their former commercial independence had been gradually disappearing and they were becoming simply a manufacturing unit of Unilever. A large number of sales routine staff remained at Warrington, but control of selling and advertising was centred in London.

Already then, in 1939, one could see the shape of things to come. In that year, however, the world was once again plunged into war. The effects upon Crosfield's were much the same as in 1914–18, but Government control was imposed earlier and more stringently. The oil-milling, hardening, and refining plants were at once taken over by the Ministry of Food, and during the war production was greatly increased to meet the demands for margarine and cooking and fish-frying fats, as well as for soap. Output from the pressing plant leapt from 3/4,000 tons of oil in 1939 to an average of 14/15,000 tons during the war years; that from the extraction plant, which had stood idle before the war, reached the same figure by 1942, but dropped to not much more than half that amount in the following years, owing to reduced Ministry allocations, reflecting the growing world shortage of raw materials for oil-milling and soapmaking. Production of hardened and refined oils rose with similar rapidity in the early years of the war, but then fell off. Output of hardened oils more than doubled from nearly 26,000 tons in 1939 to over 55,000 in 1941, then dwindled gradually to 28/29,000 in 1945; for the same years, refined oils rose from 9/10,000 tons to 24/25,000, then fell to 16,000. Output of cattle cake, nuts, and meal, of course, followed similar trends.

As in the first World War, production of soap was as essential as bullets and block-busters, owing to the increased demand for glycerine for explosives, anti-freeze mixtures, etc., while considerable quantities of soap itself were supplied to the Armed Forces. Government control and standardization, however, resulted in the disappearance of old-established brands—'Perfection', 'Pinkobolic', 'Carbosil', 'Glitto', etc.—all these went into limbo, most of them never to return. Thus war-time requirements hastened a process already under way before the war, reducing the number of competing brands sold by Unilever soap companies. And once the old trade names had gone, the manufacture itself might soon follow.

Even during the war, Crosfield's hard soap production continued to decline, from about 25,000 tons in 1939 to little more than 8,000 tons in 1943. Most of the export trade was lost, soap rationing was introduced in 1942, and manufacture of some soaps was transferred to Watson's at Leeds. Output was raised to around 15,000 tons annually in 1944–5, as a result of Admiralty contracts, but the lapse of these at the end of the war left Crosfield's with an output of only 11,000 tons in 1946, mainly of special textile and other industrial soaps.

Output of powders was also reduced. That of 'Persil' continued to rise remarkably—from 26,554 tons in 1939 to 35,617 tons in 1945—but production of 'Hudson's Extract', after jumping from 5,225 tons in 1939 to 9,076 in 1940, was discontinued towards the end of the following year, while manufacture of 'Carbosil' was also stopped, so that the total powders output declined somewhat. The continued success of 'Persil', however, augured well for the post-war years.

The increasing demand for the 'Persil' soap base led to the development and patenting in 1944–6 of a new and revolutionary method of 'continuous soapmaking' in place of the traditional batch process. This, a revival of pre-war developments, involved a continuous series of operations—jet saponification, counter-current brine washing, and fitting—by accurately controllable methods, resulting in enormous savings in time, labour, steam, and stock-in-process, much higher glycerine extraction and concentration, and a considerable increase in output capacity. In this soapmaking revolution, Crosfield's soapery manager, R. V. Owen, played a leading role. Many of the old soap pans, some of which were over fifty years old, could now be scrapped, making more space available; but the old soapery buildings were still used.

The glycerine refinery was kept very busy during the early years of the war, producing for explosives manufacture. By 1942, output of single distilled dynamite glycerine was 4,750 tons, two to three times the 1939 figure, but demand slackened off in the later years of the war and output was negligible in 1945. Conversely, production of double-distilled chemically pure glycerine, after falling from about 2,500 tons to only a few hundred annually, picked up rapidly towards the end of the war and reached over 3,500 tons by 1945.

Silicate was still required during the war for making packing materials, etc., but production declined from nearly 29,000 tons of 'glass' in 1939 to 25,000 in 1944. The demand for 'Doucil' was at first affected by the war-time slump in the domestic softener trade, output dropping from 174 tons in 1939 to only

69 in 1940; but cessation of imports of Australian greensand brought about recovery to 211 tons in 1942. Production was entirely of the 'high-silica' type, the 'full gel' product going off the market. In the later years of the war, output of 'Doucil' fell to an annual average of little more than seventy tons, after erection of a plant for manufacture of the new carbonaceous zeolite, or base-exchange material, 'Soucol', developed just before the war. Granulated coal was sulphonated by the action of sulphur trioxide gas, obtained from oleum, and the product was then neutralized in soda ash solution, washed, and centrifuged. The new plant—the fruits of prolonged research and development by R. Furness, H. J. Wheaton, and C. Billington —came into operation towards the end of 1941 and was subsequently extended, as a result mainly of increasing demand from the Permutit Company. Output soon rose to between 400 and 500 tons annually.

Another more purely war-time achievement of Crosfield's chemical staff was the production of 'Silver Doucil' (silver zeolite), for making sea water drinkable by airmen and sailors adrift in dinghies and lifeboats. War also brought new uses for the vapour-absorbent silica gel, 'Sorbsil', in keeping bomb and shell fuses dry, and likewise the compressed-air systems of aircraft gun turrets, to prevent freezing and sticking, and in protective packaging of wireless, radar, and other delicate instruments, especially for shipment to the tropics. The Ministry of Supply, the Ministry of Air, and the Admiralty took most of the output, which rose from a mere 35 tons in 1939 to 442 in 1945; new plant had therefore to be erected, in the soapery, adjacent to the 'Doucil' plant.

Thus war was accentuating the trend at Crosfield's towards manufacture of chemicals. This trend was also reflected in the rapidly increasing output of alkaline detergents—sodium metasilicate or 'Metso', etc.—for various industrial cleaning purposes. Production rose from 4,000 tons in 1939 to about 11,000 tons annually by the end of the war. At the same time, Crosfield's continued to market caustic soda, now supplied by I.C.I. Sales fluctuated between 31,000 and 35,000 tons annually, about two-thirds of which went to allied companies, both at home and abroad.

Crosfield's chemicals helped the war effort in various other ways. Aluminium stearate was manufactured for incorporation in napalm bombs and flame-thrower solutions. New uses for silicate of potash were found in camouflage paint and search-light carbons. Sulphite soaps provided protection against der-matitis in explosives and shell-filling factories. The firm's expertise in other departments was also applied to war-time needs, such as packing dried egg powder and bottling orange juice for the Ministry of Food. The skills of the engineering department were turned to munitions and armaments, includ-ing the production of Oerlikon shells—about two and a half million had been machined by the end of the war—the manu-facture of gun mountings, parts for aeroplanes and tanks, jigs and tools for production of smoke floats and bombs, cannon guides for the first 20-mm. guns on fighter planes, etc. A section of the factory was converted to covering aircraft wings, tails, and fins with fabric: by the end of the war enough had been completed to equip 160 squadrons.

These remarkable war-time achievements were accomplished despite the dislocation caused by enlistment of over a thousand employees in the Armed Forces and other forms of National Service. About half the total labour force had to be replaced by temporary workers, including a large proportion of women and girls. A Works Committee and Council were formed in 1942, which helped to improve labour relations. At the same time, the Company had to cope with shortages of raw materials, rationing, the black-out, the hazards of air raids, and the mani-fold calls upon civilian energy by the A.R.P., Home Guard, and Civil Defence generally.

Inevitably there had to be more 'rationalization' and what we may call 'interchangeability' of manufacturing and selling within Unilever, as the Directors' report for 1945 pointed out. With the assistance of Lever Brothers & Unilever Ltd. (the parent or 'Holding Company'), it was explained,

it has been possible during the war period to arrange for the manu-facture and distribution of some of your company's products by other subsidiary companies of the Holding Company. Your com-pany, in turn, has manufactured and distributed products for those other subsidiary companies. These arrangements have proved both convenient and economical and it is intended to continue them in the future.

349

It is therefore considered desirable to place these arrangements on a more permanent footing and, accordingly, agreements operative from 1st January, 1945, have been entered into with the Holding Company and with other of its subsidiary companies engaged in the same industries as your company to pool results [*i.e.* there was now to be a 'U.K. Soap Pool' and a 'U.K. Oils Pool' in which Crosfield's would share].

There was little change during the war in the Company's capital structure. The share capital (£4,900,000 issued and fully paid) remained unaltered, and the assets were much the same. The value of land, buildings, and plant in the balance sheet actually declined from £1,110,564 at the end of 1939 to £812,151 at the end of 1944, an indication of the curtailment of capital expenditure, which averaged less than £20,000 annually during the war. This reduced value, however, was a result of making substantial provision for depreciation (£877,000), without taking account of war-time inflation. It was still based, in fact, on the 1930 valuation. The Company's physical assets were therefore very much undervalued. Nevertheless, there is no doubt that by the end of the war much of Crosfield's buildings and plant were outdated and in need of replacement. Shares in subsidiary and allied companies, on the other hand, continued to rise, from £3,991,670 to £4,323,118 between 1939 and 1944. At the time of the above pooling agreement Crosfield's sold the shares of their own subsidiaries—the Erasmic Company, C. Thomas & Bros. Ltd., and J. & E. Atkinson Ltd.—to the parent company; but they continued to hold shares in allied or fellow subsidiary companies.

Crosfield's trading profits did not rise to anything like the same extent in the second as in the first World War, mainly because of more stringent price control by the Government. From about £1,000,000 per annum in the later 'thirties they increased to around £1,200,000 annually during the war. 'Persil' was still the biggest profit-earner; profits on chemicals went up by about half, to over £150,000, but those on oils and fats, glycerine, and munitions were comparatively small. Dividends from investments in subsidiary and allied companies, on the other hand, leapt up from around £300,000 annually to over £700,000 by 1944. At the same time, however, the Company had to bear a gradually increasing burden of taxation (income tax and 'national defence contribution'), rising to £457,000 in 1944.

During these difficult war years, John Inglis remained Chairman. On his retirement in September 1944, he was succeeded by William T. Kipps, the son of John Crosfield's former coachman, who had started as an office boy fifty years earlier and had been responsible for the Chemical Sales Department since 1921: in recognition of such long and honourable service, he was appointed Chairman in his final year before he, too, retired. His successor was Percy A. W. Came, who had been brought in as a Director two years previously. Meanwhile, there had been another notable retirement, that of Dr. Charles W. Moore, who had for many years held general responsibility for technical affairs at Crosfield's. Early in the war, Henry W. Pring had retired, while George A. Worsley, formerly Secretary, had been appointed a Director. (At the end of the war, however, he moved to Lever Brothers & Unilever Ltd.) But while Directors came and went, the Company was fortunate in still retaining the managerial services of such as Gordon Duff, Rex Furness, Clifton Billington, William Jackson, Sidney Newall, and R. V. Owen, who, though now older, yet preserved the technical dynamism of earlier years and were to record further notable achievements after the war.

Peace did not bring an end to business difficulties. The post-war years 1945–50 were marked by shortages of raw materials, rationing, fuel crises, and continuance of heavy taxation and Government controls. In the early 'fifties, the economic and political climate began to change: controls were removed, many of the shortages disappeared, rationing was ended, and trading became generally more profitable. The post-war slump, which many had forecast, never materialized, prices continued to rise, and near-full employment was maintained. In the soap trade, however, there was a renewal of fierce competition between the Unilever and Hedley (Procter & Gamble) giants— described and analysed by Dr. H. R. Edwards[1]—which necessitated a further tightening-up of the former's manufacturing

[1] *Competition and Monopoly in the British Soap Industry* (1962), chaps. 10 and 11.

and selling organization. Crosfield's hard soap and powders manufactures were to be critically involved. In the chemicals trade, on the other hand, conditions were easier.

By the end of 1946, the Chairman reported that the Company had 'almost completed the change-over from . . . war production to the manufacture and marketing of goods for industrial and domestic consumption'. Post-war reorganization was prepared for by the establishment of two new administrative sections for Works Development and Production Planning. Another important innovation was the Technical Sales Service, to co-operate with customers in extending and improving applications of Crosfield products. There were, however, some serious problems to be faced. The coal shortage was critical, 'but as fast as materials and labour permit we are pushing ahead with the conversion from coal to oil fuel where such a course is practicable'. At the same time, more machinery was being converted to electrical drive, but power cuts were another problem. The Chairman also referred to 'the world shortage of oils and fats', which showed no signs of being rectified. He was concerned, too, about the possible effects of the Government's proposals for nationalization of transport, and about their policy in relation to the proportioning of production between home and export markets; there was a large export potential for the Company's products, but shipping difficulties had to be overcome. The brightest prospects were provided by their manufacture of chemicals, which was 'far above the maximum pre-war production, and the upward curve will continue in the coming year as fast as equipment can be installed or adapted. In this vastly important section of the business we are stepping into an enormous demand and one that shows signs of increasing.'

This was, indeed, where Crosfield's future lay. But the Company continued to carry on a wide range of other manufacturing activities. The oil-milling, hardening, and refining plants were profoundly affected, of course, by the post-war shortage of oils and fats; prices and supplies were controlled by the Ministry of Food until 1954. The pressing and extraction plants had to be operated far below capacity. Output of extracted oil fell from about 8,000 tons annually in 1945–6 to an average of little more than 4,000 tons per annum in the late 'forties; that of pressed oil also fell, from 14/15,000 to 11/12,000 tons per annum. The supply situation improved thereafter and output from the extraction plant soared to nearly 22,000 tons in 1953; but the pressing plant remained in the doldrums. Production of meal and cattle cake, of course, followed much the same patterns.

The adjoining hardening plant and refinery, meanwhile, were breaking output records, principally with whale oil, owing to the shortage of tallow and vegetable oils. Production of hardened oil doubled from 27,000 tons per annum in 1945–6 to 54,000 in 1949, around which level it remained in the early 'fifties, with a record of over 59,000 tons in 1954. New hydrogenators were installed, together with new plant for producing hydrogen and nickel catalyst (Crosfield's supplied the latter to several associated companies), while in prior treatment of oils continuous neutralization and washing were introduced, along the same lines as in continuous soapmaking. The refinery's output similarly soared from 16,000 tons in 1945 to around 27,000 annually in the early 'fifties, with a record of over 30,000 in 1953. Few could have guessed that this was to be the final flourish of these departments.

The shortage of fats and oils necessitated the maintenance of soap rationing until 1950. By that year Crosfield's output had gradually recovered to 20,000 tons, near which figure it remained throughout the 'fifties. The main market was still in textile and other industrial soaps, but they recovered some of their lost ground in household and export qualities (still including the traditional 'blue mottled'). The new continuous soapmaking plant, however, which came into full operation by 1947–8, catered primarily for 'Persil' and other soap powders. As a result of powerful advertising, production of 'Persil' rose even more dramatically than in the past, from about 32,000 tons per annum in 1946–8 to 107,000 tons in 1955. It was now easily the leading washing powder in the country, accounting for about one-third of total U.K. household consumption (including non-soapy products). To meet this increasing demand, further technical improvements were introduced: vertical (instead of horizontal) blowing and cooling towers, which greatly reduced 'weathering' and made possible continuous manufacture and packing; chemical additives, which produced 'New

Whiter Persil', to substantiate the well-known advertising claims; and more and more printing and packing machines to pour out over a million packets a day!

In addition to 'Persil', Crosfield's continued to manufacture relatively small quantities of other soap powders, such as 'Hudson's Extract' and Watson's 'Stella'. In the post-war period, however, they had to face growing competition from new 'synthetic' or soapless detergents. Crosfield's themselves were pioneers in the development of such products. Even before the war, they were experimenting in this field (see above, p. 333), and the war-time and post-war shortage of natural oils and fats stimulated research into the production of non-soapy detergents from petroleum fractions.[1] In 1943 they succeeded in producing such a washing powder, incorporating 'Teepol' (an alkyl sulphate, produced by Shell Chemicals Ltd., the petro-chemical subsidiary of the Shell Petroleum Co.). This new product was trade-marked 'Sparkla', but did not prove successful. Crosfield's also experimented with other soapless powders and at combining phosphates with them. (Indeed, they had done so before the war, when, as we have seen, they themselves began to produce small quantities of sodium hexametaphosphate and other polyphosphates for these purposes.)

Hedley's, however, were allowed by Unilever to seize the initiative in the post-war period. First of all, in 1948, they revived their soapless powder 'Dreft' (originally introduced just before the war). Then, in the following year, they introduced a new type of organic detergent base, an alkyl aryl sulphonate—obtained by sulphonating hydrocarbon oils, obtained from oil refineries, and then neutralizing with caustic soda—which was combined with phosphate builders.[2] This new type of soapless powder had been developed by Procter & Gamble in the U.S.A., but in this country suitable petroleum fractions were not readily available until the late 'forties. Hedley's changed 'Dreft' over to this new material in 1949, and in the following year they brought out a superior product, 'Tide'.

---

[1] It is interesting to note that sixty years earlier Crosfield's had been among the first to investigate the possibilities of refined mineral oils as a source of raw materials for soapmaking (see above, p. 81).

[2] See Edwards, *loc. cit.* Edwards, however, has overlooked Crosfield's pioneering achievements in developing soapless detergents.

(a) external view

16 (a and b) Powders building in the late 'fifties

(b) internal view

17. Silicate furnace, 1950

These soapless detergents have some important advantages over soap powders, especially in hard waters, since they do not (like soap) react with calcium and magnesium salts to produce scum. At first Unilever did not fully appreciate their possibilities, while Hedley's were able to draw upon Procter & Gamble's research in the U.S.A. during and immediately after the war. Unilever were clearly at a disadvantage, but from the late 'forties onwards they began rapidly to catch up. Crosfield's were now encouraged to press forward vigorously with their developments, and they immediately brought out a 'Teepol'-based product, 'Wisk', which was put on the market towards the end of 1948. Output rose to 5,000/6,000 tons annually in 1949-50, but it did not prove successful. Meanwhile, as a result of intensive research, development and engineering— by the old team of Furness, Billington, and Duff—Crosfield's rapidly succeeded in erecting a plant for production of sulphonated alkylate (or alkane) in 1948-9. In doing so, they improved on the original American process, which involved the use of oleum for sulphonating the hydrocarbon oils and the disposal of large amounts of impure sulphuric acid; Crosfield's, instead, successfully applied their experience of gaseous sulphur trioxide sulphonation, previously developed for production of 'Soucol'.[1]

Crosfield's skills in research and development thus helped Unilever to strike back at Hedley's. 'Wisk' was soon dropped and 'Surf' was brought out in 1952. Production of this powder at Warrington quickly rose from about 9,000 tons in that year to over 20,000 in 1954, but then stabilized at around 15,000 tons in the following years. Increasing competition led to the incorporation of fluorescent whitening agents in washing powders. Crosfield's participated in Unilever development of these substances, which were used in 'Persil' and 'Surf' and also in a new blue powder, 'Omo', brought out in answer to Hedley's 'Daz'. Some 'Omo' was produced at Warrington in 1954, but thereafter it was manufactured entirely at Port Sunlight. At the latter plant, and in Sweden and Austria, Crosfield's patent gaseous sulphonation process was used. The

[1] They did not, however, continue their production of phosphates for use as builders in non-soapy detergents, but drew supplies from Albright & Wilson Ltd., who became the dominant British firm in this field.

355

Company has thus played a key role in this modern revolution in the detergents industry.

These achievements reflect Crosfield's traditional strength in chemical research and development. At the same time, the Company continued to improve its established chemical manufactures and to find new uses for its chemical products. Along with soaps and soap powders, glycerine was still produced. The new counter-current soap washing process, giving a much higher glycerine yield and concentration from the spent lyes, greatly reduced evaporating costs in this department. Considerable improvements were also made in high-vacuum distillation. Crosfield's continued to receive crude glycerine from various associated companies, and their total output of the refined product, after dropping from 5,000 tons in 1945 to about 3,750 annually in 1946–7, then rose more rapidly than ever before to a record figure of 7,125 in 1957.

Remarkable developments also occurred in the manufacture of sodium silicate and other chemicals. Immediately after the war, steps were taken to modernize the whole silicate plant. As in soapmaking, a continuous process of manufacture was introduced, in place of the traditional batch process. The old method was to mix the charge of sand and soda ash and load it into the furnace in three-ton units, tapping the white-hot liquid glass every hour and a half. The glass was allowed to cool in large trays and was then smashed to fragments by brute strength; it then had to be moved to the dissolvers. In the new plant, the sand and soda ash, conveyed mechanically, were continuously and automatically mixed and fed into the furnace and the molten glass was continuously tapped from the other end, falling in a glowing stream into small metal saucers on a slow-moving elevator, on which it was cooled, so that it arrived at the top in solid discs, which were automatically tipped into bins. It was then conveyed either to the dissolvers or to storage silos.

These innovations, it was reported in 1950, not only saved much manual labour, but also enabled them to produce a third more glass per week. At the same time, the furnaces were converted to firing by oil instead of coal (producer gas). Production of glass increased dramatically, from 26,901 tons in 1945 to 87,589 in 1955. Most of this was dissolved; only about one-tenth usually was sold in lump or powdered form. From a quarter to a third was sent to the dissolving and evaporating plant at Bow, while an increasing proportion (over five-eighths in 1955) was converted to liquor at Warrington, mainly for internal consumption, in making 'Metso', 'Doucil', and other chemicals, 'Persil', and soap. More and more, indeed, the silicate plant was becoming the heart of the factory. From a quarter to a third of total output was sold as liquors, dispatched in bulk tankers or in drums. Many different grades were produced—varying in silica/soda ratio and concentration—and marketed mostly under the well-established 'Pyramid' brand; mixed with clay, it formed 'Claysil' adhesives. The industrial applications of this versatile material were ever widening, both at home and abroad.

Among the many processes in which it plays an important part are laminated board making, soap and paper manufacture, the processing of textiles, barrel lining, paint and enamel manufacture, ore extraction, ceramics, and the manufacture of abrasive wheels and acid-proof cements . . . Potassium silicates, which Crosfield's are now producing in growing quantities [over 1,000 tons in 1955], are employed by the manufacturers of electrodes, paints and building materials and in welding. (*Progress*, Spring 1950.)

Silica gel ('Sorbsil') continued to be marketed in increasing quantities in the post-war period, mainly as a moisture vapour absorbent in packaging, to prevent rusting and deterioration of goods during transit and storage, and also for industrial air and gas drying. Output dropped just after the war to only 127 tons in 1947, but rose fairly steadily in the following years to 650 tons in 1955. New uses were found for this highly porous material, e.g. as a catalyst support.

The base-exchange materials 'Doucil' and 'Soucol', on the other hand, failed to live up to their earlier promise as water softeners. Annual output of the former, after rising to around 300 tons in the late 'forties, gradually sank to below 100 tons by the late 'fifties. For 'Soucol' similarly, there was a sharp post-war demand, when output rose to around 600 tons annually, but this too had dropped below 100 tons by the end of the 'fifties. These materials were being displaced by new synthetic ion-exchange resins (cation and anion exchangers), which, when used in series, were capable of producing the equivalent of distilled water from hard water. Crosfield's collaborated with

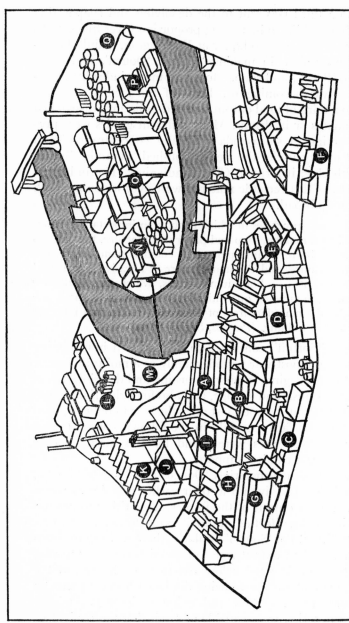

KEY TO PLATE 18

A Soapery
B Chemicals (Doucil,
   Metso, etc.)
C Offices
D Glycerine plant

E Engineers' plant
F Institute
G Printing building
H Soap tablet building
I Export building

J S.F.C. plant
K Powders building
L Silicate plant
M Wharf warehouse
N Oil hardening plant

O Oil extraction and
   pressing plant
P Oil refinery
Q Cooperage

the Permutit Company in development of such products, marketed as 'Resex' and 'Rezanex'.

A far more important application of silicate was in the rapidly expanding manufacture of sodium metasilicate ('Metso') and a widening range of derived alkaline detergents. By 1954 there were fourteen varieties, differing in alkalinity and other properties. Trade marks multiplied: 'Trimetso', 'Solgon', etc. for highly alkaline detergents, used for heavy plant cleaning and bottle washing; 'Metso' itself, 'Metrax', 'Calmet', 'Sulmet', and 'Bryta' in the medium strength range, for laundry washing, dairy-can cleansing, metal degreasing, etc.; 'Acorn', 'Calphos', and 'Hexo', of low alkalinity, for general hand-cleansing operations; but most of these products were specially blended for particular industrial purposes. Their total output more than trebled between 1945 and 1955, from 10,500 to 33,000 tons.

The most outstanding development of these ten post-war years, however, was the erection in 1951 of a large new plant for producing Synthetic Fluid Catalyst (S.F.C.). This product, supplied under agreement to five major oil-refining companies (who were thereby saved dollars on American imports), for improved cracking of their crude petroleum oils, to give higher octane yields, was developed by the Davison Chemical Corporation, of Baltimore, U.S.A., who assisted in the erection of the Warrington plant. Crosfield's, of course, already had an established reputation in production of nickel catalyst for hydrogenation of natural oils, and as manufacturers of silica gel for catalyst support, and many years earlier T. P. Hilditch, and subsequently R. Furness, had carried out research into silica-alumina catalysts. It was therefore very appropriate that this new manufacture should now be established at Bank Quay. In this process, sodium silicate was combined with aluminium sulphate, the product being filtered and spray-dried to microspheroidal form and fluid-like appearance. The plant, which was erected next to the Powders Building, on part of the former site of Robinson's glassworks, was extended in the following years to double its original capacity. Its total cost eventually was about £1,400,000.

Whilst Crosfield's were thus widening the scope of their activities in the chemical field, they continued to market caustic soda supplied by I.C.I., under the 1939 agreement. Sales rose to over 42,000 tons in 1955, but declined thereafter, following a modified arrangement, and finally ceased after 1959, as a result of a new agreement with I.C.I.

By the early 'fifties, Crosfield's were emerging from the post-war difficulties and were vigorously developing their manufacturing activities. Capital expenditure, which had been reduced to almost negligible proportions during the war, rose prodigiously afterwards. From little more than £13,000 in 1945, it gradually rose to nearly £365,000 in 1950, then leapt to £1,167,000 in 1951 and averaged well over £500,000 annually in the next four years. The largest item, of course, was the S.F.C. plant, but, as we have seen, substantial improvements and extensions had been made to other parts of the works.

At the end of 1955, the total value of land, buildings, and plant—based on a new Directors' valuation of 1st January 1953, with additions at cost—was very nearly £5,000,000, against which about £1,200,000 had been provided for depreciation. At that same date, shares in fellow subsidiaries also totalled (at cost) about £5,000,000, so that total fixed assets were put at rather more than £8¾ millions. The Company's issued capital, however, was not increased until December 1954. By that time a General Reserve of £1,500,000 had been accumulated,[1] which was then capitalized, thus raising the Ordinary capital to £3,000,000. (Preference capital still stood at £3,400,000.) Unappropriated profits in the business totalled £800,000.

The Company's trading profit, or 'operating profit' as it was now called, doubled from £809,000 in 1945 to £1,636,000 in 1955, while interest and dividends from the parent company and fellow subsidiaries remained at about £350,000.[2] Despite an increasingly heavy burden of taxation—the combined provision for income tax and profits tax in the Profit and Loss Accounts rose from £406,000 to £959,000 during this period—Crosfield's were enjoying considerable prosperity, especially in the early 'fifties. A noticeable feature was the growth of

---

[1] Prior to 1953, when a more realistic value was placed on the Company's assets, substantial amounts had been allocated annually out of profits to a Fixed Assets Replacement Reserve, but as this was no longer necessary, it was added to the General Reserve.

[2] In view of the pooling arrangements in 1945, however, comparisons with earlier years are of little value, and the published profits provide no direct indication of the prosperity of Warrington operations.

profits on chemicals (in which the Company traded independently): these more than trebled, from £172,000 to £549,000,
mainly from silicate and 'Metso'. Those from oils and fats remained comparatively small until 1954, owing to continued
price control by the Ministry of Food.

The total number of the Company's employees tended to fall
immediately after the war, from over 2,200 in 1945 to just
below 2,000 in 1948, but then rose steadily, despite increasing
mechanization, to nearly 2,500 by the middle 'fifties. Replacement of temporary employees by those returning from the
Forces was carried through smoothly. A five-day week was in-
stituted throughout the factory and offices immediately after
the war. Labour relations were stated to be excellent. The
Office and Works Committees and Councils functioned very
well, helping to overcome post-war difficulties. Regular courses
for 'Training within Industry' were started, the Company
continuing to stress the value of technical and commercial
education. Eventually, in 1957, the modern Training Centre
was built.

The emphasis on *esprit de corps* led in 1950 to the revival of
a house journal, but under a new name, the *Crosfield Chronicle*,
instead of the *Crosfield's Flag* of a quarter-century earlier. Its
pages reveal a still vigorous social life, with works' societies and
clubs of all kinds, including close links with the Company's
pensioners. They also record many long periods of service to the
firm, sometimes extending over several generations; the most
notable example is that of the Gleave family, five generations
of whom have worked at Bank Quay since the soapery was
founded.

Wages were steadily increased during the war and post-war
period, as prices and productivity rose. The basic weekly wage
for soap workers, for example, rose from £3 4s. at the end of
1939 to £4 6s. (including supplementary war allowance) in
1945, and then to £7 6s. 6d. in 1955, on top of which extra
'job rates' were paid. At the same time, payments for sickness
and pensions were still continued, alongside those of the Welfare
State. Despite the dislocations of war and the distractions of
peace, much of the old corporate loyalty survived, and Crosfield's were still 'a good firm to work for'.

CHAPTER XXI

AN END AND A NEW BEGINNING
1956–65

THE middle 'fifties formed a watershed in Crosfield's history, the beginning of a revolution at Bank Quay. Far-reaching plans of reorganization were then worked out, involving wholesale closure and scrapping on the one hand, and massive re-development on the other, bringing about a sweeping physical transformation, completing the long drawn-out process of 'rationalization', and finally establishing the Company in the specialized role of chemical manufacturers. This metamorphosis is only now nearing completion.

At that period, too, there were important changes in the directorship. Within a few years, indeed, the whole Board was changed. In June 1953 the Chairman, P. A. W. Came, who had done so much for Crosfield's post-war expansion, suddenly died. In September J. A. Fox, who had been raised to the Board in 1945, resigned on being appointed Chairman of Price's (Bromborough) Ltd. Dr. J. E. Taylor, who had just joined the Board from Unilever Technical Division, became the new Chairman, while A. C. H. Cairns, formerly chemical sales manager, and W. J. Deverall, formerly works manager, were appointed Directors. Two years later G. F. Greaves, the Finan-cial Director, retired after many years' service, while Deverall left to become Chairman of John Knight's. Their successors were R. D. Cameron, from the U.K. Soap Executive, and R. Morris, from British Oil & Cake Mills Ltd. In 1957–8 there were further changes. Cairns became Managing Director of Unilever Export Ltd., and was succeeded as Chemical Sales Director by G. W. Hemy, previously manager of the drugs and perfumery department of the United Africa Company Ltd. Soon afterwards Cameron moved up the Unilever ladder and was replaced as Financial Director by W. Rigby, previously Chairman of Lever Brothers (Pakistan) Ltd., who remained at Warrington until his retirement in 1963.

With the new men came new policies. These were first publicly announced by Dr. J. E. Taylor on 2nd November 1956, when a major factory rebuilding programme was outlined, which would take eight years to complete and cost £5 millions. The main features of this plan were the demolition of the old structures in the central part of the works—the soapery and soap export building, the clutter of buildings in which 'Doucil', 'Metso', etc., were manufactured, and also the wharf warehouse—and their replacement by a new soapery and crude glycerine plant, a new chemicals building, and a new technical centre containing laboratories, etc., while space would be left for future developments. At the same time, road and rail facilities within the works would be completely reorganized. Some buildings would still remain—the powders building, the tablet building (which would be completely modernized to house the new soapery), the silicate and S.F.C. plants, the printing and paper stores building, the office block and fire station. But most of those on the Cheshire side, including the oil-milling, hardening, and refining plants, and also those for 'Soucol' and sulphonated alkylate, were evidently doomed, for it was the Company's ultimate intention to concentrate production on the Lancashire side of the Mersey.

The Cheshire works were, in fact, closed down in 1959-60, except for the boiler plant (still feeding steam across to the Lancashire side), the melting-out department, oil-bleaching plant, and storage tanks. Crosfield's oil-milling, hardening, and refining plants were now to a large extent out of date; it was also inconvenient and costly moving materials and men across the river, and production could be carried on more economically in the larger modern Unilever plants at Bromborough, Purfleet, Erith, and Selby. So 'rationalization' finally carried the day. Perhaps it might also be said that Crosfield's were paying the penalty of their early pioneering in oils and fats, which left them with obsolescent plant on a congested and inconvenient site.

By the time the Cheshire works were closed, more far-reaching plans for reorganization of the whole of Unilever U.K. soap trade had been developed, following the report in 1960 of a study group under the Chairmanship of Dr. E. G. Woodroofe. This report can be compared with that of Geoffrey Heyworth (later Lord Heyworth) nearly thirty years previously, which had resulted in a large measure of 'rationalization'. Now, in the 'fifties, under increasing competitive pressure from Procter & Gamble, there was urgent need for further 'rationalization', so as to unify both manufacturing and selling, thereby increasing efficiency and reducing costs.

In 1960, therefore, the existing soap-selling companies— Lever Brothers Ltd., Crosfield's (C.W.G.) Ltd., and Hudson & Knight Ltd.—were merged into a single organization, Lever Brothers & Associates Ltd. At the same time, the manufacture of soap, soap powders, and non-soapy detergents was concentrated at Port Sunlight and Warrington; production of soap at John Knight's (Silvertown) was transferred to Port Sunlight. Moreover, there was a redistribution of production between Port Sunlight and Warrington. The former was burdened with excess capacity on a large factory area, while Crosfield's, though producing at lower costs than Lever Brothers, were on a comparatively restricted site, which could be more advantageously developed for chemicals manufacture. It was therefore decided to transfer Crosfield's hard soap and flakes production to Port Sunlight, and in 1960 manufacture of these products at Bank Quay finally ceased. Soapmaking operations, however, would still be carried on there, for it was decided to concentrate production of soap powders at Warrington, where by this time 'Persil' had outstripped all other such rivals. The new soapery, therefore, completed in 1962 and embodying the latest improvements in continuous manufacture, would be employed solely in producing the soap base for 'Persil' and other powders such as 'Rinso', which were transferred from Port Sunlight. On the other hand, however, Port Sunlight took over all non-soapy detergents, as well as hard soap, so that Crosfield's lost 'Surf' and other such products, and their alkylate sulphonation plant was closed.

The natural sequel to these changes was the complete integration of the manufacturing and selling of all these products. As from 1st January 1964, therefore, the soap and non-soapy manufactures of Lever Brothers (Port Sunlight) Ltd. and of Crosfield's were brought under the control of a single new company, Lever Brothers & Associates Ltd., which also controlled the selling and advertising of such products. Manufacture was still continued at Warrington, but this new integrated company took over the soap side of Crosfield's business. There would now be, in effect, two factories on the Bank Quay site, one for Crosfield's chemicals and the other for the soap powders of L.B. & A. Ltd., though Crosfield's would continue to provide general services (engineering, steam and power, personnel, etc.) for the latter. Thus the split between soap and chemicals, which had been mooted several times in earlier years, but had then proved impracticable,[1] was finally brought about.

Meanwhile, the rationalization of the soap and detergents business had been accompanied by a similar rationalizing process in Unilever chemicals, with the formation in 1960 of the Unilever U.K. Chemical Group, embracing Crosfield's, Price's (Bromborough), Knight's (Silvertown), Glycerine Ltd., and various other companies. The Woodroofe Committee regarded Warrington as a particularly 'important base for Unilever's expansion in the chemical business'. Demolition and rebuilding therefore went on furiously at Warrington in the late 'fifties and early 'sixties. All the old buildings in the central part of the factory were gradually knocked down, and the new chemicals building and technical centre rose from their ruins. The glycerine refinery was also closed, production being concentrated at Port Sunlight, and the buildings were renovated and re-equipped for production of nickel catalyst.

Thus Crosfield's were preparing for a leading role in the Unilever U.K. Chemical Group. Within that Group there has recently—in March 1964—been an important combination of Unilever chemical firms in the north-west, comprising Crosfield's, Price's (of Bromborough), and the Walker Chemical Company Ltd. (of Bolton), with the object of achieving coordination in this vital Merseyside area. This is, in fact, a piece of regional 'rationalization', the results of which are yet hardly visible. At the same time, 'rationalization' has been made easier by Unilever Ltd. buying out Crosfield's Preference shareholders.

Understandably, this long programme of closures and reorganization has created some feelings of bitter regret among the older generation, who could remember the battles of nearly half a century earlier and were still inclined to think of Crosfield's as a separate entity. It has been said that all has come to

[1] See above, pp. 229, 283-4, and 291-2.

pass as the Crosfields and their successors had feared; that the great days of the Company are now over; that Lever's have at last been able to seize this opportunity of swallowing up Crosfield's soapmaking and glycerine business; that the Company has been 'sold down the river', despite its continued technical efficiency; and that all this would never have happened if there had not been such sweeping changes in Crosfield's Board in the middle 'fifties.

These criticisms are understandable, but do not take into account the necessities of a changing business world. We have, in fact, been witnessing the final and logical consequences of 1911 and 1919. Hitherto Unilever had proceeded slowly and cautiously with 'rationalization', but they were now faced with the problem of excess capacity, in several factories, with consequently heavy overheads, at a time when they were struggling against a powerful monolithic competitor. Further 'rationalization' was therefore essential. Nor were these changes really surprising, in the light of previous history. In the 'twenties and 'thirties, as we have seen, the Company's oil-milling, hardening, and refining departments had been in constant difficulties; its hard soap trade had been steadily declining; and although Crosfield's were justifiably proud of their technical efficiency, a good deal of their buildings and equipment were outdated, and there is no doubt of the economies that were to be achieved by concentrating and streamlining production.

Not surprisingly, these changes have aroused some fears and misgivings. Gossage's had long been a skeleton in Crosfield's cupboard. What had happened at Widnes could happen at Warrington. But though much of Crosfield's works, like Gossage's in the early 'thirties, has been razed to the ground, modern buildings are rising phoenix-like from the ashes and a new future for the Company is being compounded in chemicals. Crosfield's have acquired a deservedly high reputation for their expertise in chemical research and development, and in their more specialized present-day role as chemical manufacturers their chemists and engineers—the successors of Markel, Hilditch, Furness, Duff, and the rest—are continuously revealing new possibilities for application of their products.

Interactions of sodium silicate with acids or soluble salts have been utilized for the development of 'Neosyl' fine silicas,

19 New soapery: (*a*) external view; (*b*) internal view

20 (*a*) New chemicals building

20 (*b*) New technical centre

'Microcal' and 'Alusil' calcium and aluminium silicates, all fine powders, with numerous uses as fillers, matting agents and extenders in rubber compositions, paints, printing inks, polishes, adhesives, cosmetics, etc., and also as free-flowing anti-caking agents in various powdered or granular products. Similarly, micronized silica gels, extremely fine powdered silicas, have been produced and marketed under the revived brand name 'Gasil',[1] being supplied, like the previous products, with carefully controlled chemical and physical characteristics (particle size, surface area, absorptive and suspensive capacity), for use principally as matting and flatting agents in paints, paper, and plastics. The Company has developed new techniques in the manufacture of nickel catalyst ('Nicat') for hydrogenation of oils. Numerous 'development products', mainly silica derivatives, are being brought out for a wide variety of industrial applications. The new technical centre is equipped with laboratories for research and development, for testing of raw materials and control of products at all stages of manufacture; pilot plant facilities are also provided.

New plant has been erected for production of anhydrous sodium metasilicate ('Metso') by direct fusion as in a silicate or glass furnace, and the Company has continued to add to the number of alkaline detergents in the 'Metso' family. Total production has risen from 33,000 tons in 1955 to over 44,000 in 1963. Output of 'Sorbsil' has also continued to rise, reaching nearly 1,000 tons, and that of 'Doucil' is also recovering, but now chiefly for use as a catalyst base rather than for water-softening. The ten-year loan on the Synthetic Fluid Catalyst plant has been paid off, and the oil companies are still customers for 'Synclyst', though production has tended to fall somewhat.

At the heart of all these chemical developments, of course, are the furnaces, dissolvers, and evaporators of the silicate plant. In 1957 a new furnace was erected at the Bow factory in London, to supplement the dissolving and evaporating plant built there just before the war, and so save transport of 'glass' from Warrington. Production of 'glass' at that factory quickly rose to between 20,000 and 25,000 tons annually; it was converted into liquors for use mainly as an adhesive in the

[1] The earlier use of this brand for silica gel has been dropped, 'Sorbsil' having become the sole trade mark for this product.

manufacture of cardboard and corrugated paper. As a result, Warrington's output of 'glass' was correspondingly reduced, from over 86,000 tons in 1956 to below 62,000 in 1963.

By the latter year, however, circumstances had changed and a reappraisal was necessary. Indirect costs at Bow proved higher than was anticipated, while the market situation was altered by a swing from silicate to starch adhesives; at the same time, productive efficiency at Warrington was being improved, and transport costs were being reduced. It was therefore decided to close the Bow factory, arrangements being made for silicate liquors to be manufactured by an associated company, John Knight Ltd., at its neighbouring Silvertown factory, to which 'glass' would be transported from Warrington. Output from the Warrington plant has therefore risen again.

The recent changes at Warrington, involving closures, demolition, and rebuilding, together with continuing mechanization, have resulted in some reduction of the Company's labour force. From a total of 2,451 in 1955, it fell to 2,046 in 1960, but following completion of the new buildings, has since tended to rise, reaching 2,138 in 1963. (These figures refer to the end of each year.) But there has been no consequent labour redundancy. The Company has been particularly concerned to prevent this, and the reduction in the number of employees has been brought about by 'natural wastage', i.e. by retirements and normal labour turnover. At the same time, employees have co-operated fully with management in necessary changing of jobs and retraining within the works. Wages, meanwhile, have continued to rise: the minimum or basic weekly rate in the factory has been increased from £7 6s. 6d. in 1955 to £10 7s. 6d. in 1964, on top of which evaluated 'job rates' are paid, averaging about 35s. in the latter year, while earnings, including overtime, are considerably higher.

The *Crosfield Chronicle* continues to publish lists of employees with long service records. The Company still has many workers, foremen, and managers who have spent most if not all of their working lives at Bank Quay. But there has been an increasing infusion in recent years of new managerial talent, products of Unilever training schemes, usually with University degrees or other professional qualifications; this has been particularly noticeable in research and development. This is not, however, something new at Crosfield's, who were early in adopting such a progressive policy, under Markel's inspiration, fifty or sixty years previously. Indeed this policy accounted for their technical leadership in soap and allied chemicals. It has, however, been adopted on a greater scale and has been accompanied by much more inter-company mobility.

This mobility has been most marked in the Directorship, a striking contrast to earlier years, when it was customary for Chairmen and Directors, often promoted from within the Company, to spend long periods on the Board. Since 1953, Directors (mostly from other parts of the Unilever business) have been constantly coming and going. We have already noticed such changes in the 'fifties. In 1960 the Chairman, Dr. Taylor, left to become head of the new Unilever U.K. Chemical Group. His successor, A. D. Wilson, from Unilever Technical Division, after ushering in the changes in the early 'sixties, left for Unilever Merseyside Ltd. in the spring of 1964, and J. Arnold Fox returned to Warrington to take over the Chairmanship.

This change was associated with the new combination of Unilever chemical firms in the north-west, comprising Crosfield's, Price's, and Walker's. J. Arnold Fox, the new Chairman of Crosfield's, is a former Director, with long experience of their chemicals trade. At the same time, he remains Chairman of Price's, and also of an Executive Committee co-ordinating the activities of the three associated chemical companies. Meanwhile, W. Rigby had retired and R. Morris left to become Production Director of Lever Brothers & Associates Ltd. D. Angel, previously Commercial Assistant to the Chief Accountant of Unilever Ltd., was appointed Financial Director, and was joined on the Board by H. Stromberg, Chairman of Walker's, and D. Perry, Vice-Chairman of Price's. These three, under the Chairmanship of J. Arnold Fox, form the co-ordinating executive committee for Crosfield's, Price's, and Walker's. G. W. Hemy remains on Crosfield's Board as their Chemical Sales Director.

These frequent changes, coinciding as they have with the physical transformation of the Warrington factory and the disappearance of some old landmarks, have severed many of the Company's links with the past and are preparing the way for its new leading role in Unilever's chemical development. Crosfield's future is now inextricably bound up with that of the

369

Unilever Chemical Group, and within that Group there will no doubt have to be more co-ordination, more unified research and development. But future prospects are bright. As the Woodroofe Committee observed, 'expansion in the speciality chemical business seems to us to offer considerable possibilities'. Crosfield's, with their silicate, S.F.C., and nickel catalyst plants, their new chemicals building, research centre, and traditional strength in applied science, are well placed to seize such opportunities. It is in this light that the recent changes should be viewed.

It is rather saddening, of course, to see the objects of so much human scheming and endeavour rendered obsolete, razed to the ground, or standing derelict—to view the empty waste where the busy soapery once stood, to look across the river at the old oil-milling, hardening, and refining plants now standing idle, the tall silos gaunt and empty against the sky, and emptier still the words 'Perfection Soap' emblazoned upon them. Yet while we may stand awhile gazing at these relics of the past—our thoughts drifting back to the foundation of 'the soapery at Bankey', to the heyday of 'Perfection' and the triumphs of hydrogenation—time does not stand still: 'The moving finger writes, and having writ moves on.' Or in biological terms, businesses are like living organisms, subject to the law of evolution—the fittest survive and the weakest go under—and the fittest are those who change and adapt themselves to their changing environment. If there is one lesson which the history of Crosfield's teaches it is this: only by constant research and innovation, by ruthless scrapping and rebuilding, can a firm survive in the modern competitive world.

Joseph Crosfield himself established his soapery in a converted wire-mill, where a rosin works once stood. And the present-day Chairman of Crosfield's can look out of his office window at the new soapery in the modernized tablet building, the new chemicals building near the site of the former caustic plant, and the new technical centre where the wharf warehouse was once erected. Even as these words are written, a chemicals warehouse is being put up on the site of the old soapery, the former oil-hardening buildings are being pulled down to make room for a new steam-raising plant, and a new bridge is to be flung across the river. Crosfield's are moving into the future!

THE CROSFIELDS OF WARRINGTON
(male issue)

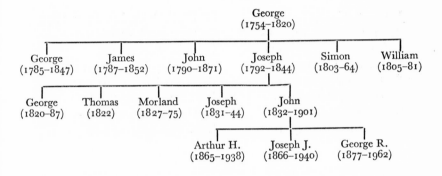

George
(1754–1820)

George (1785–1847)   James (1787–1852)   John (1790–1871)   Joseph (1792–1844)   Simon (1803–64)   William (1805–81)

George (1820–87)   Thomas (1822)   Morland (1827–75)   Joseph (1831–44)   John (1832–1901)

Arthur H. (1865–1938)   Joseph J. (1866–1940)   George R. (1877–1962)

CHAIRMEN OF JOSEPH CROSFIELD & SONS LTD.

J. Crosfield 1896–1901
A. H. Crosfield 1902–1908
J. J. Crosfield 1909–1915
F. W. Brock 1915–1916
R. Brunner 1916–1917
C. Haslam 1917–1919
G. Hunt 1919–1923
C. F. Huffam 1923–1926

G. H. K. Kingdon 1926–1929
G. Heyworth 1929–1931
J. Inglis 1931–1944
W. T. Kipps 1944–1946
P. A. W. Came, 1946–1953
J. E. Taylor 1953–1960
A. D. Wilson 1960–1964
J. A. Fox 1964 to date

APPENDIX III

SOAP AND GLYCERINE MANUFACTURE
c. 1900

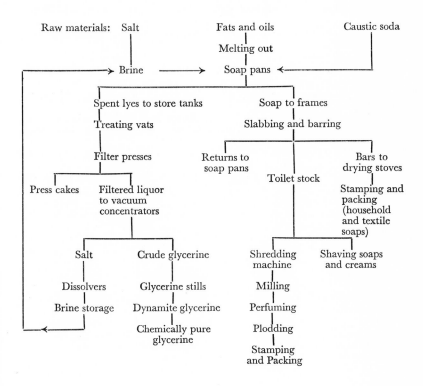

INDEX

Acetone production (First World War), 147, 272

'Acsil' (activated earth, for oil bleaching), 272, 300, 310, 314, 338

Administration. *See* Company organization

Advertising, 100–4, 142, 186–91, 195, 196, 197, 199, 212–13, 228, 254, 268–9, 270, 276, 292–3, 294–6, 304–7, 315, 329–30, 354

Ainsworth, G., and Bank Quay Wire-mill, 15–16

Albright & Wilson Ltd., 355n.

Alkali. *See* Soda

Alkaline detergents ('Metso', etc.), 339–40, 341, 348, 359, 367

Allan, J., 147, 167, 179, 319, 343

Alum works, St. Helens, 42–3, 58

Aluminium stearate, 349

'Alusil' (aluminium silicate), 367

Ambulance brigade, 153

Angel, D., 369

Anti-Corn-Law League, 51, 128

Apol Ltd., 179, 218, 256, 283, 290, 301

Ardol Ltd., 172, 250, 253

Armstrong, Dr. E. F., 276, 310, 317, 318–19

Associated Enterprises Ltd., 251–2, 279, 283

Associations. *See* Combines

Atkinson Ltd., J. & E., acquired by Crosfield's, 302, 342, 350

Australia, trade in, 100, 141, 185, 196, 238

Bag-making, 209, 212, 261, 267, 301

Ball, E., 148, 167, 344

Ballantyne, H., 174, 250

Banking transactions, 6–7, 18, 36–8, 45–6, 58, 59, 65, 105–6, 267, 273, 275

Bank Quay, Warrington, location and industrial development, 14–16, 32–3, 60–3, 83

Bank Quay Foundry, 61–2, 299

Bank Quay Glassworks, 15, 32, 61, 83, 89, 99, 211, 298

Bank Quay Mission, 120–1, 162n., 212

Base-exchanging materials. *See* Water-softening

Baxter, A. V., 196, 319

Bedford & Williams, hydrogenation patent, 172, 173, 249–50

Benzine (solvent extraction) plant, 145, 162

Bernhard, E. E. and E. H., 186

Bibby's, of Liverpool, 293, 304, 310

Billington, C., 148, 167n., 244, 314, 343, 348, 351, 355

Blake & Maxwell, soap manufacturers, Liverpool, 70–1, 141

Boby & Co., of London, 314

Bow (London) silicate factory, 337, 357, 367–8

Box-making (wood, cardboard, and tin), 25, 33, 76, 84, 145, 204, 209, 211, 212, 261, 267, 301, 311, 331

Brass band, 153, 317

Bremen Besigheimer Oelfabriken (B.B.O.), 173, 249, 252

Bridgewater Canal. *See* Transport

Bright, John, 51, 128, 129

British Oil & Cake Mills Ltd., 293, 304

Brock, F. W., 247, 248, 251, 256, 257–9, 276–8

Bromborough, Planter's Margarine Co.'s factory at, 307–8, 324

Brunner, John (Sir), 72–3, 241n., 243, 246, 248, 254, 277, 283

Brunner, Mond & Co. Ltd., introduction of Solvay (ammonia-soda) process, 72–3; links with Crosfield's, 72–3, 76, 79, 82, 141, 146, 148, 204, 219, 236 *et seq.*; purchase of Crosfield's and Gossage's, 241–4; relations

374

377

competition in soap trade, 62, 67, 80, 83, 100–1, 106, 107, 112–14, 116, 139, 169, 180, 181, 182, 183, 186–7, 188, 220–1; participation in Soap Makers' Association, 114, 116, 186–7, 219, 221 *et seq.*; proposed combine ('Soap Trust'), 188, 225–7, 228–9; relations with Crosfield's and Brunner Mond's, 80, 100–1, 112, 169, 174, 186–7, 188, 190, 195, 196, 197, 201, 219, 225–31, 234, 239–44, chap. XVI, 276–84; take-over and control of Crosfield's, 3, 283–4, 286–98, 316–19, 320–1

Lever, William Hulme (second Viscount Leverhulme), 288, 319

Lime, use and production of, 24, 94, 205, 213, 299, 312

Limited liability, Crosfield's adoption of, 139–41

Liverpool, trade with, 6, 11, 12, 14, 23, 35–6, 37, 41–2, 90–1, 94–6, 97, 98, 99, 101, 179, 184, 213; Crosfield's soapworks in, 141–2, 143, 145, 177, 195–6

Loewig (or Ferrite) process, caustic soda manufacture, 82, 203

London soap trade, 98, 108–9, 110, 114–15, 142, 181, 184, 221, 222; tallow market, 90, 179, 224

London & North Western Railway Co., 59, 61, 62, 65, 83, 94, 99

'Lux' soap flakes, 201, 306

Machenhauer, German chemist, 146, 147, 167, 187

Managerial staff, 145–9, 343–4, 351, 368–9

Manchester Ship Canal, 36, 95–6, 99, 210–11, 213–14

Margarine. *See* Oil refining

'Margol' (refined oil), 324

Markel, Dr. K. E., 79–83, 139–41, 143–5, 146–7, 157, 159, 167n., 168n., 176, 214, 217, 219, 230, 235, 244, 247, 366, 369

Medley, E. G., 148

Medley & Sons, Liverpool, Crosfield's purchase and sale of, 141–2, 148

Mersey, River. *See* Transport

Mersey Flint Glass Works. *See* Robinson, Son & Skinner

Merseyside chemicals and soapmaking, 11, 14, 23, 41–4

'Metso' (metasilicate of soda). *See* Alkaline detergents

'Microcal' (calcium silicate), 367

Ministry of Food, control by, 346, 361

Mond, Alfred (Sir), 246

Mond, Emile, 288

Mond, Ludwig, 72–3, 79

'Monut' (vegetable butter), 161, 170

Moore, Dr. C. W., 147, 343, 351

Morris, R., 362, 369

Motor transport. *See* Transport

Mount process, caustic soda manufacture, 312

Munitions manufacture (Second World War), 349

Muspratt, J., 42

Myers' box-making machine, 76

Natal Soap Works Ltd., 182, 255, 267, 273, 277, 283, 301

National Service League, 150, 152–3, 244, 265

'Neosyl' fine silicas, 366

Newall, J., 148

Newall, S., 305–6, 331, 343, 351

Nickel catalyst ('Nicat'), 165–9, 174, 353, 359, 365, 367, 370

Niger Company, 286, 290, 342

Non-soapy detergents, 333, 338, 354–6, 364

Normann, Dr. Wilhelm, and hydrogenation patent. *See* Oil hardening

Northern Soap Makers' Association. *See* Combines

Ockel, R., 146, 160, 161, 163, 166–7

Offices. *See* Commercial and clerical work

Oil fuel, change-over to, 352, 356

Oil hardening (hydrogenation), production and trade, 81, 157, 158, 164–74, 179, 215, 241n.2, 243, 249–53, 257, 258, 259, 260, 266, 270–1, 277, 278, 281, 285, 290–1, 307, 308, 309–10, 323–4, 346, 352, 353, 363, 370